ČERENKOV RADIATION AND ITS APPLICATIONS

(*Reproduced by permission of the United Kingdom Atomic Energy Authority.*)

PLATE I. Čerenkov radiation in the water surrounding the core of the "swimming-pool" reactor LIDO at the Atomic Energy Research Establishment, Harwell, England. Reactor power 100 kW. Exposure 10 min at f/8 on Ektachrome film, daylight type (Weston speed 10).

ČERENKOV RADIATION
and its applications

by

J. V. JELLEY
B.Sc. (Birmingham)
Ph.D. (Cantab.)

Published for the
United Kingdom Atomic Energy Authority

PERGAMON PRESS
NEW YORK · LONDON · PARIS · LOS ANGELES
1958

PERGAMON PRESS LTD.
4 & 5 *Fitzroy Square, London W.*1

PERGAMON PRESS, INC.
122 *E. 55th Street, New York* 22, *N.Y.*
P.O. Box 47715, *Los Angeles, California*

PERGAMON PRESS, S.A.R.L.
24 *Rue des Écoles, Paris Ve*

Library of Congress Card Number 58–9691
Printed in Great Britain by Page Bros. (Norwich) Ltd.

ONULP

CONTENTS

v

5. THE PHOTOMULTIPLIER

6. ČERENKOV DETECTORS AND THEIR APPLICATIONS

7. OPTICAL CONSIDERATIONS

8. DESIGNS OF SOME PRACTICAL COUNTERS

9. ČERENKOV RADIATION IN THE ATMOSPHERE

10. GAS COUNTERS

11. MISCELLANEOUS IDEAS AND APPLICATIONS

APPENDICES

AUTHOR'S PREFACE

THE vast and rapid development of high energy nuclear physics in recent years has provided a great stimulus to research on new types of radiation detectors. But for this, and the advent of the photomultiplier, the subject of Čerenkov radiation might well have remained only of academic interest. The field itself occupies only a very restricted niche in modern physics; nevertheless it impinges on a wide range of topics, including not only nuclear physics but also optics, high frequency radio techniques, astrophysics and cosmic rays.

The development of the Čerenkov detector has followed closely on that of the scintillation counter, both being remarkable for their simplicity and sensitivity. Although the Čerenkov detector does not possess the versatility and precision of the scintillation counter, its unique properties have led to the development of an extremely useful instrument in the fields of high energy machine physics and cosmic-ray research.

As far as the author is aware, this is at the present time the only monograph devoted exclusively to the subject of Čerenkov radiation and its applications. In view of this the aim has been to present as complete an account of the whole field as is possible in a volume of this size.

On the theoretical side, the classical treatment of the normal Čerenkov effect in isotropic media is presented in detail, together with an account of the underlying physical basis of the phenomenon. For the many and varied special cases, for example anisotropic media and ferromagnetics, only the results however are presented; the mathematical treatments are often very lengthy and their inclusion would serve very little purpose.

The book has been written primarily for the experimentalist, but technical details of specific types of Čerenkov counters have purposely been restricted, since developments are rapidly taking place all the time, and present designs may well become obsolete within a few years. Emphasis has therefore been laid on the general properties and applications of counters of various types, with inclusion of sufficient technical data to allow the design to be worked out for an instrument for any particular purpose.

ix

Special attention has been paid to the assembly of a complete bibliography on all aspects of the subject; this includes, in particular, most of the references to the considerable amount of theoretical work carried out in the U.S.S.R., and the very extensive developments and applications of the techniques to high energy problems centred around the large accelerators in the U.S.A.

The author would like to express his thanks to innumerable colleagues at Harwell with whom the individual chapters have been discussed, and he is grateful to Professor W. E. Burcham, F.R.S., of Birmingham University who has had the difficult task of reading the manuscript.

He would also like to express his appreciation to Dr. E. Bretscher and Mr. W. J. Whitehouse, both of A.E.R.E. Harwell, who have encouraged and stimulated the work carried out there by the author and his colleagues on various aspects of the subject. In conclusion he wishes to express his gratitude to Mr. J. E. Terry, of the Harwell Information Office, for the laborious work of producing an excellent bibliography which greatly lightened the task of writing this monograph.

CHAPTER 1

INTRODUCTION

1.1 Historical

The very faint emission of a bluish-white light from transparent substances, in the neighbourhood of strong radioactive sources, had been observed by many workers in the field of radioactivity prior to an understanding of its origin. Those who have read the life of Mme Curie (1941), may recall the account of how she found bottles of concentrated radium solutions aglow with this uncanny pale blue light. Her preoccupation with the much more significant discoveries in radioactivity no doubt stifled an investigation of the causes and nature of this luminescence. This was in 1910, twenty-four years before Frank and Tamm produced the correct explanation for the origin of this radiation. The early observations of Čerenkov radiation were made at a time when the electromagnetic theory of light had been well established and the study of optics and luminescence featured large in the field of physics. Thus, in principle, the theoretical interpretation of the effect might have appeared many years earlier than it did. The delay in the study of the phenomenon was due to a number of causes. For instance, at the time of these early observations, much work was going on in the systematic study of the fluorescence and phosphorescence of materials irradiated by ultra-violet light, x-rays and the newly discovered radiations from the radioactive elements. The diverse and relatively complicated phenomena associated with these forms of luminescence only helped to postpone the discovery of Čerenkov radiation; the latter in any case was so weak that it was frequently masked by the presence of these other effects. Nevertheless, it was through studies of fluorescence and phosphorescence that the work on Čerenkov radiation finally developed. The absence of really sensitive light detectors also contributed to the delay in the discovery of Čerenkov radiation; the early work had to be carried out either by visual observation or by photographic recording with long exposure.

The first deliberate attempt to study the phenomenon was made by Mallet (1926, 1928 and 1929) whose work has unjustly been either forgotten or ignored. He found that the light emitted from a wide variety of transparent bodies placed close to a radioactive source always had the same bluish-white quality, and that the spectrum was continuous, not possessing the line or band structure characteristic of fluorescence. He was the first to appreciate the generality of the effect and to notice that in a number of other respects also, it was very different from fluorescence and other known forms of luminescence. Unfortunately Mallet did not pursue the work, nor did he attempt to offer an explanation for the origin of the light. The subject then lay dormant until, in 1934, Čerenkov commenced an exhaustive series of experiments which he continued until 1938. These experiments were remarkable for their simplicity and for the excellent agreement between their results and the theory, which had in the meantime been proposed by Frank and Tamm, in 1937. Čerenkov appears to have been unaware of the earlier work of Mallet, though he too met the problem accidentally, through studies of fluorescence; his experiments covered a wider range than did those of Mallet. The next contribution was due to Ginsburg who in 1940 produced a quantum theory of the phenomenon which was henceforward known as Čerenkov radiation.

The war years caused a further lapse in research in the field, though at the same time they heralded the development of the photomultiplier. The advent of this remarkable instrument, the most sensitive light detector known, gave a great impetus to the subject, which has since been growing at an ever increasing rate. It was the development of this same instrument that allowed Curran and Baker in 1944 to devise the first form of the modern scintillation counter. The latter has proved to be an extremely versatile tool in studies of nuclear and cosmic-ray physics; the Čerenkov counter, having less numerous applications, has developed more slowly but is becoming increasingly important, for its most significant applications lie in the high energy field, where so much progress is now being made. The development of ever larger accelerating machines places an increasing demand on instruments for the measurement of beams of particles of very high energies and intensities.

Returning to the historical survey, the first proposal to use a photomultiplier and a simple optical system for detecting single particles by the Čerenkov effect, was made by Getting (1947). After an unsuccessful attempt by Dicke (1947) to detect cosmic-rays by this means, and some experiments of Weisz and Anderson (1947) who observed small effects with light-sensitive Geiger counters, it was Jelley (1951) who first detected single fast charged particles with high efficiency, using distilled water and a photomultiplier. Almost immediately, Mather (1951) and Marshall (1951) published accounts of the first Čerenkov detectors to be used for the direct measurement of particle velocities, in beams from high energy accelerators. Since 1951 there has been a steady increase in the number of practical applications of the Čerenkov counter to nuclear and cosmic-ray physics. These are now too numerous for individual mention in this introductory review, but perhaps special reference should be made here to the first detection of Čerenkov radiation in a gas by Ascoli in 1953, the observation of light pulses from the night sky by Galbraith and Jelley, also in 1953, and, more recently, the vital rôle of the Čerenkov detector in the discovery of the anti-proton by Chamberlain *et al.* in 1955.

On the theoretical side considerable interest has been shown by Fermi and others (1940) in the effects on the specific ionization produced by fast particles in dense media, produced by the local polarization associated with the Čerenkov effect. Čerenkov radiation was suggested by Ginsburg (1947) as a possible source of microwaves, and its relationship with other physical processes has also been widely discussed. Other problems investigated include studies of Čerenkov radiation in anisotropic media and in ferromagnetics, the radiation produced by electric and magnetic dipoles, and modifications introduced by the quantum theory. The ultimate resolution of the focusing type of counter has been worked out in terms of the effects produced by scattering, diffraction and dispersion.

1.2 Descriptive account of the Čerenkov effect

While the complete mathematical theory is presented in Chapter 2, it is nevertheless appropriate at this point to explain the basic principles of the effect in a qualitative manner. This should enable the reader to appreciate more fully the interpretation of the early experiments which are described in the next sections.

Suppose an electron to be moving relatively slowly through a piece of glass or other transparent medium. Fig. 1.1(a) shows a section of the glass in the vicinity of the track AB of this electron, the circles representing the individual atoms composing the glass. Normally these will be roughly spherical in shape, and undistorted. However, in the region close to the passing electron, which at a particular instant in time is for instance at the point P, the electric field of the particle distorts the atoms so that the negative charges of the electrons are displaced to one side of the heavier positive charges of the nuclei of these atoms. The medium thus becomes polarized about the point P. When now the electron moves on to another point, say P', the elongated atoms around P return to their normal shape. While the atoms are distorted they behave like elementary dipoles, with the negative poles pointing away from the track if the passing particle is a negative electron, or vice versa for a positron or proton. Thus, as the particle passes through the medium, each elemental region of the glass along the track will in turn receive a very brief electromagnetic pulse. Owing to the complete symmetry of

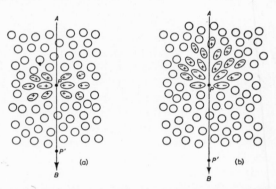

FIG. 1.1. The polarization set up in a dielectric by the passage of a charged particle. (a) At low velocity. (b) At high velocity.

the polarization field surrounding the electron, there will be no resultant field at large distances and therefore no radiation. There is symmetry both in azimuth and along the axis, in this case.

If however the electron is moving fast, that is at a speed comparable to that of light in the medium, the picture is quite different (see Fig. 1.1b). In this case the polarization field is no longer completely symmetrical. In the azimuthal plane, symmetry is preserved, but along the axis there is a resultant dipole field which will be apparent even at large distances from the track of the electron. Such a field will be momentarily set up by the electron at each element along the track in turn, each element then radiating a brief electromagnetic pulse. The radiation will be spread over a band of frequencies corresponding to the various Fourier components of this pulse.

In the general case, the radiated wavelets from all parts of the track interfere destructively so that, at a distant point, the resultant field intensity is still zero. However, if the velocity of the particle is higher than the phase velocity of the light in the medium, it is possible for the wavelets from all portions of the track to be in phase with one another so that, at a distant point of observation, there is now a resultant field. It will be understood from the Huygens construction shown in Fig. 1.2 that this radiation is only observed at a particular angle θ with

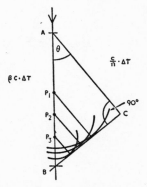

FIG. 1.2. Huygens construction to illustrate coherence.

respect to the track of the particle, namely that angle at which the wavelets from arbitrary points such as P_1, P_2 and P_3 on the track AB are coherent and combine to form a plane wave front BC. This coherence takes place when the particle traverses AB in the same time that the light travels from A to C. If the velocity of the particle is βc where c is the velocity of light $in\ vacuo$ and n the refractive index of the medium, in a time $\Delta\tau$ the particle will travel a distance $AB = \beta c \cdot \Delta\tau$, and the light a distance $AC = \Delta\tau \cdot (c/n)$. From this we obtain:

$$\cos\theta = \frac{1}{\beta n} \qquad (1.1)$$

which is known as the "Čerenkov relation".
It is seen that:

(i) For a medium of given refractive index n, there is a threshold velocity $\beta_{min} = (1/n)$, below which no radiation takes place.

At this critical velocity the direction of radiation coincides with that of the particle.

(ii) For an ultra-relativistic particle, for which $\beta = 1$, there is a maximum angle of emission, given by $\theta_{max} = \cos^{-1}(1/n)$.

(iii) The radiation occurs mainly in the visible and near-visible regions of the spectrum, for which $n > 1$. Emission in the x-ray region is impossible for n is then less than unity and (1.1) cannot be satisfied.

Figure 1.2 has been drawn in one plane only. There is of course complete symmetry about the axis of the particle. The light originating from

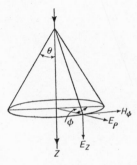

Fig. 1.3. The formation of the Čerenkov cone, and the polarization vectors.

each element of track is propagated along the surface of a cone whose apex is at this element, whose axis coincides with the track, and whose semi-vertical angle is the angle θ (see Fig. 1.3). The distribution in θ of the light intensity approximates to a δ-function, and the polarization is such that the electric vector E is everywhere perpendicular to the surface of the cone, and the magnetic vector H tangential to this surface.

From what has already been said, it will be seen that the phenomenon is in some ways analogous to the V-shaped shock wave observed in acoustics when a projectile travels through the air at a velocity in excess of the speed of sound, the quantity βn taking the place of the Mach number in aerodynamics. A more familiar case is that of the formation of a bow wave from a ship moving through water when its speed is greater than that of surface waves on the water.

Returning to the optical case, it will be realized that there are two further conditions to be fulfilled to achieve coherence, in addition to that stated in (i). First, the length l of the track of the particle in the medium shall be large compared with the wavelength λ of the radiation in question, otherwise diffraction effects will become dominant and the light distributed over an angle $\delta\theta \sim \lambda/l \sin\theta$, instead of appearing at only one angle θ as in (1.1). Secondly, the velocity of the particle must be constant during its passage through the medium, or, to be more specific, the differences in the times for the particle to traverse successive distances λ shall be small compared with the period (λ/c) of the emitted wave.

In anticipation of section 3.10 in Chapter 3, it is appropriate here to emphasize that this radiation phenomenon should not be confused with either recombination or excitation radiation associated with ionization caused by the particle. Neither should it be confused with Bremsstrahlung, which is an acceleration radiation produced if the particle enters the sphere of influence of the electrostatic field of an atomic nucleus.

1.3 The early observations of Mallet

Mallet describes his first observations in a paper in 1926 entitled "Luminescence de l'eau et des substances organiques soumises au rayonnement γ". In his first experiment he immersed a 30 mg radium source of γ-rays in distilled water which was placed in a wooden container to eliminate possible luminescence of the latter. He found that the light was bluish-white and that its total intensity increased as the depth of water was raised to 10 cm, suggesting that there was little or no self absorption of the light. The same effect occurred if the γ-ray source was outside the water, and running water was found to behave in the same way as still water. He then succeeded in taking a photograph of the light with the source 15 cm away, obtaining an intense blackening after 17 hr exposure, while the darkening from the direct action of the γ-radiation was five or six times weaker. It was also shown that 1 mm glass was more absorbing to the radiation than 5 mm quartz or 5 mm of albumen. The significance of this experiment was that most of the radiation was evidently of short wavelength.

In his second paper, in 1928, Mallet described his first attempt to analyse the spectrum of the radiation, to see if it had a line or band

B

structure like that associated with fluorescence. His spectrograph, designed by Fabry, consisted of a collimator having an aperture of 54 mm at f/2·0 and two 30° flint glass prisms. Using two radium sources each of strength 250 mg, he obtained spectra from water and carbon disulphide after exposures lasting for between two and four days. He was the first to find that the spectrum was continuous and extended to 3700 Å, the cut-off imposed by the apparatus. He continued the spectrographic work and published a third paper in 1929. With a new spectrograph having quartz lenses and two hollow quartz prisms, each of angle 45° and filled with water, he obtained spectra with a dispersion of 22 mm on the plate, between wavelength limits of 2400–4360 Å. In these last experiments he used a 250 mg RaE source, and required between four to eight days to obtain adequate exposures for the light from water and carbon disulphide.

Mallet did not observe the asymmetry in the angular distribution of the light with respect to the exciting radiation, discussed in section 1.2, and made no attempt to study its polarization.

1.4 Čerenkov's original experiments

In 1934 Čerenkov first noticed a very weak visible radiation from pure liquids under the influence of γ-rays. A study of a variety of liquids led him to the conclusion, unaware as he was of Mallet's earlier work, that this was a phenomenon of a different nature from that of fluorescence. Since most of his early experiments were carried out visually, he had to use γ-ray sources of a strength which, on present standards of tolerance dosage, was very high. Since the accounts of the early experiments are not easily accessible to many readers, they will be described in some detail.

In his first experiment Čerenkov used the very simple apparatus shown in Fig. 1.4. A small phial containing 104 mg of radium was inserted at position R_1 in a wooden block B in which stood a platinum crucible A. The liquid under investigation was placed in A above the radium source. By means of the optical system consisting of the collimator L_1, reflecting prism P and telescope $L_2 L_3$, it was possible to observe at E the faint glow in the liquid near the source. The field of view was defined by the diaphragm D; other elements of the optical system were a graded wedge W, used to measure relative intensities, filters F of different colours, for crude spectral analysis, and a Nicol prism N used for investigating the polarization of the radiation. With the eye accommodated to the dark, Čerenkov was able to measure the relative intensities of the light from 16 pure liquids, among which were distilled water, paraffin, xylol, toluene, glycerine and various alcohols. In these measurements he used as criterion the point of visual extinction of the light in the optical wedge. His main conclusions from these first observations were that the range of relative intensities was found to be comparatively small, that the spectral distribution varied little from one liquid to another, and that the light was concentrated in the blue and violet.

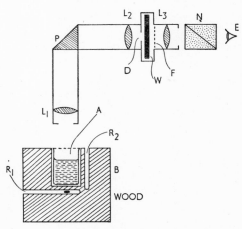

FIG. 1.4. Apparatus used by Čerenkov in his first experiment (1934).

There was, moreover, no diminution of the light by the addition of silver nitrate, potassium iodide and other compounds known to be strong quenching agents in the case of fluorescence. Furthermore, and again unlike fluorescence, changes of temperature produced no changes in the intensity of the radiations. In the polarization experiments a small effect, $\sim 20\%$, was observed, indicating a partial polarization in which the electric vector lay in the same direction as that of the exciting γ-radiation.

Shortly after these first experiments, Vavilov (1934) suggested that the effect might be due to the slowing down of the electrons in the medium, Bremsstrahlung, but this idea presented difficulties and was found to be untenable. (See section 3.10 for further discussion on this topic.)

Čerenkov then commenced a new series of experiments. For instance, in 1936 he investigated the influence of a magnetic field on the exciting radiation using a γ-ray source and water, and concluded that the light must be attributed to the secondary electrons produced in the medium by the γ-rays, rather than to the γ-rays themselves. Then, in 1937, just about the time Frank and Tamm produced their theory, two further papers appeared. In the first (1937a) it was announced that the phenomenon could be observed with β-rays, and in the second (1937b), an account was given of a simple experiment that showed for the first time the asymmetry of the light intensity with respect to the direction of the exciting radiation, as predicted by Frank and Tamm. With a γ-ray source of poor collimation, and an extended medium, only a crude check however could be made of the fundamental relation $\cos \theta = (1/\beta n)$.

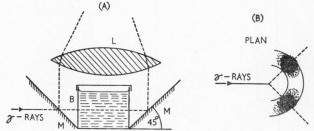

FIG. 1.5. Čerenkov's first apparatus using photographic recording.
(a) Apparatus.
(b) The photographic images obtained with this apparatus. (Čerenkov, 1937c.)

The first publication in the English literature, and at the same time the first photographic observation of the characteristic asymmetry of the light, appeared also in 1937(c). Figure 1.5(a) shows the simple apparatus for this experiment. A γ-ray source equivalent to 794 mg of radium was mounted to one side of a conical mirror M containing a thin-walled glass beaker B, filled with water or benzene. The light emitted through the sides of the beaker was reflected upwards and focused by the camera-lens L (f/1·4) on to a photographic plate. With exposures of 72 hr, images were obtained of the general form shown in Fig. 1.5(b), revealing the asymmetrical light distribution having two areas of intensity brighter than elsewhere.

Čerenkov concluded his work with a group of experiments in 1938 of a more thorough nature, with the deliberate aim of verifying the theory of his colleagues Frank and Tamm.

(i) *The spectrum of the radiation* (1938a) was studied with the apparatus shown in Fig. 1.6(a). β-rays from a 100 mc radon source Rn in a small glass phial were used to irradiate benzene in a thin-walled glass vessel V. An image of V was focused on the slit S of the first of the two

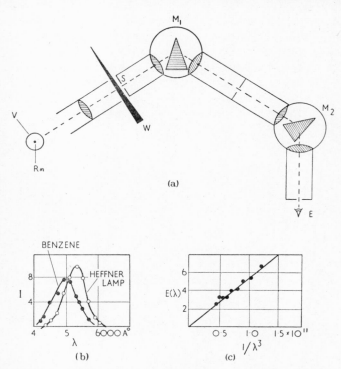

FIG. 1.6. Čerenkov's experiment to determine the spectral distribution of the radiation. (Čerenkov, 1938a.)
(a) The spectrometer.
(b) The observed intensity distribution compared with that from a Heffner lamp.
(c) The derived intensity function $E(\lambda)$ plotted as a function of $(1/\lambda^3)$.

monochromators M_1 and M_2 in cascade. The light was observed visually at E and a neutral tinted wedge W was used in the method of threshold extinction, to determine the relative intensities of the radiation at wavelengths in the range 4300–6000 Å. Comparisons were then made with the spectrum of the light from a standard Heffner lamp which illuminated a magnesium oxide screen situated at the position previously occupied by the source Rn. The intensity distribution curves for the two sources are shown in Fig. 1.6(b). From the known spectral distribution from a Heffner source and the two measured curves, the true distribution of the radiation from the benzene was obtained, $E(\lambda)$. The plot of $E(\lambda)$ versus $(1/\lambda^3)$, shown in Fig. 1.6(c), shows the excellent agreement between experiment and theory. The $(1/\lambda^3)$ law is derived in Chapter 2.

(ii) *The absolute intensity* of the radiation was then measured with the arrangement shown in Fig. 1.7 (1938b). A 150 mc radon source,

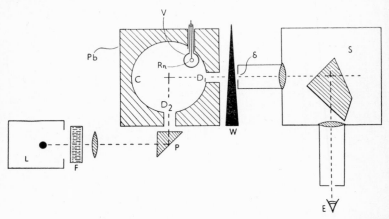

FIG. 1.7. The apparatus used by Čerenkov (1938b) to determine the absolute intensity of the radiation.

sealed in an ampule Rn, was mounted at the centre of a small spherical vessel V containing water. V was situated near the surface of an integrating spherical cavity C (whitened with magnesium oxide) cut out of a lead block Pb which screened the observer from the intense γ-radiation from the source. The Čerenkov radiation from the water, assumed uniform throughout C and emerging from the aperture D_1, was observed visually at E through a constant deviation spectrometer S. By suitable choice of slit-width δ, a band of wavelengths 5360–5560 Å was observed, centred on 5460 Å, the wavelength of the green line in the mercury spectrum. The wedge W was used as before, again with the criterion of threshold extinction. Comparisons were then made with the intensity observed from a mercury lamp L, the light of which entered the integrating sphere through the aperture D_2, via a prism P. The absolute intensity of the light was measured by a thermopile placed inside C over the aperture D_2, the liquid filter F absorbing all but the green part of the spectrum. The thermopile was calibrated in turn from a Heffner lamp. From this experiment the absolute light intensity was found to be $4\cdot1 \times 10^{-4}$ erg/sec/mc of radon, while that calculated from the theory of Frank and Tamm under the same conditions was $3\cdot5 \times 10^{-4}$

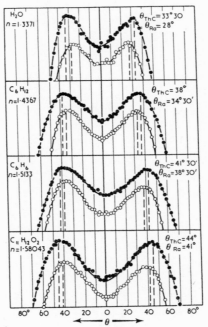

FIG. 1.8. The variation of θ with n, for two different sources of γ-rays. (Čerenkov, 1937d and 1938c.)

in the same units. This agreement is remarkable in view of the large number of inter-comparisons. The same apparatus was also used to measure relative intensities for different liquids, again for comparison with the theory. Among the following liquids: water, benzene, *cyclo*-hexane, carbon disulphide, *iso*butyl alcohol and carbon tetrachloride, ranging in refractive index from 1·334 to 1·637, the observed relative intensities agreed with those calculated, to within 12 % in the worst case, while the average deviation was $\approx$ 6 %.

(iii) *The dependence of θ on* n *and β.* In concluding this series of early experiments, Čerenkov used the photographic technique already described (1937c) to study the dependence of θ on n and β. In this work he used γ-rays, both from radium (1937d), and later from ThC" (1938c), measuring the angles θ from microphotometer tracings. These results are shown in Fig. 1.8. The variation of θ with β was obtained from a knowledge of the energies of the two sources of γ-rays and the Klein-Nishina theory (Heitler, 1944) of the Compton scattering process, while the variation of θ with n was studied using the liquids water, *cyclo-hexane*, benzene and ethyl cinnamate. In both cases the results agreed satisfactorily with theory.

It will be realized from the above account of these early experiments, that the lack of beams of particles strictly monoenergetic in energy, the poor collimation, and the relatively crude ways of measuring the light intensities, all combined to set a limit to the precision of the observations. The more thorough tests of the theory, which were made possible as techniques improved, are too numerous to list here, though the more significant developments will be mentioned in their appropriate place in later chapters.

CHAPTER 2

THEORETICAL INTERPRETATION

2.1 The classical theory of Frank and Tamm

In their original treatment of the problem of the radiation of an electron moving uniformly in a dielectric medium, Frank and Tamm (1937) made the following simplifying assumptions:

(i) The medium is considered as a continuum, so that the microscopic structure is ignored; the dielectric constant is then the only parameter used to describe the behaviour of the medium.

(ii) Dispersion is ignored, at least in the first approximation.

(iii) Radiation reaction is neglected.

(iv) The medium is assumed to be a perfect isotropic dielectric, so that the conductivity is zero, the magnetic permeability $\mu = 1$, and there is no absorption of radiation.

(v) The electron is assumed to move at constant velocity; i.e. the slowing down due to ionization, and the multiple Coulomb scattering are ignored.

(vi) The medium is unbounded and the track length infinite.

With the above assumptions, following Frank and Tamm, we proceed as follows:

Taking the dynamical relation between the polarization $\mathbf{P}$ and the electric intensity $\mathbf{E}$ (see, for example, Sommerfeld, 1954, p. 90),

$$\frac{\partial^2 \mathbf{P}}{\partial t^2} + \sum_s \omega_s^2 \mathbf{P}_s = a\mathbf{E} \tag{2.1}$$

where ω_s are the frequencies of the molecular oscillators of the medium, and $a = Ne^2/m$. (N is the number of electrons, of charge e and mass m, per unit volume.)

$\mathbf{E}$ and $\mathbf{P}$ are obtained by expanding all the field variables in Fourier series, of the type

$$\mathbf{E} = \int_{-\infty}^{+\infty} \mathbf{E}_\omega e^{i\omega t} \cdot d\omega, \qquad \mathbf{P} = \int_{-\infty}^{+\infty} \mathbf{P}_\omega e^{i\omega t} \cdot d\omega, \text{ etc.} \tag{2.2}$$

It is necessary to introduce the following connexion between $\mathbf{P}_\omega$ and $\mathbf{E}_\omega$:

$$\mathbf{P}_\omega = (n^2 - 1)\, \mathbf{E}_\omega \tag{2.3a}$$

where n is the refractive index of the medium at the frequency ω. There is, likewise, a connexion between $\mathbf{E}_\omega$ and the dielectric induction $\mathbf{D}_\omega$, of the form

$$\mathbf{D}_\omega = n^2.\, \mathbf{E}_\omega. \tag{2.3b}$$

The Maxwell equations in the medium are then:

$$\operatorname{div} \mathbf{H}_\omega = 0 \tag{2.4a}$$

$$\operatorname{curl} \mathbf{H}_\omega = \frac{1}{c}\left(4\pi \mathbf{j}_\omega + \frac{\partial \mathbf{D}_\omega}{\partial t}\right) \tag{2.5a}$$

$$\operatorname{div} \mathbf{D}_\omega = 4\pi\rho \tag{2.6a}$$

$$\operatorname{curl} \mathbf{E}_\omega = -\frac{1}{c}\frac{\partial \mathbf{H}_\omega}{\partial t} \tag{2.7a}$$

where c is the velocity of light in free space, $\mathbf{j}$ is the current density, and ρ the density of free charges.

Re-writing these equations as functions of the vector and scalar potentials $\mathbf{A}$ and ϕ, we arrive at the following set:

$$\mathbf{H}_\omega = \operatorname{curl} \mathbf{A}_\omega \tag{2.4b}$$

$$\nabla^2 \mathbf{A}_\omega + \frac{\omega^2 n^2}{c^2} \mathbf{A}_\omega = -\frac{4\pi \mathbf{j}_\omega}{c} \tag{2.5b}$$

$$\nabla^2 \phi_\omega + \frac{\omega^2 n^2}{c^2} \phi_\omega = -\frac{4\pi}{n^2} \rho \tag{2.6b}$$

$$\mathbf{E}_\omega = -\frac{1}{c}\frac{\partial \mathbf{A}_\omega}{\partial t} - \operatorname{grad} \phi_\omega \tag{2.7b}$$

where we have made use of the connexion between the vector and scalar potentials:

$$\operatorname{div} \mathbf{A}_\omega + \frac{i\omega}{c} n^2 \phi_\omega = 0.$$

If an electron of charge e is moving through the medium along the axis z with a constant velocity v, the corresponding current density $\mathbf{j}$ is equal to

$$j_z = ev \; \delta(x)\delta(y)\delta \; (z - vt),$$

where δ denotes Dirac's function. The components j_x and j_u are both zero. Expanding j_z one gets:

$$j_z(\omega) = \frac{e}{2\pi} \cdot e^{-iwz/v} \cdot \delta(x) \; \delta(y)$$

or, introducing cylindrical co-ordinates ρ, ϕ and z,

$$j_z(\omega) = \frac{e}{4\pi^2\rho} \cdot e^{-iwz/v} \cdot \delta(\rho).$$

Inserting this expression into (2.5b), and putting

$$A_\rho = A_\phi = 0 \text{ and } A_z(\omega) = u(\rho) \; e^{-iwz/v} \tag{2.8}$$

we obtain:

$$\frac{\partial^2 u}{\partial \rho^2} + \frac{1}{\rho}\frac{\partial u}{\partial \rho} + s^2 u = \frac{e}{\pi c \rho}\delta(\rho) \tag{2.9}$$

where

$$s^2 = \frac{\omega^2}{v^2}(\beta^2 n^2 - 1) = -\sigma^2. \tag{2.10}$$

Thus u is a cylindrical function satisfying the Bessel equation:

$$\frac{\partial^2 u}{\partial \rho^2} + \frac{1}{\rho}\frac{\partial u}{\partial \rho} + s^2 u = 0 \tag{2.11}$$

everywhere with the exception of the pole $\rho = 0$. To find the condition to be satisfied by u at $\rho = 0$, we first replace the right-hand side of (2.9) by f, such that

$$f = -\frac{2e}{\pi c \rho_0} \text{ if } \rho < \rho_0, \text{ and } f = 0 \text{ if } \rho > \rho_0;$$

then integrate (2.9) over the surface of the disc of radius ρ_0 and lastly go over to the limit $\rho_0 \to 0$. In this way we obtain:

$$\lim_{\rho \to 0} \rho \frac{\partial u}{\partial \rho} = -\frac{e}{\pi c}. \tag{2.12}$$

We now consider two different cases.

An electron moving at low speed, namely at a velocity such that $\beta n < 1$. In this case $s^2 < 0$ and $\sigma^2 > 0$. The solution of (2.11) satisfying (2.12) and vanishing at infinity, is:

$$u = \frac{ie}{2c} H_0^{(1)}(i\sigma\rho), \tag{2.13}$$

where $H_0^{(1)}$ is the Hankel function of the first kind. If $\sigma\rho \gg 1$, one can use the asymptotic value of $H_0^{(1)}$ and obtain according to (2.8) and (2.13),

$$A_z = \frac{e}{c} \int\limits_{-\infty}^{+\infty} \frac{\exp\left[-\sigma\rho + i\omega(t - z/v)\right]}{\sqrt{(2\pi\sigma\rho)}} \, d\omega. \tag{2.14}$$

Thus, in the case of small velocities, the field of the electron decreases exponentially with ρ, so that at a point remote from the track of the electron, no radiation will be observed.

At *high velocities*, namely those for which $\beta n > 1$, the parameter s in (2.10) is real and the general solution of equations (2.9) and (2.11) represents, at infinity, a cylindrical wave. Specifying u in this case to represent an outgoing and not an ingoing wave, we obtain the following solution of (2.11) satisfying (2.12):

$$u = -\frac{ie}{2c} H_0^{(2)}(s\rho) \text{ if } \omega > 0 \tag{2.15}$$

and a complex conjugate expression if $\omega < 0$, s being assumed to be positive. Using the asymptotic value of $H_0^{(2)}$ for $s\rho \gg 1$, one gets from (2.8) and (2.15):

$$A_z(\omega) = -\frac{e}{c\sqrt{(2\pi s\rho)}} \cdot \exp\left[i\omega\left(t - \frac{z}{v}\right) - i\left(s\rho - \frac{3\pi}{4}\right)\right]$$

when $\omega > 0$.

With the aid of (2.10) one can transform the exponent as follows:

$$A_z(\omega) = -\frac{e}{c\sqrt{(2\pi s\rho)}} \cdot \exp\left[i\omega\left(t - \frac{z\cos\theta + \rho\sin\theta}{c/n}\right) + \frac{3}{4}\pi i\right],$$

$$\omega > 0$$

where θ is defined by the coherence relation $\cos\theta = 1/\beta n$.

Thus, if $\beta n > 1$, a wave is propagated, at infinity, along the direction θ. The electric vector of the wave lies in the meridian plane (z, ρ).

Calculating the field intensity in the wave zone with the aid of (2.4) and (2.5), there are three and only three non-vanishing field vectors, namely:

$$\left. \begin{aligned} H_\phi &= -\frac{a}{\sqrt{(\rho)}} \int \sqrt{(s)} \cdot \cos \chi \cdot d\omega \\[2mm] E_\rho &= -\frac{a}{c\sqrt{(\rho)}} \int \frac{\sqrt{(\beta^2 n^2 - 1)}}{\beta^2 n^2 \sqrt{(s)}} \cdot \cos \chi \cdot \omega \, d\omega \\[2mm] \text{and } E_z &= +\frac{a}{c\sqrt{(\rho)}} \int \left(1 - \frac{1}{\beta^2 n^2}\right) \cdot \frac{1}{\sqrt{(s)}} \cdot \cos \chi \cdot \omega d\omega \end{aligned} \right\} \quad (2.16)$$

where $a = \dfrac{e}{c} \sqrt{\dfrac{2}{\pi}}$ and

$$\chi = \omega \left[t - \frac{z \cos \theta + \rho \sin \theta}{c/n} \right] + \frac{\pi}{4}.$$

See Fig. 1.3.

The integrations of (2.16) have to be carried out only over values of ω for which $\beta n(\omega) \geqslant 1$. The total energy radiated by the electron through the surface of a cylinder of length l whose axis coincides with the line of motion of the electron track, is equal to:

$$W = 2\pi \rho l \int_{-\infty}^{+\infty} \frac{c}{4\pi} [\mathbf{EH}] \, dt.$$

With the aid of the formula

$$\int_{-\infty}^{+\infty} \cos (\omega t + \alpha) \cos (\omega' t + \beta) \, dt = \pi \delta (\omega - \omega'),$$

we arrive at the fundamental equation for the output of radiation, namely

$$\boxed{\frac{dW}{dl} = \frac{e^2}{c^2} \int_{\beta n > 1} \left(1 - \frac{1}{\beta^2 n^2}\right) \cdot \omega d\omega.} \qquad (2.17)$$

Since no frequency cut-off has been imposed in deriving this result, the radiation output represented by (2.17) is infinite. In practice, however,

there are two factors which set an upper limit to the frequency spectrum
and cause the radiation yield to be finite.

In the first place, a real medium is always dispersive, so that radiation
is restricted to those frequency bands for which $n(\omega) > 1/\beta$. The
absorption bands in media which are transparent at visible wavelengths

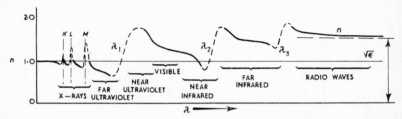

FIG. 2.1. The dispersion curve of a typical transparent medium over the whole
electromagnetic spectrum. (After Jenkins and White, 1937.)

are such as to limit the radiation to the near ultra-violet and longer
wavelengths; there may even be absorption bands in the infra-red. In
the x-ray region $n(\omega)$ is always < 1 and radiation is therefore forbidden,
while at radio frequencies $n(\omega) = \sqrt{(\epsilon)}$ (where ϵ is the dielectric constant of the medium) and there is again a pass-band as in the visible
region. Radiation in regions of absorption is discussed in greater detail
in Chapter 3.5. The general form of the dispersion curve for a typical
transparent medium over the entire spectrum is shown in Fig. 2.1,
while dispersion curves for a number of glasses, in the visible region,
are shown in Fig. 2.2.

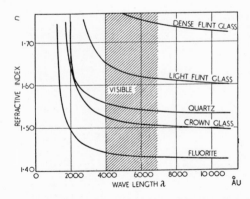

FIG. 2.2. Dispersion curves for a variety of glasses. (After Jenkins and White, 1937.)

The second factor which limits the spectrum in (2.17) is the finite size of the electron. To satisfy the coherence condition it is obvious that the radiation of the electron must be limited to wavelengths which are greater than the classical "diameter" d of the electron. If we integrate (2.17) from $\omega = 0$ to $\omega = c/nd$ (i.e. from $\lambda = \infty$ to $\lambda/2\pi = d$) we obtain:

$$\frac{dW}{dl} = \frac{e^2}{2n^2d^2} \left(1 - \frac{1}{\beta^2 n^2}\right). \tag{2.18}$$

Since $d = 5 \cdot 6 \times 10^{-13}$ cm, $\lambda_{min} = 2\pi d = 3 \cdot 5 \times 10^{-4}$ Å. This limitation to the radiation yield is however very artificial, since such a wavelength occurs in the γ-ray region of the spectrum.

It is nevertheless interesting to note that Sommerfeld (1904, 1905) obtained an expression very similar to (2.18) for the radiation losses from an electron moving *in vacuo* with a constant velocity $v > c$. This of course was prior to the establishment of the theory of relativity from which we know that the condition $v > c$ can never be realized.

2.2 Radiation yield and spectral distribution

We may calculate the order of magnitude of the radiation yield (2.17) in the following way. The approximate value for $n^2(\omega)$ may be written in the form (see Sommerfeld, 1954, p. 91, equation 10):

$$n^2(\omega) = 1 + \left(\frac{A}{\omega_0^2 - \omega^2}\right), \quad n^2(o) = \epsilon = 1 + \left(\frac{A}{\omega_0^2}\right) \tag{2.19}$$

where ω_0 is the frequency of the first resonance in the spectrum. Substituting (2.19) in (2.17), we obtain the following approximate expression for the energy loss per unit path by Čerenkov radiation for a fast electron ($\beta \sim 1$):

$$\frac{dW}{dl} = \frac{e^2 \omega_0^2}{2c^2} (\epsilon - 1) \ln \left(\frac{\epsilon}{\epsilon - 1}\right). \tag{2.20}$$

In a typical medium $\omega_0 = 6 \cdot 10^{15}$/sec, so that (dW/dl) is of the order of several keV per cm, or $\sim 0 \cdot 1\%$ of the energy loss by ionization for a relativistic particle.

It is frequently more useful to express the radiation intensity in terms of the number of photons. From (2.17) it is easy to deduce that the number of photons emitted by an electron within a spectral region defined by wavelengths λ_1 and λ_2 is equal to:

$$N = 2\pi a l \left(\frac{1}{\lambda_2} - \frac{1}{\lambda_1}\right) \cdot \left(1 - \frac{1}{\beta^2 n^2}\right) \tag{2.21}$$

or, since $1/\beta n = \cos \theta$, (the coherence condition derived in Section 1.2),

$$N = 2\pi a l \left(\frac{1}{\lambda_2} - \frac{1}{\lambda_1}\right) \sin^2\theta \tag{2.22}$$

where a is the fine structure constant $= e^2/\hbar c = 1/137$ and n is the average refractive index of the medium. Consider for instance a 500 keV electron moving through a depth of 1 mm of water. From (2.21) we find that between wavelengths of 4000 and 6000 Å (the visible region of the spectrum) about 10 photons are emitted by a single electron of this energy, for which $\beta^2 = 0.75$, taking $n = 1.33$.

The spectral distribution of the radiation may be expressed in several ways. Since the intensity of light of frequency ν, $(\omega/2\pi)$, may be written as $W = N \cdot h\nu$ where h is Planck's constant, the spectral distribution may be written in any of the following four ways:

$$\left.\begin{array}{ll}
\left(\dfrac{d^2 W}{dl\, d\omega}\right) \propto \omega. & \text{(energy per unit path per unit} \\[0.3em]
 & \text{frequency interval)} \\[1em]
\left(\dfrac{d^2 W}{dl\, d\lambda}\right) \propto \dfrac{1}{\lambda^3}. & \text{(energy per unit path per unit} \\[0.3em]
 & \text{wavelength interval)} \\[1em]
\left(\dfrac{d^2 N}{dl\, d\omega}\right) \propto \text{const.} & \text{(number of photons per unit} \\[0.3em]
 & \text{path per unit frequency interval)} \\[1em]
\left(\dfrac{d^2 N}{dl\, d\lambda}\right) \propto \dfrac{1}{\lambda^2}. & \text{(number of photons per unit path} \\[0.3em]
 & \text{per unit wavelength interval)}
\end{array}\right\} \tag{2.23}$$

2.3 Developments of the theory

Two years after the appearance of the paper by Frank and Tamm, the latter (1939) published a more general treatment of the problem, some of the main points of which are now mentioned.

In their original theory, outlined above, Frank and Tamm made use of the asymptotic expansions of the Hankel functions for large values of the argument. However, the arguments $\sigma\rho$ and $s\rho$ in (2.13) and

(2.15) tend to zero for a fixed value of ρ if ω tends to zero. A more rigorous treatment, which does not involve asymptotic expansions, was presented by Tamm; the final expression obtained for the radiation yield is nevertheless identical with (2.17).

Field Strengths near the Wavefront

Neglecting dispersion and taking the case $\beta n > 1$, Tamm obtains very simple expressions for the field strengths of the vectors E_z, E_ρ and H_ϕ in the proximity of the wavefront.

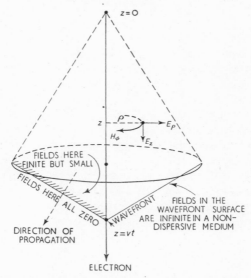

FIG. 2.3. The conical form of the wavefront in Čerenkov radiation.

The field, which is stationary with respect to the electron, is discontinuous and is bounded by the cone

$$z = vt - \rho \sqrt{(\beta^2 n^2 - 1)} \tag{2.24}$$

for which the vertex $\rho = 0$ and $z = vt$, coincides with the instantaneous position of the electron. This cone, see Fig. 2.3, is not the normal Čerenkov cone but the complementary one coincident with the wavefront.

In front of this cone the field is zero; on its surface the vectors **A**, **E** and **H** are infinite and gradually diminish as one moves backwards

C

from the surface. Thus a conical wave of discontinuity is propagated along the z-axis with the velocity of the electron. Behind this conical surface the field strengths are given by the following simple relations

$$\left.\begin{aligned} H_\phi &= -\, q\beta\rho/R^3 \\ E_\rho &= -\, q\rho/n^2R^3 \\ \text{and } E_z &= +\, q(vt-z)/n^2R^3 \end{aligned}\right\} \qquad (2.25)$$

where

$$\left.\begin{aligned} R &= \sqrt{[(z-vt)^2 - \rho^2(\beta^2n^2-1)]} \\ \text{and } q &= 2e(\beta^2n^2-1) \end{aligned}\right\} \qquad (2.26)$$

In the presence of dispersion the fields are nowhere infinite and the expressions corresponding to (2.25) and (2.26) are much more complex, containing ω and the dispersion law $(dn/d\omega)$ for the medium.

Duration of the Light Flash

Since, in a non-dispersive medium, the wavefront is infinitely thin, the duration of the light pulse at any given point within the Čerenkov cone is infinitely short. If however the medium is dispersive, the Čerenkov angle θ is different for different wavelengths and the wave trains will spread out from one another as shown in Fig. 2.4. The duration Δt of the light pulse observed along a line parallel to the axis of the particle, at a distance ρ from this axis, will be given by:

$$\Delta t = \frac{\rho}{\beta c}\,\{\sqrt{[\beta^2n^2(\omega_2)-1]} - \sqrt{[\beta^2n^2(\omega_1)-1]}\}$$

$$= \frac{\rho}{\beta c}\,(\tan\theta_2 - \tan\theta_1) \qquad (2.27)$$

where ω_1 and ω_2 are the frequency limits of the light receiver and θ_1 and θ_2 the corresponding Čerenkov angles.

As an example, suppose we consider observing the light flash at a distance of 10 cm to the side of the track of a fast electron traversing water ($\beta = 1$, $\bar{n} = 1\cdot33$ and $\theta = 41°$). From (2.27), between wavelength limits of say $\lambda = 4000$ and 6000 Å, we find $\Delta t = 5 \times 10^{-12}$ sec. With achromatic systems using focusing arrangements, intrinsic response times much shorter than this may however be obtained, as described in section 7.2.

The theoretical limits to the speed of response of various types of counter have been discussed by Frank (1956); on the experimental side the results reported by Bay *et al.* (1952) indicate that the practical limit occurs at resolving times of the order of 10^{-10} sec.

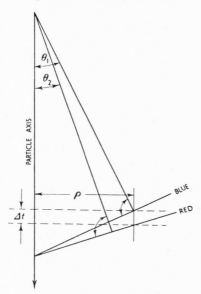

FIG. 2.4. The duration of the light pulse in a dispersive medium.

Radiation Phenomena in Moving Media

It is interesting to speculate on the effects that might occur if the observer is at rest with respect to the electron while both are immersed in a swiftly moving medium. This problem has been treated independently by Tamm (1939), Jauch and Watson (1948) and by Nag and Sayied (1956). The three groups arrive at the same conclusions, that Čerenkov radiation is still observed in this case, and that its intensity and spectral distribution are identical with those obtained in the normal system in which the observer and medium are at rest and the electron is in motion.

Since the electric field in the rest system of the electron is stationary, it follows that the magnetic intensity $\mathbf{H}'$ will vanish. The magnetic induction $\mathbf{B}'$ is however different from zero provided $n \neq 1$. This magnetic field is caused by the variations of the polarization of the medium as it moves through the inhomogeneous electric field surrounding the (stationary) electron. The presence of this vector $\mathbf{B}'$, and the influence of the motion of the dispersive medium on the field of the electron, are responsible for the radiation that would be observed in a system moving with respect to the medium and stationary with respect to the charged particle.

By transforming the frame of reference in two stages, Nag and Sayied go further, and deduce the results of the Frank and Tamm theory directly from the invariance of the electrodynamic equations of Maxwell. In the first stage they calculate the electromagnetic field experienced by an observer at rest with respect to the charged particle with the medium moving past at a constant velocity (as considered by Tamm and by Jauch and Watson). In the second stage the observer is supposed to move with the medium at the same velocity (i.e. observer at rest with respect to the medium but both moving with respect to the charged particle); the electromagnetic field as seen by him is then calculated using the Lorentz-Minkowski transformation relations for electromagnetic fields in moving media given by the special theory of relativity.

It might be pointed out that although it is possible to detect a moving medium in this way, the induced fields only exist if the dielectric constant ϵ or the permeability μ of the medium $\neq 1$; there is therefore no possibility of detecting an "ether drift".

Since Nag and Sayied assume their medium to have magnetic as well as dielectric properties, their results are more general than those of Frank and Tamm. The radiation yield, for instance, is of the form:

$$\frac{dW}{dl} = \frac{e^2}{c^2} \int\limits_{\beta n > 1} \mu \left(1 - \frac{1}{\epsilon\mu\beta^2}\right) . \, \omega d\omega \qquad (2.28)$$

in agreement with that obtained by Sitenko, equation (3.21), section 3.2.

The asymmetry of ϵ and μ in equation (2.28) stems from the asymmetry between $\mathbf{D}$ and $\mathbf{B}$ in the divergence equations (2.4a) and (2.6a), arising in turn from the non-existence of free magnetic poles.

The Effects of Slowing Down

Returning to the case of normal Čerenkov radiation, we may ask how stringent is the condition, assumed throughout the treatment by

Frank and Tamm, that the velocity of the particle is constant. As the particle traverses the medium it will lose energy by ionization and Bremsstrahlung, and its direction of motion will also be affected by these processes and by non-radiative Coulomb scattering. As the particle slows down, the value of β will change and hence the Čerenkov angle θ. To ensure that the coherence is preserved it is only necessary that the deceleration of the particle shall not be too rapid. The condition to be satisfied may be expressed in the form

$$T \cdot \left(\frac{dv}{dt}\right) \ll (c/n) \tag{2.29}$$

where T is one period of the wave in question and (dv/dt) is the deceleration of the electron. This condition in practice is easily satisfied in the visible region, even for the dominant source of energy loss, namely ionization, which is $(dW/dl) \sim 2$ MeV . g^{-1} . cm^{-2}.

Other effects of the slowing down are discussed elsewhere, see Sections 3.8 and 7.3.

2.4 Modifications introduced by the quantum theory

In the classical theory of Čerenkov radiation presented above, effects due to the reaction of the emitted radiation on the motion of the particle have been ignored. When these effects are taken into account, the expressions for the radiation condition and the energy production have forms which differ slightly from those obtained in the original theory. Ginsburg (1940a) has presented a treatment of the theory of the Čerenkov effect based on the quantum theory, and has introduced the necessary modifications by allowing for the recoil experienced by the particle when it emits the radiation. Quantum treatments have also been presented by Sokolov (1940), Beck (1948), Schiff (1949), Taniuti (1951), Neamtan (1953), Tidman (1956) and others. The modifications are naturally expected to be small, since the energy of the radiated quanta is small compared with the kinetic energy of the particle.

It is possible to arrive at the radiation condition by quite simple arguments about the conservation of momentum and energy, in a manner similar to that used in discussing the Compton effect. Following Cox (1944), let a charged particle of rest mass m be travelling through the medium at a constant velocity u. Assume now that at some stage along its track it emits a photon of energy $h\nu$ at an angle θ with respect to the original direction of the particle. The latter will experience an instantaneous loss of energy and it will be assumed that it now travels with velocity v at some angle ϕ with respect to its original direction. Conservation of momentum leads to the equations:

$$mv(1 - v^2/c^2)^{-\frac{1}{2}} \cos \phi + \frac{h}{\lambda} \cos \theta = mu(1 - u^2/c^2)^{-\frac{1}{2}} \quad (2.30)$$

and

$$mv(1 - v^2/c^2)^{-\frac{1}{2}} \sin \phi - \frac{h}{\lambda} \sin \theta = 0, \quad (2.31)$$

while conservation of energy leads to:

$$mc^2(1 - u^2/c^2)^{-\frac{1}{2}} = mc^2(1 - v^2/c^2)^{-\frac{1}{2}} + h\nu \quad (2.32)$$

Eliminating ϕ and v and writing $\nu = c/n\lambda$, where n is the refractive index of the medium, we get:

$$\cos \theta = \frac{c}{nu} + h(1 - u^2/c^2)^{\frac{1}{2}}(n^2 - 1)/2mun^2\lambda \quad (2.33)$$

which may in turn be written as:

$$\cos \theta = \frac{1}{\beta n} + \left(\frac{\Lambda}{\lambda}\right) \cdot \left(\frac{n^2 - 1}{2n^2}\right) \quad (2.34)$$

where Λ is the de Broglie wavelength of the particle

$$\Lambda = \frac{h\sqrt{(1 - \beta^2)}}{mu} = \frac{\sqrt{(1 - \beta^2)}}{\beta} \lambda_0 \quad (2.35)$$

and λ_0, the Compton wavelength, $= 0.024$ Å.

We see that the second term in (2.34) by which this differs from the classical radiation condition, $\cos \theta = 1/\beta n$, is extremely small in any practical case. For example, for electrons at the Čerenkov threshold in water (260 keV), $\beta = 0.75$, so that from (2.35) we have $\Lambda \approx 0.021$ Å and $(\Lambda/\lambda) \approx 5 \cdot 10^{-6}$. λ in (2.30) and (2.31) is the wavelength of the light *in the medium*. The validity of these equations rests on the assumption that the momentum of a photon in the medium is $(h\nu n/c)$ and not $(h\nu/c)$, a point discussed elsewhere by March (1931).

While the medium has been assumed to modify the momentum of the photon, no such modification has been made for the particle. The justification for this is that the wavelength of the photons (in the optical region) is so large compared with interatomic distances that the radiation is influenced by the macroscopic properties of the medium, whereas the particle, owing to its small de Broglie wavelength, finds itself travelling most of the time through space, its dimensions being small compared with these interatomic distances. It is for this reason that in (2.30) and (2.31) the ordinary relativistic equations for momenta in free space are used. These questions are discussed in detail by Cox and also appear in the work of Michels and Patterson (1941).

It is appropriate at this point to say something about coherence in the quantum picture of Čerenkov radiation. It may be asked how the phases of the individual quanta are defined, so that the coherence may be preserved. The answer to this question is that in a light wave the uncertainty of the phase ϕ is related to a corresponding uncertainty of the number of quanta N in the wave, by the expression $\Delta N . \Delta\phi \sim 1$. Thus, for a number of quanta emitted from the track of our particle, the phases may be defined as closely as we please, in which case either the number of quanta in a given wavelet is entirely undetermined, or, the total intensity may be known but it is then not possible to say which quanta are associated with which part of the wavefront. These questions are discussed by Heitler (1944, Chapter II, p. 66).

With the quantum condition for radiation (2.34), Ginsburg (1940a) uses Schrödinger's equation to obtain the following expression for the radiation output from a charge e, which it is assumed has no magnetic moment:

$$\frac{dW}{dl} = \frac{e^2}{c^2} \int \left\{ 1 - \frac{1}{\beta^2 n^2(\omega)} \left[1 + \frac{n^4}{4} \left(\frac{\hbar\omega}{mc^2}\right)^2 + n^2 \left(\frac{\hbar\omega}{mc^2}\right) \right] \right\} \omega d\omega. \quad (2.36)$$

Strictly speaking, (2.36) is only valid in the non-relativistic case. Since $\beta n > 1$ we must therefore assume n to be large. However, (2.36) will not differ appreciably when we extrapolate to high velocities. We see that (2.36) differs from the classical expression only by the presence of two small terms of higher order. It is interesting that whereas the classical expression for (dW/dl) diverges for a *non*-dispersive medium, (2.36) does not.

Using Dirac's equation, Ginsburg extends the treatment to consider the radiation of a non-relativistic electron *with* an associated magnetic moment μ_0, which he assumes is polarized along the axis of motion. The radiation yield now contains two terms; the first arises from the charge and is identical with (2.36), and the second arises from the magnetic moment, and has the form:

$$\left(\frac{dW}{dl}\right)_{\mu_0} = \frac{\mu_0^2}{\beta^2 c^4}\int n^2(\omega)\omega^3\left\{1 - \frac{1}{\beta^2 n^2(\omega)}\left[1 + \frac{n^4}{4}\left(\frac{\hbar\omega}{mc^2}\right)^2 + n^2\left(\frac{\hbar\omega}{mc^2}\right)\right]\right\}d\omega. \quad (2.37)$$

This may be compared with the classical expressions for the magnetic Čerenkov effect (see section 3.1). Again there is similarity between the quantum and classical results, with the exception of the higher order terms. In addition to the direct magnetic radiation represented by (2.37), there should be yet a further term arising from transitions in which there is spin flip, the dipole moment reversing during the passage of the electron through the medium. The method used by Ginsburg to calculate this effect leads however to erroneous results, the cause for which he discusses at length.

Ginsburg finally uses Dirac's electron theory to obtain the radiation output in the case of an ultra-relativistic "magnetic" electron. This leads to the result that at very high energies the magnetic radiation is absent, in agreement with the classical theory when the dipole axis lies along the line of motion; see section 3.1, equation (3.3). When $\beta \to 1$, $(dW/dl)_\mu \to 0$.

In addition, when $v \to c$, photon recoil effects become negligible and the yield of radiation is then identical with that obtained for a *non* magnetic electron in the classical theory.

Spin Effects

It has recently been shown by Sokolov and Loskutov (1957) that if the particle has spin, the polarization, the threshold condition and radiation yield are slightly modified. The total radiation, expressed in units of energy per unit path length, may be written as the sum of a number of separate components $W\binom{s}{j}$, where the index s refers to the spin ($s = \frac{1}{2}$, 0) and j refers to different types of polarization ($j = 2$, 3, $+ 1$, $- 1$). The co-ordinate system for defining these polarizations is the following: $j = 3$ corresponds to a linearly polarized photon in the plane containing the photon and the particle (with its axis perpendicular to the direction of motion of the photon), $j = 2$ corresponds to the orthogonal case (i.e. the E-vector tangential to the surface of the

Čerenkov core) and $j = \pm 1$ corresponds to the two cases of circular polarization.

On this basis, the normal Čerenkov radiation in the case of a particle without spin may be written

$$W(^0_2) = 0, \quad W(^0_3) = \frac{e^2}{c^2} \int_0^{\omega_{max}} \omega(1 - \cos^2 \theta)\, d\omega. \tag{2.38}$$

But for the radiation of particles with half-integral spin, we have an additional contribution, of the form:

$$W(^{\frac{1}{2}}_2) = \frac{e^2}{c^2} \int_0^{\omega_{max}} \omega \left[\frac{n^2 \omega^2 \hbar^2}{4 c^2 p^2}\right] \cdot \left(1 - \frac{1}{n^2}\right) d\omega \tag{2.39}$$

and the total yield is:

$W(^{\frac{1}{2}}_3) = W(^0_3) + W(^{\frac{1}{2}}_2)$, with the additional condition

$W(^{\frac{1}{2}}_{-1}) = W(^{\frac{1}{2}}_{+1})$

(2.39) is a quantum effect, and it is seen that if $\hbar \to 0$ (classical approximation) the radiation, as for particles without spin, will again be completely linearly polarized.

The spin effect leads then to a contribution to the radiation which does not disappear at the threshold $(E = E_0)$, whereas the linearly polarized portion of the radiation vanishes at the threshold, and slightly above the threshold it increases linearly with $(E - E_0)$:

$$\text{For} \quad (E - E_0)/E_0 \ll 1, \quad W(^0_3) = 2\frac{e^2}{c^2} \left(\frac{E - E_0}{mc^2}\right) \int_0^{\omega_{max}} n^2 \cdot \omega d\omega \tag{2.40}$$

Although Harding and Henderson (1948) report non-polarized radiation at the threshold, this observation cannot be attributed to spin effects, because the $\hbar^2$ factor in (2.39) leads to a value for $W(^{\frac{1}{2}}_2)$ which is far below detectability with present techniques.

Spin effects have also been worked out by Ginsburg (1942 and 1943), who calculated the radiation from a particle with spin 3/2, and by Shirobokov (1949) who considers the case of a particle with spin 2.

CHAPTER 3

EXTENSIONS TO THE THEORY*

3.1 Radiation from dipoles, multipoles and oscillators

(a) *Electric and Magnetic Dipole Radiation*

We have so far only considered the radiation produced by the passage of a point charge through a dielectric, i.e. the normal Čerenkov effect. However, Čerenkov radiation will also be produced when an electric or magnetic dipole passes through a dielectric medium, provided of course its velocity is above the threshold. The radiation mechanism is the same as for the normal effect, though the intensity is much lower since the field associated with a dipole falls off more rapidly with distance.

It is easy to see superficially why the effect is so much weaker. Consider for instance an electric dipole of moment p orientated so that its axis lies along the direction of motion. This dipole may be considered as consisting of two charges ϵ of opposite sign separated by a distance $d = p/\epsilon$. The fields associated with the charges ϵ have opposite sign and therefore practically cancel each other when d is small. Each charge will pass in turn through a given point in the medium, with a time lag of $\Delta\tau = (d/v) = (p/\epsilon v)$. If the value of the polarization field for one of the charges is $P_\epsilon = A\,\epsilon e^{i\omega t}$, the resultant field for the two charges is

$$P_p = A\,\epsilon e^{i\omega t}\,[1 - \exp(-i\omega p/\epsilon v)] = \frac{i\omega p}{v}\,Ae^{i\omega t} = \left(\frac{i\omega p}{v\epsilon}\right).P_\epsilon.$$

The resultant field from the dipole thus depends on the frequency ω of the radiation in question; this would be expected, since the degree of cancellation will depend on the ratio of the time lag $\Delta\tau$ to the period of one oscillation of the field, $1/\omega$. The significance of this is that since the radiation output per unit bandwidth is proportional to the square of the fields, i.e. $W \propto P_p^2$, it follows that an extra factor ω^2 appears in

---

* The contents of this chapter are included for the sake of completeness; an understanding of these specialized topics is unnecessary for the general reader. Since the inception of this book, the comprehensive work of Bolotovsky (1957) has appeared, which covers much of the theoretical work in the field.

32

the expression for the total radiation yield, so that the spectral distribution of this type of Čerenkov radiation falls off much more steeply with the wavelength λ; it will vary as $\omega^3 d\omega$, or $(1/\lambda^5) d\lambda$. It will be remembered that for normal Čerenkov radiation $W \propto \omega d\omega$ or $(1/\lambda^3) d\lambda$.

Classical treatments of the problem of Čerenkov radiation from moving dipoles have been given by Frank (1943), Eidman (1956) and by Balazs (1956). There are two cases, the first in which the dipole axis is parallel to the axis of motion of the particle, and the second in which these axes are perpendicular to one another. We shall consider those cases in which the "particle", in its own frame of reference, is either a pure electric dipole or a pure magnetic dipole. A moving magnetic dipole will not however appear pure as seen in the rest frame of the observer, for it will acquire an electric dipole, and vice versa. Temporarily neglecting these induced effects, and assuming that the particle has either an electric moment p_0 (when at rest) or a magnetic moment μ_0, Balazs* obtains the following expressions for the radiation from dipoles moving with a velocity v through an isotropic dielectric of refractive index n; the yields are expressed in units of energy per unit bandwidth and per unit time:

(i) *Electric Dipole Radiation*

$$p_0 \parallel v \qquad W_{\mathrm{EL}} = \frac{p_0^2(1 - \beta^2)}{vc^2} \int \omega^3 \left(1 - \frac{1}{\beta^2 n^2}\right) d\omega \qquad (3.1)$$

$$p_0 \perp v \qquad W_{\mathrm{EL}} = \frac{p_0^2}{2vc^2} \int n^2 . \omega^3 \left(1 - \frac{1}{\beta^2 n^2}\right)^2 d\omega. \qquad (3.2)$$

(ii) *Magnetic Dipole Radiation*

$$\mu_0 \parallel v \qquad W_{\mathrm{MAG}} = \frac{\mu_0^2(1 - \beta^2)}{vc^2} \int n^2 . \omega^3 \left(1 - \frac{1}{\beta^2 n^2}\right) d\omega \qquad (3.3)$$

$$\mu_0 \perp v \qquad W_{\mathrm{MAG}} = \frac{\mu_0^2 v}{2c^4} \int n^4 . \omega^3 \left(1 - \frac{1}{\beta^2 n^2}\right)^2 d\omega. \qquad (3.4)$$

The factor $(1 - \beta^2)$ in (3.1) and (3.3) arises from the Lorentz contraction of the dipole, which reduces its effective moment relative to the medium. In those cases (3.2) and (3.4), in which the dipole axis

---

* Balazs has pointed out, in a private communication, that the corresponding expressions obtained by Frank are in error by a factor of 2, and furthermore that his equations for $\mu_0 \perp$ to v and $p_0 \perp$ to v, are inconsistent with each other.

is perpendicular to the line of motion, the radiation intensity varies in azimuth round the surface of the Čerenkov cone and is greatest in the plane perpendicular to that containing the dipole axis and the axis of motion.

Returning now to the secondary effects, when a magnetic dipole of moment μ_0 moves so that its axis is perpendicular to the line of motion, it will acquire an electric moment. Both dipole moments will then be normal to the direction of motion and their electric fields mutually orthogonal. These fields will not interfere, and the total energy loss will be the sum of the effects due to the separate moments. The general expression for the radiation in this case is then (in the same units as before):

$$\mu_0 \perp v \quad W'_{MAG} = \tfrac{1}{2} (\beta^2 n^2 - 1)^2 . (\mu^2 + p_1^2/n^2) . \int (\omega/v)^3 \, d\omega$$

where p_1 is the induced electric dipole moment. In this particular case we have $p_1 = \beta\mu = \beta\mu_0$ so that we get

$$\mu_0 \perp v \quad W'_{MAG} = \frac{\mu_0^2 v}{2c^4} \int n^4 \omega^3 . \left(1 - \frac{1}{\beta^2 n^2}\right)^2 . \left(1 + \frac{\beta^2}{n^2}\right) d\omega \qquad (3.4a)$$

(3.4a) differs from (3.4) by the extra term (β^2/n^2) due to this induced electric dipole. When $\beta \sim 1$, the term is of the order of 0·6 for water. The effect of the induced dipole is not therefore negligible. When, however, μ_0 is parallel to v, the induced moment is zero and equation (3.3) is therefore exact.

Taking first the case of the electric dipole, let us compare the radiation intensity with that of the normal Čerenkov radiation for a point charge. If we re-write the equation for radiation yield for the latter, (2.17), in units of energy . (unit bandwidth)$^{-1}$. (unit time)$^{-1}$, it will have the form:

$$W_e = \frac{e^2 v}{c^2} \int \omega \left(1 - \frac{1}{\beta^2 n^2(\omega)}\right) d\omega \qquad (3.5)$$

from which we deduce:

$$(W_{\parallel\,EL}/W_e) = \frac{p_0^2 \omega^2 (1 - \beta^2)}{e^2 v^2}. \qquad (3.6)$$

To take a practical case, consider a fast moving atom having a typical electric dipole moment p_0 of say 3×10^{-18} (e.s.u. $\times$ cm) travelling at a velocity $v = 2 \cdot 10^{10}$ cm/sec, so that $\beta = 0 \cdot 7$. At a wavelength

$\lambda \sim 4000$ Å, $\omega \sim 5 \cdot 10^{15}$. Comparing the Čerenkov radiation from this with that of an electron, for which $e \approx 5 \times 10^{-10}$ e.s.u., from (3.6) we get $(W_{\parallel \text{ EL}}/W_e) \sim 10^{-6}$, which is a quite negligible and undetectable amount of light.

In the case of magnetic radiation also, the light yields are too small to detect. Consider the case of an electron, with its magnetic moment $\mu_0 \approx 10^{-20}$ erg. gauss^{-1}, oriented parallel to the line of motion. From (3.3) and (3.5), we have in this case:

$$(W_{\parallel \text{ MAG}}/W_e) = (1 - \beta^2) \left(\frac{\mu n \omega}{ev}\right)^2 \approx 3 \times 10^{-11} \tag{3.7}$$

if $v = 2 \cdot 10^{10}$ cm/sec, $\omega = 5 \cdot 10^{15}$ and $n = 1 \cdot 6$.

Ginsburg (1940a, 1952), who also derives expressions for the properties of "magnetic" Čerenkov radiation, by a method different from that used by Frank, points out that if the particle has charge *and* a magnetic moment, and if furthermore the axis of the latter is perpendicular to the line of motion, there is a further contribution arising from cross-terms in the Poynting vector, so that the radiation yield due to the magnetic moment will be considerably larger than that calculated from (3.4). This *extra* term W'' amounts to:

$$W'' = \left(\frac{2\mu n \omega}{ev}\right) . W_e \tag{3.8}$$

which, with the same constants as before, is $\approx 1 \cdot 6 \times 10^{-5} W_e$. Again, however, it is seen that such an effect is far below present attainable threshold sensitivities.

(b) *Radiation from Multipoles*

This has been discussed by Frank (1952) and by Muzikář (1955). Using the same notation as before, and indicating only orders of magnitude, the latter obtained the following relation for the intensity of radiation from an electric quadrupole having a moment p_Q:

$$(W_Q/W_e) \sim \left(\frac{p_Q}{2e}\right)^2 . \left(\frac{\omega}{v}\right)^4 . \tag{3.9}$$

For instance, an atom with a typical quadrupole moment $p_Q \sim 3 \cdot 10^{-27}$ e.s.u $\times$ cm, $\omega \sim 10^{15}$ and $v \sim c$, will yield Čerenkov radiation of an intensity $\sim 10^{-17}$ of that for a single electron, again obviously unobservable.

(c) *Motion of an Oscillator through a Medium*

Having seen that Čerenkov radiation may be produced when a "static" dipole traverses a medium, one may ask what phenomena will occur when an oscillator (e.g. an excited atom) replaces the dipole. At low velocities there is the normal Doppler effect, while at velocities exceeding the phase velocity of light in the medium, diverse and complicated phenomena occur. There is a "complex" Doppler effect, in which *two* line frequencies may be produced; there is, however, in this case, *no* true Čerenkov effect. These various phenomena have been discussed at length by Frank (1942 and 1943), Akhiezer *et al.* (1950) and by Ginsburg and Frank (1947a).

3.2 Radiation in isotropic ferrites

A ferrite is here defined as a substance having zero conductivity, and a magnetic permeability μ which is assumed to be greater than unity; it may also in general possess a dielectric constant ϵ which is greater than unity. A fast charged particle traversing such a medium will produce Čerenkov radiation of a character similar to normal Čerenkov radiation, provided the medium is isotropic, i.e. both μ and ϵ the same in all directions.

Sitenko (1954) found that the radiation output per unit path-length in such a "magnetic" medium was:

$$H = \frac{e^2}{c^2} \int \mu \left(1 - \frac{1}{\beta^2 \epsilon \mu} \right) . \omega d\omega \tag{3.10}$$

with the normal coherence condition $\cos \theta = \dfrac{1}{\beta n}$, where n is here equal to $\sqrt{(\epsilon \mu)}$. Equation (3.10) differs from the Frank and Tamm expression by the factor μ; the radiation intensity is therefore μ times as great as that for a similar non-magnetic medium. Ferrites would thus seem preferable to dielectrics for the possible generation of microwaves (see Section 3.4) but unfortunately, in the centimetre region, the present known ferrites have $\mu < 2$ and the gain is therefore small.

Other treatments of the problems of Čerenkov radiation in ferromagnetics have been given by Ivanenko and Gurgenidze (1949) and by Ivanenko and Tzytovich (1955).

3.3 Čerenkov radiation in anisotropic and optically active media

The Čerenkov radiation produced by charged particles traversing media which are anisotropic in ϵ or μ, has properties different from and more complex than those met in the case of isotropic media. In general, the coherence conditions, polarizations and radiation intensities are different for the emission of the two types of waves, the ordinary and the extraordinary. In the most general case, there may be an arbitrary angle between the direction of the particle and the optic axis, the medium may be isotropic in μ but not in ϵ, or vice versa, or it may be anisotropic in both. Furthermore, in the extreme cases there may be two optic axes, or the optic axes for the dielectric and magnetic properties may not coincide. Some but not all of these more general problems have been worked out by Pafomov (1956), Tanaka (1951 and 1954) and Kaganov (1953a).

The results for certain specific cases only will be presented here. The media (uniaxial crystals) will possess anisotropy in either ϵ or μ, but not in both simultaneously, and the results will be quoted only for the two specific cases of the charge moving parallel to the optic axis or perpendicular to it. The following notations will be used: W and H will denote the radiation yields per unit path length, for media that are anisotropic in ϵ or μ respectively. o and e refer to ordinary and extraordinary waves respectively, while $\parallel$ or $\perp$ will denote whether the particle is moving parallel or perpendicular to the optic axis. θ will have the normal interpretation, though the coherence conditions in aniso-tropic media are more specific than those in isotropic media. Since in some cases the intensities of the radiation are different on different generatrices of the radiation cones, the angle ϕ is introduced to denote the azimuth angle on a given cone. In some cases W and H are given with respect to ϕ and expressed as a yield per unit azimuth range $d\phi$.

(a) *Anisotropic Dielectrics*

With the coordinate system shown in Fig. 3.1(a) it is assumed that $\epsilon_o = \epsilon_x = \epsilon_y$, $\epsilon_e = \epsilon_z$ and μ is isotropic. In this case there is no emission of ordinary waves, so that we have:

$$W_{o\,\parallel} = 0. \qquad (3.11)$$

There is only one Čerenkov cone, belonging to extraordinary waves and this, by symmetry, is a circular cone with an intensity uniform over its surface, for all values of ϕ.

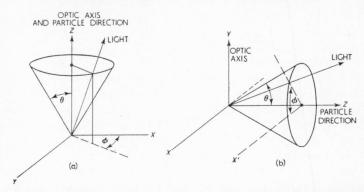

FIG. 3.1. The co-ordinate system used for the discussion on anisotropic media. Particle moving (a) along, and (b) perpendicular to the optic axis.

The refractive index at angle θ for e-waves is given by:

$$\frac{\mu}{n_e^2} = \frac{\cos^2\theta}{\epsilon_o} + \frac{\sin^2\theta}{\epsilon_e} \tag{3.12}$$

and the threshold condition is

$$(\epsilon_e/\epsilon_o) \cdot (\beta^2\mu\epsilon_o - 1) > 0. \tag{3.13}$$

The radiation yield is given by:

$$W_{e\,\|} = \frac{e^2}{c^2} \int \left| \left(\mu - \frac{1}{\beta^2\epsilon_o} \right) \right| \omega \, d\omega. \tag{3.14}$$

These results, obtained by Pafomov, are the same as those found by Ginsburg (1940b) for a pure dielectric if we put $\mu = 1$ in (3.12), (3.13) and (3.14). The coherence relation for a pure dielectric in this case is:

$$\cos\theta_{e\,\|} = \frac{1}{\beta\sqrt{\epsilon_e}} \sqrt{\left[\frac{1}{1 + \dfrac{1}{\beta^2\epsilon_e}(1 - \epsilon_e/\epsilon_o)} \right]} \tag{3.15}$$

If, instead, the particle is moving perpendicular to the optic axis, Fig. 3.1(b), there is emission of both types of waves. There are now two refractive indices, n_e defined by (3.12) and n_o given by $n_0^2 = \mu\epsilon_o$. (3.16)

Ordinary waves—The coherence condition is now

$$\cos\theta_{o\,\perp} = \frac{1}{\beta n_o} = \frac{1}{\beta\sqrt{(\mu\epsilon_o)}}. \tag{3.17}$$

This does not contain ϕ so we again have a cone of circular form, though the intensity distribution is now non-uniform over its surface. The radiation yield is given by:

$$W_{o\perp} = \frac{e^2}{2\pi c^2} \int \frac{\mu(\beta^2 \epsilon_o \mu - 1) \cos^2\phi \; \omega \; d\omega \; d\phi}{\beta^2 \epsilon_o \mu \cos^2\phi + \sin^2\phi}. \tag{3.18}$$

Extraordinary waves—In this case the conic surface has a complicated shape and again the intensity varies over this surface. The yield is of the form:

$$W_{e\perp} = \frac{e^2}{2\pi c^2} \int \frac{(\beta^2 \epsilon_e \mu - 1) \sin^2\phi \; \omega \; d\omega \; d\phi}{\beta^2 [\beta^2 \epsilon_o \mu \cos^2\phi + \sin^2\phi] [\epsilon_o + (\epsilon_e - \epsilon_o) \sin^2\phi]}. \tag{3.19}$$

Equations (3.17), (3.18) and (3.19) are valid for a pure dielectric ($\mu = 1$) in which case the coherence relation relevant to (3.19) is:

$$\cos^2\theta_{e\perp} = \frac{\cos^2\phi + \left(\dfrac{\epsilon_e}{\epsilon_o}\right) \sin^2\phi}{\beta^2 \epsilon_e \left[1 - \dfrac{1}{\beta^2 \epsilon_e} \left(1 - \dfrac{\epsilon_e}{\epsilon_o}\right) \sin^2\phi\right]}. \tag{3.20}$$

Polarizations—In the case of a particle travelling along the optic axis, the polarization of the e-ray is always radial to the Čerenkov cone as in the normal isotropic case. In the second case, Fig. 3.1(b), the radiation of the o-rays is polarized in the plane XZ while that of the e-rays is polarized in the principal plane, so that the polarization on different generatrices of the cone depends on ϕ.

(b) *Anisotropic Ferrites*

With the same coordinate system as in Fig. 3.1(a) we will assume the medium has the following characteristics: $\mu_o = \mu_x = \mu_y$, $\mu_e = \mu_z$ and ϵ is isotropic. The refractive indices for the two types of rays are now

$$n_o^2 = \mu_o \epsilon \quad \text{and} \quad \frac{\epsilon}{n_e^2} = \frac{\cos^2\theta}{\mu_o} + \frac{\sin^2\theta}{\mu_e}. \tag{3.21}$$

For motion along the optical axis, there is no radiation of e-type waves, in contradistinction to the case of anisotropic dielectrics, so that

$$H_{e\parallel} = 0. \tag{3.22}$$

D

For the yield of o-type waves, Pafomov obtains:

$$H_{o\parallel} = \frac{e^2}{c^2} \int \left(\mu_o - \frac{1}{\beta^2 \epsilon} \right) \omega \, d\omega, \tag{3.23}$$

with the simple threshold condition

$$\beta^2 \mu_o \epsilon > 1. \tag{3.24}$$

For motion perpendicular to the axis there are, as in anisotropic dielectrics, two radiation cones, each having an intensity distribution non-uniform in ϕ. The radiation yields for the two wave-types are given by:

$$H_{o\perp} = \frac{e^2}{2\pi c^2} \int \frac{(\mu_o - 1/\epsilon\beta^2) \sin^2\phi \; \omega \, d\omega \, d\phi}{\beta^2 \epsilon \mu_o \cos^2\phi + \sin^2\phi} \tag{3.25}$$

and

$$H_{e\perp} = \frac{e^2}{2\pi c^2} \int \left| \frac{\mu_o^2 (\beta^2 \epsilon \mu_e - 1) \cos^2\phi \; \omega \, d\omega \, d\phi}{[\beta^2 \epsilon \mu_o \cos^2\phi + \sin^2\phi] [\mu_o + (\mu_e - \mu_o) \sin^2\phi]} \right| \tag{3.26}$$

The difference between Čerenkov radiation in media which are anisotropic in their magnetic properties from that in media anisotropic in their dielectric properties is clear by comparing (3.18) with (3.25) and (3.19) with (3.26). The value ϕ which corresponds to a maximum in a magnetically anisotropic medium, is the angle at which zero intensity is observed in an anisotropic dielectric, and vice versa.

This is true for both types of waves.

A numerical example—We will consider the case of a single (uniaxial) crystal of titanium dioxide, an anisotropic dielectric with $\mu = 1$.

In most practical cases the difference between the two refractive indices is small, so that the resulting intensities differ only slightly from that calculated for an isotropic medium having the same refractive index as that for the o-wave in the crystal. For example, let us consider 340 MeV protons travelling through rutile TiO_2, for which:

$$n_e = 2.9029 \qquad \epsilon_e = 8.41 \qquad \beta = 0.68$$
$$n_o = 2.6158 \qquad \epsilon_o = 6.81$$

Neglecting dispersion, and expressing the normal Čerenkov intensity relation in terms of the output per unit angle of ϕ

$$\text{i.e.} \qquad W_{\text{isotropic}} = \frac{e^2}{2\pi c^2} \int \omega \left(1 - \frac{1}{\beta^2 \epsilon_{\text{isotropic}}} \right) d\omega \tag{3.27}$$

we find that the intensities of the various components in the TiO_2 *relative* to $W_{isotropic}$ are given by the figures in the column I in Table 3A; this table also shows the corresponding Čerenkov angles θ.

TABLE 3A

Particle direction	Wave	ϕ	I	θ
‖ to optical axis	o	all	0	—
	e	all	1·06	52° 16′
⊥ to optical axis	o	o	1·00	55° 45′ ⎱ *
	o	$\pi/2$	0	55° 45′ ⎰
	e	o	0	59° 32′
	e	$\pi/2$	1·22	56° 55′

* Same as for an isotropic medium.

In the case of biaxial crystals the radiation characteristics are essentially the same though more complex in detail. Two peculiarities however arise, namely the effects of the dispersion of axes and conical refraction, see for example Jenkins and White (1937, p. 344).

It should be noted that the above results do not take into account optical activity.

(c) *Optically Active Media*

The general problem of the radiation produced by a charged particle moving in a medium which is anisotropic and possesses optical activity, has been solved by Sitenko and Kolomenskii (1956). We will here confine ourselves to a more restricted case which had been investigated by Kolomenskii at an earlier date (1953), namely the case of a gyrotropic medium.*

The dielectric constant ϵ for such a medium, in the simplest case for which there is only a single gyrotropic parameter, may be written in tensor form

$$\epsilon_{\alpha\beta} = \begin{pmatrix} \epsilon & -i\epsilon_g & 0 \\ i\epsilon_g & \epsilon & 0 \\ 0 & 0 & \epsilon \end{pmatrix} \tag{3.28}$$

* A gyrotropic medium is one in which waves propagated in it have elliptical polarization.

where ϵ_g is the gyration constant; see for example Sommerfeld (1954, p. 160) or Born (1933, p. 410). In such a medium the electric displacement will be expressed by the three equations.

$$\left. \begin{array}{l} D_1 = \epsilon\, E_1 - i\epsilon_g\, E_2 \\ D_2 = \epsilon\, E_2 + i\epsilon_g\, E_1 \\ D_3 = \epsilon\, E_3 \end{array} \right\} \tag{3.29}$$

An example of a physical medium which has those properties is that of quartz, which has rotational dielectric symmetry and the gyration vector is aligned with the principal axis which will be denoted by z.

The following results were obtained by Kolomenskii in the two particular cases of main interest.

(i) *An electron moving along the z-axis*—In this case, owing to symmetry, the two cones representing the o- and e-waves are both circular, with their axes collinear with the z-axis, and have a uniform distribution of intensity over their surfaces. The coherence condition is given by:

$$\cos^2\theta_{o,\,e} = \frac{\beta(2\epsilon^2 - \epsilon_g) \mp \epsilon_g\sqrt{(4\epsilon + \epsilon_g^2\beta^2)}}{2\beta[\beta^2\epsilon(\epsilon^2 - \epsilon_g^2) - \epsilon_g^2]} \tag{3.30}$$

$$0 \leqslant \cos^2\theta_{o,\,e} \leqslant 1$$

with the further restrictions

$$\left. \begin{array}{l} \text{(a)} \;\; \epsilon \geqslant \dfrac{1}{\beta^2},\; \epsilon_g^2 \leqslant \dfrac{(\epsilon\beta^2 - 1)^2}{\beta^4}; \\[2mm] \qquad\qquad -\dfrac{1}{\beta^2} \leqslant \epsilon < 0,\; -\dfrac{4\epsilon}{\beta^2} \leqslant \epsilon_g^2 \leqslant \dfrac{(\epsilon\beta^2 - 1)^2}{\beta^4} \\[3mm] \text{(b)} \;\; \epsilon \geqslant \dfrac{1}{\beta^2},\; \epsilon_g \geqslant \dfrac{\epsilon\beta^2 - 1}{\beta^2};\; 0 \leqslant \epsilon \leqslant \dfrac{1}{\beta^2},\; \epsilon_g \geqslant \dfrac{1 - \epsilon\beta^2}{\beta^2}; \\[2mm] \qquad\qquad\qquad\qquad \epsilon \leqslant 0,\; \epsilon_g \leqslant \dfrac{\epsilon\beta^2 - 1}{\beta^2} \\[3mm] \text{(c)} \;\; \epsilon > \dfrac{1}{\beta^2},\; \epsilon_g \leqslant \dfrac{1 - \epsilon\beta^2}{\beta^2};\; 0 \leqslant \epsilon \leqslant \dfrac{1}{\beta^2},\; \epsilon_g \leqslant \dfrac{\epsilon\beta^2 - 1}{\beta^2}; \\[2mm] \qquad\qquad\qquad\qquad \epsilon \leqslant 0,\; \epsilon_g \geqslant \dfrac{1 - \epsilon\beta^2}{\beta^2} \end{array} \right\} \tag{3.31}$$

In ranges (a) both types of waves are radiated, in ranges (b) only o-waves, and in (c) only e-waves.

Finally, the radiation yield is given by:

$$\left(\frac{dW}{dz}\right)_{o,\,e} = \frac{e^2}{2c^2} \int \left(1 - \frac{1}{\epsilon\beta^2}\right) \cdot \left[1 \pm \frac{\epsilon_g\beta(1 + \epsilon\beta^2)}{(1 - \epsilon\beta^2)\sqrt{(4\epsilon + \epsilon_g^2\beta^2)}}\right] \omega\, d\omega \tag{3.32}$$

(ii) *An electron moving perpendicular to the z-axis*—In this case the radiation pattern does not possess circular symmetry with respect of the z-axis. The surface of the cones for both o and e-type waves now have a complicated form and the radiation intensity depends on the azimuth angle ϕ. With δ given by:

$$\delta^2 = 1 - \frac{\cos^2\theta}{\sin^2\phi}, \text{ the Čerenkov relation is now expressed by:}$$

$$\delta^2_{o,\,e} = \frac{\beta[2\epsilon^2 - \epsilon_g\cos^2\phi] \mp \epsilon_g\sqrt{[\epsilon_g^2\beta^2\cos^4\phi + 4\epsilon(\epsilon\beta^2 - 1)\sin^2\phi]}}{2\beta[\epsilon(\epsilon^2 - \epsilon_g)\beta^2 + \epsilon_g^2\sin^2\phi]} \tag{3.33}$$

$$0 \leqslant \delta^2 \leqslant 1$$

and the ranges of the parameters ϵ, ϵ_g and β, inside which radiation takes place, are:

$$(a) \quad \epsilon \geqslant \frac{1}{\beta^2}, \; \epsilon_g \leqslant \frac{\sqrt{[\epsilon(\epsilon\beta^2 - 1)]}}{\beta}$$

$$(b) \quad \epsilon \geqslant \frac{1}{\beta^2}, \; \epsilon_g \geqslant \frac{\sqrt{[\epsilon(\epsilon\beta^2 - 1)]}}{\beta};$$

$$(b') \quad \epsilon \leqslant 0, \; \epsilon_g \leqslant -\frac{\sqrt{[\epsilon(\epsilon\beta^2 - 1)]}}{\beta}$$

$$(c) \quad \epsilon \geqslant \frac{1}{\beta^2}, \; \epsilon_g \leqslant -\frac{\sqrt{[\epsilon(\epsilon\beta^2 - 1)]}}{\beta};$$

$$(c') \quad \epsilon \leqslant 0, \; \epsilon_g \geqslant \frac{\sqrt{[\epsilon(\epsilon\beta^2 - 1)]}}{\beta} \tag{3.34}$$

As before, in (a) both types of waves are radiated, in (b) only o-waves and in (c) only e-waves. The radiation yield in this case is given by:

$$\left(\frac{dW}{dz}\right)_{o,\,e} = \frac{e^2}{4\pi c^2} \int_\omega \int_{\phi=o}^{2\pi} \left(1 - \frac{1}{\epsilon\beta^2}\right) \times$$

$$\times \left\{1 \pm \frac{\epsilon_g\beta\cos^2\phi}{\sqrt{[4\epsilon(\epsilon\beta^2 - 1)\sin^2\phi + \beta^2\epsilon_g^2\cos^4\phi]}}\right\} \omega\,d\omega\,d\phi \tag{3.35}$$

3.4 Radiation in the microwave region of the spectrum

It has already been pointed out that there is no limit to the spectrum of Čerenkov radiation on the long-wave side, provided the medium is free from absorption bands in this region. Ginsburg (1947a, b) was the first to propose that the Čerenkov effect could in principle be used to produce microwaves, in a range of wavelengths difficult of access by other methods, namely in the range $\lambda \sim 0.01$ to 1.0 cm. Since the yield of radiation falls with decreasing frequency, as $\omega d\omega$, or $(1/\lambda^3)\, d\lambda$, it is obvious that it is unlikely to be an efficient way of producing radio frequency radiation, and it would be difficult to obtain high powers. The source, furthermore, would give a continuous spectrum, whereas in most radio applications the aim is to produce oscillators that run on a single frequency.

There are however three points of interest in this rather special application of Čerenkov radiation. The first is that by using electron beams in which the electrons are "bunched", it is possible to enhance the radiation output by a very large factor. The second point is that by causing an electron beam to travel down a narrow channel in the dielectric medium, of dimensions small compared with the wavelength, the main source of energy loss, namely ionization, may be completely eliminated; this enables relatively low-energy electrons to produce radiation over a long path. The third and perhaps most important point is that by using circuit or resonator systems, having definite modes, it is in principle possible to concentrate the energy of the Čerenkov radiation into these modes, so that the source will then emit a line rather than a continuous spectrum. These ideas, essential to a practical application of the Čerenkov effect to microwave problems, will now be discussed.

Effects of Electron "Bunching"

First consider a single electron travelling a distance l in a medium which has a refractive index $n = 7$ in the microwave region. (Such refractive indices are realized in selected materials in certain regions of the spectrum; at this value of n the kinetic energy of the electrons has only to be ~ 5 keV to make $\beta n \approx 1$.) The output of radiation, neglecting dispersion, is then:

$$\Delta W = \frac{e^2 l}{2c^2} \cdot \omega \Delta\omega = 1.28 \times 10^{-40}\, l \cdot \omega \Delta\omega \text{ ergs} \qquad (3.36)$$

in which we have neglected dispersion, and assumed that the factor $(1 - 1/\beta^2 n^2) \approx 1$.

In a typical case, let $\omega = 2 \times 10^{12}$ (i.e. $\lambda \sim 1$ mm), $\Delta\omega = 2 \times 10^{11}$ and $l = 20$ cm. From (3.36), $\Delta W \approx 10^{-15}$ erg. If now we have a current of 10 mA of electrons radiating independently, $W \approx 60$ erg/sec, or $6\ \mu$W.

If however the electrons are "bunched", so that the dimensions of the bunches are small compared with the wavelength, the electrons in any one bunch will radiate coherently. If there are ν electrons/bunch and N bunches/sec, the radiation output will be:

$$W_{\text{coherent}} = \frac{\nu^2 e^2 f^2(\omega) l}{2c^2} N \cdot \omega d\omega \qquad (3.37)$$

where $f(\omega)$ is a form factor which depends on the size of the bunch. This will be unity for small bunches and small for bunches exceeding one wavelength, measured in the direction of emission of the radiation. In particular, for a bunch of length L (measured in the direction of the radiation),

$$f(\omega) = \sin(\omega L n/2c)/(\omega L n/2c) \qquad (3.38)$$

If the conditions are such that we may put $f(\omega) = 1$, (3.37) may be re-written:

$$W_{\text{coherent}} = \frac{el}{2c^2} I\nu \cdot \omega\Delta\omega = 8 \times 10^{-22} I I_{\text{amp}} \nu \cdot \omega\Delta\omega \qquad (3.39)$$

where the mean current $I = e\nu N$.

If we take, as before, $I = 10$ mA and put $\nu = 10^8$, W from (3.39) = 600 W. It should be mentioned that such conditions would be difficult to attain in practice. With $\nu = 10^8$ and $\beta = 0.14$, the instantaneous current for bunches 1 mm long will be 0·7 A, and the resulting space charge will cause considerable spreading of the bunches after they have travelled only quite short distances. Also, since an output power of 600 W is itself greater than the input power, it is evident that means must be provided for steadily feeding power into the beam. There are of course considerable technical problems, among which is that of the bunching itself, at such short wavelengths. The condition for the size of the "bunch" is that $(\lambda/n) \geqslant L$.

Radiation from a Particle in the Proximity of a Dielectric

The elimination of the ionization energy loss, by directing the electrons down a channel of width $\ll \lambda$ is important. The ionization loss amounts to ~ 2 MeV. g^{-1}. cm^{-2} for a relativistic particle in a light material, whereas the Čerenkov radiation energy loss is ~ 2 keV. cm^{-1} (over the whole spectrum) in say Perspex, i.e. only $\sim 0 \cdot 1 \%$ of the available particle energy can at best be utilized.

The output of Čerenkov radiation from a particle passing in close proximity to a dielectric medium will now be discussed, in terms of the ratio of its distance from the dielectric surface, to the wavelength of the radiation. The first case, that of electrons on the axis of a hollow evacuated cylindrical tunnel inside an infinite dielectric, was worked

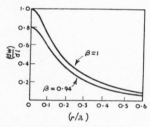

FIG. 3.2. Čerenkov radiation from a charge moving down a tunnel in a dielectric; the variation of yield as a function of the radius of the tunnel. (Ginsburg and Frank, 1947b.)

out by Ginsburg and Frank (1947b). Their results are shown in Fig. 3.2, in which the radiation output (dW/dl) is plotted against the ratio (r/λ), where r is the radius of the tunnel and λ the wavelength of the radiation ($= 2\pi c/\omega$). Both curves apply to $n = 1 \cdot 50$, the upper one to $\beta = 1$ and the lower one to $\beta = 0 \cdot 94$ (electrons of energy 1 MeV). It will be seen that a significant loss of yield occurs when $r > 0 \cdot 1 \lambda$, so that for radiation of wavelength 1 mm the tunnel would be of extremely small bore.

The energy losses and field associated with a charge moving through a channel in a dielectric have also been discussed by Bogdankevich and Bolotovsky (1957).

Application of this principle in the optical region is clearly not feasible; for instance, with $\lambda \sim 4000$ Å, high energy electrons travelling through a tunnel only 1 cm long in Perspex would have to be collimated to an accuracy of ~ 1 second of arc, for $r \sim (\lambda/10)$.

Linhart (1955) worked out the problem of Čerenkov radiation emitted by an electron moving over the surface of a dielectric sheet. This case is of interest since it was used by Danos *et al.* (1953) in the first successful experiments to detect microwave Čerenkov radiation; see Chapter 4.5. Linhart obtains the following expression for the radiation output per unit angular frequency, at a mid-band frequency ω.

$$W_\omega = \frac{2e^2\omega}{c^2} \cdot v \left(1 - \frac{1}{\beta n}\right) \cdot \exp\left[-2\,\frac{\omega z_0}{c}\,(\epsilon - 1)^{\frac{1}{2}}\right] \text{ ergs/sec} \quad (3.40)$$

where v is the velocity of the particle, ϵ the dielectric constant of the medium and z_0 the distance between the track of the particle and the

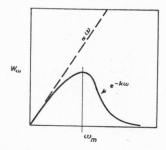

FIG. 3.3. Čerenkov radiation from a charge moving over the surface of a dielectric; the radiation yield as a function of the frequency ω, for a fixed value of z_0. (From Linhart, 1955.)

surface of the dielectric. Equation (3.40) is only strictly valid for $\beta n \approx 1$ and $\epsilon \gg 1$, though the general form still holds over a wider range of these parameters. The decrease of W with increasing z_0 follows the general form of the curve obtained for the case of the dielectric with tunnel (Fig. 3.2). When $z_0 \to 0$, (3.40) tends to the normal equation for the radiation yield, with the approximation that $(1 - 1/\beta^2 n^2) \approx 2(1 - 1/\beta n)$. Figure 3.3 shows a plot of W_ω as a function of ω, showing that there is always a frequency ω_m for given values of ϵ and z_0, at which most of the radiation appears. The position of this maximum is found by differentiating (3.40) with respect to ω and equating to zero; from this it is easily seen that the wavelength λ_m corresponding to ω_m is given by:

$$\lambda_m \approx 4\pi(\epsilon - 1)^{\frac{1}{2}} \cdot z_0 \quad (3.41)$$

Thus, for the peak of the emission curve to occur for example at a wavelength $\lambda_m = 1$ cm, when using a dielectric with $\epsilon = 2$, the optimum spacing of the electron beam from the surface would be $z_0 \approx 0.8$ mm.

Čerenkov Radiation in a Loaded Waveguide

The question whether the energy of the continuous spectrum can be concentrated in any way into certain discrete frequencies, was first solved theoretically by Abele (1952), for the specific case of electrons travelling down a loaded waveguide. Abele considers a cylindrical waveguide of radius ρ_2 within which there is a concentric dielectric cylinder of inner radius ρ_1, see Fig. 3.4. Within ρ_1 there is a vacuum,

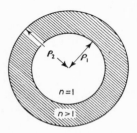

FIG. 3.4. The dielectric loaded cylindrical waveguide system considered by Abele (1952).

and the dielectric between ρ_1 and ρ_2 has a refractive index n; it is assumed the waveguide is a perfect conductor and the dielectric is both loss-less and non-dispersive. Consider an electron of charge e travelling with velocity v down the axis in such a system. At a given phase velocity there are a number of modes h for free oscillations within the guide.

The general problem of the distribution of the energy among these different modes is extremely complex, though solutions in specific cases were obtained by Abele. For instance, the output of radiation W_h in the hth mode, was obtained for the case when $(1 - \beta^2)/(n^2\beta^2 - 1) \approx 1$, $\rho_1 \ll \rho_2$ and $h \ll (\rho_2/\pi\rho_1)$. The solution is then:

$$W_h \sim \frac{e^2}{4n^2 v \rho_2} (n^2\beta^2 - 1)^{\frac{1}{2}} \omega_h \left\{ 1 - \frac{k_e^2 \rho_1^2}{2} \times \right.$$
$$\left. \times \left[\left(1 - \frac{1}{n^2} \right) \log \frac{2}{\gamma k_e \rho_1} + \tfrac{1}{2} \left(\frac{1 - \beta^2}{n^2\beta^2 - 1} \right) \right] \right\}_{\omega = \omega_h} \quad (3.42)$$

where the frequency of the hth mode is:

$$\omega_h \sim (2h - \tfrac{1}{2}) \frac{\pi v}{2\rho_2} \left[1 - h \frac{\pi^2}{4} \left(1 - \frac{1}{n^2} \right) \frac{\rho_1^2}{\rho_2^2} \right] (n^2\beta^2 - 1)^{-\frac{1}{2}}. \quad (3.43)$$

and $k_e = \dfrac{\omega}{v} (n^2\beta^2 - 1)^{\frac{1}{2}}$.

From (3.42) we see that W_h increases linearly with the frequencies of the modes in the limiting case when $\rho_1 = 0$; when $\rho_1 \neq 0$, W_h still increases with ω_h, but more slowly. Again with $\rho_1 \ll \rho_2$, but with $h \gg (\rho_2/\pi\rho_1)$, Abele obtains another expression for W_h which in this case contains an exponential factor very similar to that in (3.40), so that the radiation output W_h increases at first with ω_h and then reaches a maximum for the mode at which $h \sim (\rho_2/\pi\rho_1)$.

The Čerenkov radiation in a cylindrical guide completely filled with dielectric has also been studied by Akhiezer (1956).

An entirely different approach to Čerenkov radiation at radio frequencies has been made by Pierce (1955) who works out the effects of the interaction of charges moving close to distributed circuits, using conventional transmission line and circuit theory. He works out the energy transferred from the electron to the line, both for dispersive and non-dispersive lines. He finds, in particular, that for dispersive circuits there is always transfer of energy from the charge to the circuit, for those frequencies at which the charge velocity equals the phase velocity of the wave.

The continuous spectrum of normal Čerenkov radiation may then be interpreted in the following way: the current distribution represented by the moving charge approximates to a δ-function and therefore contains all frequencies. Radiation however will only occur at those frequencies for which there is coupling between the charge and the various modes of oscillation of the system. In a loaded waveguide the number of modes (at a given phase velocity) is finite so that the radiation spectrum then has discrete frequencies. An infinite homogeneous dielectric is however equivalent to an infinite loaded waveguide. The number of modes is then infinite and the resulting spectrum is therefore continuous.

The general problem of Čerenkov radiation in a waveguide has also been studied by Muzikář (1955) who considers a much more general case, that of an extended region of space charge travelling down a guide which is loaded with a medium of finite conductivity. In this work, only a few specific results are derived in detail, while the main solutions are left in a general form.

There are a number of other treatments of the problem of Čerenkov radiation in waveguides; for instance Schmidt (1956) considers the case of a guide with diaphragms and other restricted spaces, while Kaganov (1953b and 1953c) has studied the radiation from a beam in a waveguide loaded with an anisotropic dielectric.

There is a very close parallel between Čerenkov radiation in a loaded waveguide and the radiation mechanism in travelling-wave oscillators; see for example the review article by Kompfner (1952). The fundamental difference is that the refractive medium is replaced, in the travelling wave tube, by a different type of slow-wave structure, frequently a metal helix or resonant cavities with iris diaphragms.

Čerenkov Radiation in Coupled Resonators

A particular example of a system which yields Čerenkov radiation at discrete frequencies, of interest on account of its practical implications, see section 11.3, is that of a linear array of coupled resonators. We suppose the arrangement to consist of a chain of identical cylindrical resonators placed end to end, and coupled to one another (loosely) by small apertures along the common axis of the system. The spectrum of free oscillations of this assembly consists of discrete bands, the lowest frequency ω of which is related to the lowest frequency ω_o of a single resonator by the following relationship due to Vladimirskii (1947):

$$\omega = \omega_o \left[1 + a \left(1 - \cos kl\right)\right] \tag{3.44}$$

where k is an integer and the constant a is a measure of the coupling, given by:

$$a = \frac{2}{3\pi J_1^2(\mu_1)} \cdot \frac{a^3}{R^2 l},$$

where a is the radius of the aperture, R the radius of the resonator and l its length, J_1 the Bessel function and μ_1 the first root of J_o.

A particle of charge e moving down the axis of the system will radiate if its velocity v is greater than the phase velocity of the waves in the system, i.e. if $v > l\omega_o/\pi$. The intensity of the Čerenkov radiation in the lowest frequency band has been calculated by Akhiezer (1956) who obtains the following expression.

$$W = \frac{16e^2v^3}{R^2l^2\omega_0^2 J_1^2(\mu_1)} \cdot \frac{\sin^2(\omega_0 l/2v)}{1 - [(a\omega_0 l/v)\sin(\omega_0 l/v)]} \tag{3.45}$$

With typical resonator systems, the yield from a single particle at millimetre or centimetre wavelengths is negligible, but at high current densities and with "bunching", the radiation may then become appreciable.

3.5 The region of anomalous dispersion

The classical theory of Čerenkov radiation takes dispersion into account, though only in those spectral regions free of absorption bands, where $n(\omega)$ is varying slowly with ω. Radiation may however also be found in regions where anomalous dispersion exists, in relatively narrow frequency bands in the ultra-violet and x-ray domains. Owing to absorption, it does not necessarily follow that this Čerenkov radiation will be *observed*, at least at any reasonable distance from the track of the particle; it will, nevertheless, present a source of energy loss, to be added to those of the normal excitation and ionization processes.

Čerenkov radiation has therefore a direct bearing on the very important problems of the energy loss of fast particles traversing matter. In recent years intensive studies, both theoretical and experimental, have been concentrated on this problem; its details do not come within the scope of this book and the reader is referred to the review article by Price (1955). A few general notes will nevertheless be included for completeness.

The Density Effect and the Fermi Plateau

A plot of the most probable energy loss Δ_0 (or specific ionization), as a function of the kinetic energy T of a charged particle traversing a medium, reveals three distinct regions; see Fig. 3.5. At low energies, Δ_0 varies approximately as $1/v^2$ until, at a kinetic energy of the order of twice the rest energy of the particle, a minimum in the curve is reached. Beyond this minimum there is a logarithmic increase of Δ_0 with T; this however does not persist indefinitely, and the curve soon bends over to a nearly horizontal region which is known as the "Fermi plateau".

Following Swann's suggestion (1938), that the polarization of the

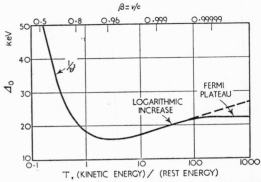

FIG. 3.5. To illustrate the three distinct regions in the curve relating the specific ionization loss Δ_0 to the particle energy T. (After Price, 1955.)

medium in the neighbourhood of the track of a fast particle will reduce the field associated with it, and hence also reduce the energy loss, Fermi (1939, 1940) worked out the theory of this, the so called "density effect". This theory, based as it was on certain simplifying assumptions, has been extended and modified by a number of investigators, notably by Halpern and Hall (1948), Schönberg (1950, 1951, 1952), Huybrechts and Schönberg (1952), Fowler and Jones (1953), Bolotovsky and Kolomensky (1952), Budini (1953) and by Budini and Taffara (1953). The particular importance of Čerenkov radiation in the problem is that in the high frequency region, among the absorption bands of the medium, the radiation intensity is no longer a negligible contribution to the total energy loss. The radiation, as we shall see, is then rapidly absorbed but this itself leads to further contributions to excitation and ionization. The "density effect", as its name implies, is most easily observed in solids.

Other treatments of the Čerenkov and polarization energy losses have been given by Kolomensky (1952) and by Sitenko and Kaganov (1955).

Complex Indices of Refraction

In the neighbourhood of absorption bands, the dielectric constant of a medium is complex, and may be written in the form:

$$\epsilon(\omega) = \text{Re } \epsilon(\omega) + i \text{ Im } \epsilon(\omega) \tag{3.46}$$

where the real part Re, is a measure of the dispersion, and the imaginary part Im, arises from absorption. The familiar form for $\epsilon(\omega)$, (see for example Sommerfeld, 1954, p. 97), is:

$$\epsilon(\omega) = 1 + a \sum_i \frac{f_i}{\omega_i^2 - \omega^2 - ig_i\omega} \tag{3.47}$$

where $a = \dfrac{4\pi Ne^2}{m}$ (N is the number of electrons per ml, and e and m are the charge and mass of the electron respectively) while ω_i and f_i are the frequency and oscillator strengths of the ith resonance, and g_i the corresponding damping coefficient responsible for the absorption.

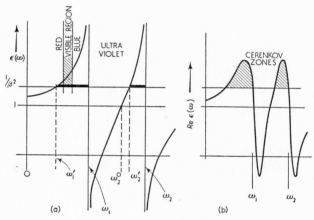

FIG. 3.6. The variation of the dielectric constant of a medium in the region of anomalous dispersion.

(a) Idealized case of zero damping.   (b) Dispersion with damping.

In an idealized dispersive medium, in which absorption is absent, $g = 0$ and $\epsilon(\omega)$ has the general form indicated in Fig. 3.6(a), for the first few resonances. Čerenkov radiation will then be emitted over narrow bands ω'_1 to ω_1, ω'_2 to ω_2, and so on, the limits being defined by the line $1/\beta^2$. When $\beta \to 1$ the bands are somewhat broader, 0 to ω_1 (which includes the visible region in transparent substances), ω_2^0 to ω_2, etc. Note that some radiation will be produced in very narrow regions for values of β well below the normal threshold as calculated for the visible region. Budini shows that the radiation output in such a case would be:

$$\frac{dW}{dl} = \frac{e^2}{c^2} \int \left(1 - \frac{\text{Re } \epsilon(\omega)}{\beta^2 |\epsilon(\omega)|^2}\right) \omega d\omega \tag{3.48}$$

which reduces to the Frank and Tamm expression, when $g_i = 0$. The integration in (3.48) is carried out over all frequencies for which the condition Re $\epsilon(\omega) > 1/\beta^2$ is satisfied.

No real medium is of course free from absorption, so that $g_i \neq 0$. Re $\epsilon(\omega)$ then takes the form shown in Fig. 3.6(b), showing that maxima now occur in the dispersion curve. The dielectric constant at the peak of a given resonance is

$$\text{Re } \epsilon(\omega_i) \approx 1 + \tfrac{1}{2} \left(\frac{4\pi \, Ne^2 f_i}{mg_i\omega_i} \right) \tag{3.49}$$

and the threshold for radiation in this band is then

$$(\beta E)^2 = \left(\frac{\beta^2}{1 - \beta^2} \right) > 2 \left(\frac{mg_i\omega_i}{4\pi Ne^2 f_i} \right) \tag{3.50}$$

where E is the kinetic energy of the particle in units of its rest energy.

The total output of radiation, covering resonance regions with damping, and observable at a radial distance ρ from the track of the particle, is then:

$$\frac{dW}{dl} = \frac{e^2}{c^2} \int \exp \left[-\frac{\omega}{v} \beta^2 \rho \,.\, \text{Im } \epsilon(\omega) \right] . \left(1 - \frac{\text{Re } \epsilon(\omega)}{\beta^2 | \epsilon(\omega)|^2} \right) \omega d\omega \tag{3.51}$$

where v is the particle velocity.

The first factor in the integrand contains the absorption, showing that radiation of a given frequency ω will only be seen, at a distance ρ, if the condition $\left[\dfrac{\omega}{v} \beta^2 \rho \,.\, \text{Im } \epsilon(\omega) \right] \ll 1$ is satisfied.

It can be shown that in dense media with narrow resonances, there should be a relativistic increase of the Čerenkov radiation at high energies which is *additional* to the relativistic increase of ionization.* A preliminary experiment designed to verify this has been reported by Bassi *et al.* (1952), while Budini has suggested that an experiment should be carried out with compressed gases, for which both phenomena could be studied simultaneously.

---

* The logarithmic increase of ionization, Fig. 3.5, after the minimum, arises from two causes: (i) the relativistic increase in the radius of action of the electric field of the particle as its velocity approaches c, and (ii) an increase in the maximum transferable energy.

The problem of radiation production in ferromagnetic media (see also sections 3.2 and 3.3) has been discussed by Ivanenko and Gurgenidze (1949), and by Ivanenko and Tsytovich (1955) who take into account a complex permeability arising from magnetic resonances with damping.

The possibility of obtaining a reasonable yield of Čerenkov radiation at microwave frequencies (see section 3.4) prompted Lashinsky (1956) to work out the radiation produced by a bunched electron beam passing over the surface of a medium for which both the dielectric constant

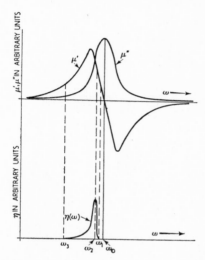

FIG. 3.7. The dispersion curve of a typical ferrite. (After Lashinsky, 1956.)

and the permeability are characterized by complex numbers. He considers, in particular, the case of ferrites, which have ferromagnetic resonances in the microwave region. In ferrites, the relative values of the real and imaginary parts of the magnetic permeability can be controlled to some extent by the application of an external field. A typical dispersion curve for a ferrite in the region of a resonance is shown in Fig. 3.7 where the two curves μ' and μ'' represent dispersion and absorption respectively, and are related to the magnetic permeability μ, by $\mu = \mu' - i\mu''$. Operation at a frequency ω_2 just below the resonance at ω_0, produces a considerable enhancement of the Čerenkov radiation relative to that of a pure dielectric. The curve $\eta(\omega)$

E

at the bottom of Fig. 3.7 represents the ratio of the radiation produced in the ferrite to that produced in a pure dielectric.

Taking also a complex form for the dielectric constant, so that $\epsilon = \epsilon' - i\epsilon''$, Lashinsky quotes the following figures for a typical ferrite: $\epsilon' = 10$, $\epsilon'' = 0$, $\mu' = 10$ and $\mu'' = 60$. With a value of $\beta = 0\cdot2$, for a reasonable beam velocity, the threshold criterion $\beta^2\mu'\epsilon' > 1$ is easily satisfied. The radiation output $\eta(\omega)$ is then found to be as high as 260 times that from a pure dielectric for which $\epsilon' = 100$, $\epsilon'' = 0$, $\mu' = 1$ and $\mu'' = 0$, at the same beam velocity.

3.6 Radiation in a plasma

The dielectric constant for an electron plasma is:

$$\epsilon(\omega) = 1 - (\omega_o^2/\omega^2) \tag{3.52}$$

where ω is the frequency of the waves being propagated, and ω_o is the plasma frequency, given by:

$$\omega_o^2 = 4\pi Ne^2/m \tag{3.53}$$

where N is the number of electrons per unit volume, and e and m are the charge and mass of the electron. Owing to their greater inertia, the positive ions in the plasma may be ignored. From (3.52) it is seen at once that the refractive index, $n = \sqrt{\epsilon}$, can never exceed unity, so that Čerenkov radiation in a simple plasma will not exist. Veksler (1956) has shown however that if the plasma is in a magnetic field, the refractive index is modified in such a way that Čerenkov radiation is then possible, in certain frequency regions and with suitable choice of magnetic field strengths and electron densities.

An electron plasma in a magnetic field behaves like a birefringent crystal, having an axis of symmetry in the direction of the magnetic field H. The refractive index of such a plasma is a function of several variables $n = n_{o,e}(\omega, \theta, \omega_o, \omega_H)$ where θ is the angle between the ray direction and the axis of the magnetic field H, and ω_H is the gyro or cyclotron frequency:

$$\omega_H = eH/mc, \tag{3.54}$$

and the subscripts o and e refer, respectively, to ordinary and extraordinary waves. Bremmer (1949) obtains the following expression for the refractive index for the propagation of waves of frequency ω in a direction making an angle θ with respect to the magnetic field direction H:

$$n^2(\theta) = 1 - \frac{2x(1-x)}{2(1-x) - y^2\sin^2\theta \pm \sqrt{\{y^4\sin^4\theta + 4y^2(1-x)^2\cos^2\theta\}}}$$

(3.55)

where $x = (\omega_o^2/\omega^2)$
and $y = (\omega_H/\omega)$.

From (3.55) it is seen that in certain regions of ω, n will exceed unity and the Čerenkov condition $\cos\Theta = 1/\beta n$ may be satisfied; (Θ is here used to denote the Čerenkov angle, i.e. the angle between the direction of motion of the charged particle and the direction of emission of the coherent radiation).

Kolomenskii (1956) followed up Veksler's suggestion, in order to obtain expressions for the coherence condition and the radiation output, for an electron of velocity βc travelling through such a plasma in a magnetic field. For simplicity Kolomenskii restricts the analysis to the specific case of the motion of an electron along the magnetic field direction, which is the case most frequently encountered in practice; we thus put $\Theta = \theta$. Under these conditions the following complicated expression is obtained for the coherence, for the two types of wave:

$$\cos^2\Theta_{o,e} = \frac{\omega^2}{2\beta^2\{(\omega^2 - \omega_o^2)^3\beta^2 - \omega_H^2\omega^2[\omega^2\beta^2 + (1-\beta^2)\omega_o^2]\}} \times$$
$$\times \{2(\omega^2 - \omega_o^2)^2\beta^2 - \omega_H^2[2\beta^2\omega^2 + (1-\beta^2)\omega_o^2] \pm$$
$$\omega_o^2\omega_H\sqrt{[4(\omega^2 - \omega_o^2)\beta^2 + \omega_H^2(1-\beta^2)^2]}\}.$$

(3.56)

From (3.56), with the condition $0 \leqslant \cos^2\Theta_{o,e} \leqslant 1$, it follows that the ranges of frequency for the radiation of o- and e-type waves, will be defined by the following limits:

$$\text{For } o\text{-type waves} \qquad \omega < \omega_o. \qquad (3.57a)$$

$$\text{For } e\text{-type waves} \qquad \omega_o < \omega < [\omega_o^2 + \omega_H^2]^{\frac{1}{2}}. \qquad (3.57b)$$

Under these conditions the regions will not overlap. Thus, only e-waves are emitted at comparatively small field strengths $H < H_1$, and for $H > H_1$ only o-waves, where

$$H_1 = 8\pi Nec\beta/(1-\beta^2)^{\frac{1}{2}} \text{ if } \beta < 1/\sqrt{2}$$

or $\qquad H_1 = 4\pi Nec/(1-\beta^2) \text{ if } \beta > 1/\sqrt{2}.$

(3.58)

In the relativistic case ($\beta \sim 1$) only e-waves are emitted, and these appear over the whole frequency range covered by (3.57b). It is worth noting that in this type of medium, Čerenkov radiation may also occur under non-relativistic conditions, i.e. when $\beta \ll 1$.

In the regions defined by (3.57), for which radiation is possible, the radiation yield and spectral distribution are given by the following complicated expression:

$$\frac{dW}{dl} = \frac{e^2}{2c^2} \int \left| \frac{(\omega^2 - \omega_H^2)(1 - \beta^2) + \beta^2\omega_o^2}{\beta^2(\omega_o^2 + \omega_H^2 - \omega^2)} \left\{ 1 \pm \cdots \right.\right.$$
$$\left.\left. \frac{\omega_H[(\omega^2 - \omega_H^2)(1 - \beta^2)^2 + \beta^2(3 - \beta^2)\omega_o^2]}{[(\omega^2 - \omega_H^2)(1 - \beta^2) + \beta^2\omega_o^2] \cdot \sqrt{[(1 - \beta^2)^2\omega_H^2 + 4\beta^2(\omega^2 - \omega_o^2)]}} \right\} \right| \omega d\omega$$
(3.59)

It is interesting to note that the integral (3.59) diverges at the frequency $\omega_{\lim} = (\omega_o^2 + \omega_H^2)^{\frac{1}{2}}$ where the range of the e-waves ends. This sort of divergence is characteristic of anisotropic media (which are also gyrotropic) and has been discussed elsewhere by Kolomenskii (1952, 1953). According to (3.56), the frequency $\omega_{\lim}$ corresponds to a value of $\Theta = \pi/2$, so that the radiation is then emitted perpendicular to the motion of the electron. Moreover, in this case, the electric vector is polarized along the direction of the emitted radiation, so that the wave of the electric field becomes longitudinal.

It will also be seen that the application of a magnetic field to a plasma changes the character of the energy losses encountered by electrons traversing the plasma; see also section 3.5. In the absence of an applied field, only polarization losses are suffered by the electron, corresponding to waves having the plasma frequency ω_o. For these waves, $\epsilon = 0$, and radiation damping causes them to decay exponentially with distance from the track of the moving electron. With the field applied, these polarization losses are replaced by true Čerenkov radiation losses. The phenomena have also been discussed by Akhiezer and Sitenko (1952).

The Čerenkov radiation produced by charged particles moving in a plasma, with an applied magnetic field, has a bearing on a number of different topics. It may have astrophysical significance in connexion with the production of radio noise, and it may arise terrestrially, through the passage of charged particles through the ionosphere. A particular astrophysical problem is discussed in section 11.4. The process is also important in connexion with the inverse Čerenkov effect, see section

11.10, suggested by Veksler (1956) as a possible mechanism for accelerating charged particles to high energies.

And finally, the Čerenkov radiation in a plasma is a process that should be considered in connexion with gas discharge phenomena at high currents and their application to the problems of producing thermonuclear reactions.

3.7 Transition radiation

In their original theory, Frank and Tamm assumed that the medium was infinite in extent and the velocity of the particle constant; in practice of course the medium has boundaries and the track length is finite. Besides diffraction effects caused by the finite path (see sections 3.8 and 3.9), the existence of boundary surfaces slightly modifies the total yield of radiation, introducing a small contribution additional to the normal Čerenkov radiation. If a charged particle, moving at constant velocity, enters a slab of dielectric (of depth d) at a point A and then emerges from the other side at a point B, radiation will be generated at these two points, in addition to the Čerenkov radiation *between A and B*. This, known as Transition Radiation, always occurs when a charged particle crosses the boundary between two media having different optical properties; the media need not necessarily be pure dielectrics. The two cases of particular interest that arise occur when a charged particle, initially travelling in a vacuum, plunges into the surface of either a pure dielectric or a perfect conductor. In both cases it is assumed that the transition is abrupt; i.e. that the boundary is sharp compared with the wavelength in question. Unlike Čerenkov radiation proper, the process does not have a threshold and will occur at any velocity of the particle, though its intensity increases with the energy.

Moreover, it is not essential that the boundary be sharp; an electron travelling at constant velocity in a medium whose refractive index is varying slowly along the track, will radiate continuously (though weakly in such a case), and this even at velocities below the normal Čerenkov threshold.

A situation alternative to that of a particle of constant velocity traversing a finite slab may arise in the following way; suppose instead that we have an infinite medium and that a charged particle, initially at rest at a point A, is rapidly accelerated up to a constant velocity (above the Čerenkov threshold) which it maintains until, at a point B, it is brought abruptly to rest. If, as in the first case, the distance $AB = d$, the output of Čerenkov radiation will be the same as before. In this case also, there will be radiation at the two points A and B; this will now be identified as a form of acceleration radiation. This and transition radiation are essentially the same; the intensities work out the same in both cases and it is only convention which decides which term shall be used.

The easier case to understand is that of a charge entering a perfect conductor, see Fig. 3.8. As the charge approaches the surface, a dipole is set up between the charge and its image below the surface. At the

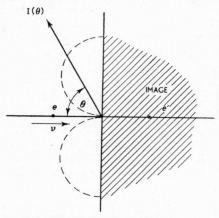

FIG. 3.8. To illustrate the origin of Transition Radiation in a perfect conductor.

instant of impact, this dipole is destroyed, and the radiation emitted is equivalent to four times the radiation from the stoppage of a single point charge. (A factor of two arises from the presence of two charges, and another factor of two because the radiation can only appear in the hemisphere outside the metal.) In this simple case the energy radiated per unit angular frequency interval, integrated over the angular distribution, is:

$$W = \frac{4e^2v^2}{3\pi c^3} \, d\omega \tag{3.60}$$

in the non-relativistic case, where v is the velocity of the charge. If we take $v \sim c$, and a bandwidth $d\omega = 10^{15}$ (i.e. 4000–5000 Å), $W \approx 3\cdot6 \times 10^{-15}$ erg, or approximately one photon per 10^3 incident electrons, indeed a very small light output. The upper limit to the frequency spectrum in this process occurs when the corresponding wavelength becomes comparable with the roughness of the surface of the metal.

Frank and Ginsburg (1945) and Ginsburg and Frank (1946) considered the more general problem in which an electron of charge e enters a medium having a complex dielectric constant ϵ'. If the first medium is a vacuum, the energy radiated at an angle θ to the path of the electron, as it enters the second medium, is:

$$W(\theta) = \frac{e^2 v^2}{4\pi^2 c^3} \left| \frac{\epsilon' - 1}{\epsilon'} \right|^2 (1 + f)^2 \sin^2\theta \, d\Omega \, d\omega \tag{3.61}$$

where $d\Omega$ and $d\omega$ refer to unit solid angle and unit angular frequency interval, respectively. In (3.61), f is the Fresnel reflexion coefficient for waves with the electric vector in the plane of incidence. ϵ' is related to the normal dielectric constant ϵ and the conductivity σ of the medium by:

$$\epsilon' = \epsilon - i \left(\frac{4\pi\sigma}{\omega} \right). \tag{3.62}$$

In a pure dielectric, $\sigma = 0$ and, for regions away from absorption lines, $\epsilon = n^2(\omega)$. By inserting the appropriate values of f, it can be shown in the non-relativistic case, that (3.61) takes the form:

$$W(\theta) = \frac{e^2 v^2}{\pi^2 c^3} \left[\frac{n^2 - 1}{n^2 \cos\theta + \sqrt{(n^2 - \sin^2\theta)}} \right]^2 \sin^2\theta \cos^2\theta \, d\Omega \, d\omega. \tag{3.63}$$

Frank and Ginsburg also work out the differential and total light yields for the case of a perfect conductor; it is of interest that Askarian (1956) has recently proposed a millimetre-wave generator based on the transition effect, gaining intensity by "bunching" the electrons so that coherence is achieved. The existence of transition radiation has never been satisfactorily established;* with dielectrics it would be difficult to observe, or isolate from other effects, such as Bremsstrahlung, fluorescence and "residual" Čerenkov radiation (see section 3.9). Its observation in the case of a metal of high conductivity should however be straightforward.

* At the time of proof-reading (January 1958), experiments are being conducted by Elliott, Goldsmith and Jelley on the Van de Graaff generator at A.E.R.E. Harwell. Polarized light has been observed from a polished aluminium target bombarded by $2\mu A$ of protons at 1·5 MeV energy. An estimate of the intensity of the light suggests that transition radiation has been observed.

Beck (1948) has also investigated transition radiation, in the course of a general treatment of Čerenkov radiation, arriving at a result very similar to that of Frank and Ginsburg. Beck concludes that at small velocities the radiation is insignificant, but increases sharply as the velocity of the charge approaches the critical value (c/n). At this critical velocity the number of photons emitted dN, per unit wavelength interval $d\lambda$, is found to be:

$$dN \approx \frac{4ne^2v^2}{h\pi c^3} \cdot \frac{\sin^3\theta \, d\theta}{[1 - n^2\beta^2 \cos^2\theta]^2} \cdot \frac{d\lambda}{\lambda} \tag{3.64}$$

which has therefore a maximum in the forward direction, at

$$\theta_{max} = \left[\frac{6}{5}(1 - n^2\beta^2)\right]^{\frac{1}{2}}. \tag{3.65}$$

Integrating over all angles, (3.64) leads to

$$W = \frac{e^2}{\pi^2 c}\left[\frac{1}{2}(1 + n^2\beta^2) \cdot \ln\left(\frac{1 + n\beta}{1 - n\beta}\right) - n\beta\right] d\omega. \tag{3.66}$$

At relativistic velocities it is possible to reach yields of one photon for approximately 100 incident electrons, still nevertheless an extremely low intensity.

A study of transition radiation has also been made by Klepikov (1952).

3.8 Diffraction and scattering effects

Even in the absence of the slowing down of the particle as it traverses the medium, the resolution of a Čerenkov counter is limited by effects of diffraction and scattering. To a first approximation these effects may be considered separately, though in a more rigorous treatment they have to be taken together, for reasons which will become clear in due course.

Diffraction Alone

The angular width of the light distribution in the Čerenkov cone is zero only in the idealized case of an infinite path length. If the track has however a finite length L, and the effective wavelength of the radiation is λ, the image will have a diffraction width $\Delta\theta \sim (\lambda/L \sin\theta)$. In any practical case, this would be extremely small. For instance in a 1 mm thick slab of Perspex, with $\theta = 48°$, $\lambda = 4000$ Å, $\Delta\theta \approx 5 \cdot 10^{-4}$ rad. Li (1950) suggested that the effective length of track L should not be the thickness of the radiator, but rather, the mean distance between the emission of successive photons, owing to deflexions of the track caused by the photon "recoil". It is true of course (again temporarily neglecting non-radiative scattering) that the track is divided into very short straight sections due to this recoil, but, as Li himself later realized (1951), the recoil is so small for photons of such low energy, that the coherence is not seriously disturbed by this effect. The effects of scattering, as we shall see, are far more serious. We may

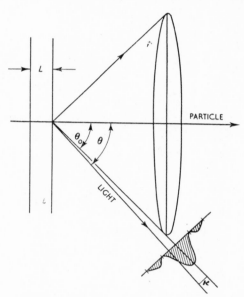

FIG. 3.9. Effects of diffraction on the angular width of the Čerenkov image. (After Dedrick, 1952.)

anticipate then that the effective length L will lie somewhere between these two extremes.

To conclude, it may be instructive to know precisely what the *pure* diffraction width will be, because it is in principle possible to eliminate the scattering if the particle moves down a narrow tunnel in the dielectric without coming in contact with the medium (see section 3.4).

Suppose we denote the normal Čerenkov angle by θ_0 and enquire what radiation intensity will be observed at small angles κ with respect to the direction θ_0, so that $\kappa = (\theta - \theta_0)$; see Fig. 3.9.

Neglecting the insignificant effects due to photon recoil, the diffraction pattern will have the form:

$$I(\theta) = I(\theta_0) \times L^2[\sin\left(\tfrac{1}{2}nkL\kappa \sin\theta_0\right)/\left(\tfrac{1}{2}nkL\kappa \sin\theta_0\right)]^2 \quad (3.67)$$

where n is the refractive index, L is now the geometrical path length, and $k = 2\pi/\lambda$ where λ is the wavelength. This pattern is essentially the same as that from a near end-fire aerial array with a progressive phase shift along its length, and the same as that from a diffraction grating.

Scattering Effects

During its passage through the medium, a particle undergoes multiple Coulomb scattering in the vicinity of the nuclei of those atoms which it encounters at sufficiently small impact parameters. This scattering produces a spread in the observed angular distribution of the Čerenkov light, in two ways. In the first place, since the particle emerges from the radiator along a different direction from that along which it entered, there will be an apparent spread in the directions of the light paths corresponding directly to the spread in the directions of the particle inside the medium. Secondly, the scattering produces a lateral displacement of the particle from its original track, and this in turn will lead to a broadening of the image in optical systems with cylindrical symmetry; see section 7.2, where this matter is discussed in more detail.

Since multiple Coulomb scattering arises mainly from a very large number of small-angle scattering events, it can be treated by statistical methods, from which values for the mean square angle of scatter $\langle\theta^2\rangle$ may be deduced.

Following the notation of Rossi and Greisen (1941), the mean square angle of scatter is given by:

$$\langle\theta^2\rangle = (E_s^2/p^2\beta^2) \cdot t \quad (3.68)$$

where p is the momentum of the particle in MeV/c, E_s is a constant, $= 21$ MeV, which is independent of the mass of the particle and the nature of the medium, and t is the path length measured in units known as radiation lengths X_0.* Radiation lengths, often expressed in g/cm^2, are different in different materials. Values of X_0 for some of the more common materials are found in Table H in Appendix I.

* The term "radiation length" emerges from electron cascade theory and is discussed in section 6.5. The term has no connexion with Čerenkov radiation.

In equation (3.68), it is assumed that the momentum of the particle is unchanged during its passage through the radiator. If the momentum change is appreciable, (3.68) is replaced by:

$$\langle \theta^2 \rangle = E_s^2 \int_{p_2}^{p_1} \frac{1}{-(dp/dt)} \cdot \frac{dp}{p^2 \beta^2} \tag{3.69}$$

where $- (dp/dt)$ is the momentum loss per radiation length and p_1 and p_2 are the momenta of the particle as it enters and leaves the radiator, respectively.

It is evident from (3.69) that for particles of a given velocity, the scattering is more severe for light particles than for heavy; in fact, for electrons, the scattering is usually one of the main sources of image spread in a focusing counter.

Diffraction Modified by Scattering

Since the scattering breaks up the track length into short sections, it will influence the effects of diffraction; this influence cannot be calculated in an elementary way because the coherence of radiation from neighbouring elements of track will be only *partially* destroyed. A solution of the problem has been found by Dedrick (1952) who has obtained expressions for the resultant angular distribution of light intensity, in the absence of slowing-down of the particles. From classical radiation theory, and the established theory of multiple scattering, he first considers the resultant radiation from a typical track, and then takes an ensemble average over all possible paths, to obtain the overall radiation pattern.

The main results of Dedrick's treatment will now be presented. There are two solutions of the problem, one valid for viewing angles θ close to the radiation maximum at θ_0, i.e. for small values of κ, and the other valid for viewing angles far away from the direction θ_0, i.e. large κ. The former is of more general use, for computing the resolution of practical detectors, i.e. to obtain the half-width of the angular distribution function of the light intensity. The solution at large viewing angles may however be important in certain cases, such as occur when it is required to resolve a weak component of Čerenkov radiation of one characteristic cone angle θ_{01}, from a much stronger component having a different cone angle θ_{02}.

The Region of Small κ

The intensity distribution for the case of small viewing angles is represented by the family of curves in Fig. 3.10. The ordinates represent the intensity relative to that at the normal Čerenkov angle θ_0, while the abscissae δ measure κ in units of the r.m.s. multiple scattering which occurs in the radiator. K is a constant, characteristic of (L/λ) and the r.m.s. multiple scattering. The dashed curve is a plot of the projected

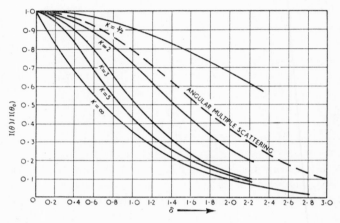

FIG. 3.10. Intensity distributions computed by Dedrick (1952) for calculating the width of a Čerenkov image due to diffraction in the presence of Coulomb scattering.

angular distribution of particles emerging from the radiator, while the curve for $K = \infty$ is the projected angular multiple scattering averaged over the thickness of the plate. The constant K is calculated from the expression:

$$K = [(6\pi/\sqrt{2})\, n \sin \theta_0 (L/\lambda) \,.\, \langle\theta^2\rangle^{\frac{1}{2}}]^{\frac{1}{3}} \tag{3.70}$$

where L is here the thickness of the radiator and n its refractive index, and δ is given by:

$$\delta = \kappa\sqrt{2}/\langle\theta^2\rangle^{\frac{1}{2}}. \tag{3.71}$$

It will be seen that in general the radiation pattern is narrower than the angular distribution of the particles emerging from the radiator. This is explained by the fact that much of the light arises from the early part of the track for which the scattering is less than it is later.

A particular example will now be worked out, taking the case of the detector designed for the proton synchrotron at Birmingham University, mentioned in Chapter 8. We have a Perspex radiator of density $1\cdot20$ g/cm^3 and effective length $L = 8$ cm. This is exposed to protons travelling along its axis with an energy of 950 MeV. These protons, see Appendix II, will have a momentum of $p = 1640$ MeV/c and a velocity ratio $\beta = 0\cdot875$. The radiator thickness, t in equation (3.68), is thus $9\cdot6$ g/cm^2 or $0\cdot185$ radiation lengths, for one radiation length in Perspex is 52 g/cm^2. From equation (3.68) we find the r.m.s. scattering angle for the protons emerging from the radiator is $\langle\theta^2\rangle^{\frac{1}{2}} = 6\cdot3 \times 10^{-3}$ rad, or $0\cdot36°$. For $\beta = 0\cdot875$ and a refractive index $n = 1\cdot50$, $\theta_0 = 40° \ 10'$. Taking an effective wavelength $\lambda = 4000$ Å, we find from (3.70) that $K = 12$. Turning now to Fig. 3.10 and interpolating between the curves for $K = 5$ and $K = \infty$ we find that the intensity is down to 50% of its maximum value when $\delta = 0\cdot8$, corresponding to a value of $\kappa = 3\cdot5 \times 10^{-3}$ rad or $0\cdot20°$. This, we see, is considerably less than the spread of the protons emerging from the Perspex. With the aid of equation (7.14), section 7.3, a spread in the Čerenkov angle of $\pm 0\cdot2°$ represents a resolution limit of ± 19 MeV at a proton energy of 950 MeV, i.e. $\pm 2\%$. From the curves of Fig. 3.10, it is only for values of $K < 1\cdot8$ that the spread in the Čerenkov light exceeds the Coulomb scattering.

The Asymptotic Region, Large κ

This is defined by the criterion $\kappa \gg \langle\theta^2\rangle^{\frac{1}{2}}$. The intensity distribution in this case takes the following form:

$$I_\kappa = 2 \left(\frac{e \sin\theta_0}{2\pi}\right)^2 \frac{9L^2}{\delta^2 K^6} \left\{ 1 - \left[\cos\left(\frac{K^3\delta}{3}\right) + \frac{K^3}{3\delta}\sin\left(\frac{K^3\delta}{3}\right)\right] \right.$$
$$\left. \times \exp\left(-\frac{K^6}{27}\right) + \frac{2}{\delta^2} \right\} \quad (3.72)$$

where K, δ and L are the same as before, and $e = 2\cdot7$.

In both solutions it can be shown that by allowing the scattering to go to zero, the intensity distributions of Fig. 3.10 and equation (3.72) tend to the form derived from simple diffraction theory, equation (3.67).

Summarizing, we may say that the angular distribution in the case of large K may be obtained by averaging the projected angular multiple scattering over the whole path length L, so that the curves for large K always fall within the dashed curve of Fig. 3.10. As K tends to smaller values, the broadening of the radiation peak increases, at first due to the effects of partial incoherence, and ultimately, at very small K, due to the diffraction over the entire path length.

3.9 Radiation below the threshold

We have seen, section 3.8, that the angular distribution function of the light intensity on the Čerenkov cone is not infinitely narrow if the track is of finite length. Coulomb scattering, diffraction, dispersion and effects of radiation reaction all combine to broaden the width of the conical shell of light. One of the results of such broadening is that there is no

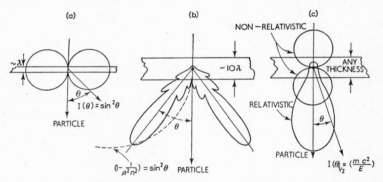

FIG. 3.11. Angular distribution functions for Čerenkov radiation and Bremsstrahlung.

(a) Čerenkov; radiator thickness $\sim \lambda$. (b) Čerenkov; radiator thickness $\sim 10\lambda$.
(c) Bremsstrahlung.

sharp cut-off of the light intensity at the threshold when $\beta n = 1$. A qualitative interpretation of this may be gained by looking at Fig. 3.11 (a) and (b). It is obvious that when the depth of the medium is $\sim \lambda$ or less (and yet thick enough for the concept of a refractive index to have a physical meaning), the polar diagram of the radiation will be much the same whether $n\beta < 1$ or > 1. Extending the argument to the rather less fictitious case (b), when the depth of the medium is say 10λ or more, the Čerenkov cone has now developed but still has considerable width. As $\beta n \to 1$, the cone-angle θ_0 collapses to zero, though part of the main lobe, and radiation in the side-lobes, will persist even when $\beta n < 1$.

The following analysis due to Lawson (1954) enables an estimate to be made of the amount of this radiation that persists below the threshold.

Coulomb scattering, dispersion and radiation reaction are ignored in this treatment of the problem, which is based on simple diffraction arguments. The problem is essentially that of finding the polar diagram of an array of Hertzian dipoles placed end to end and fed so that there is a progressive change of phase along the array.

The radiation intensity per unit solid angle from a component of single frequency may be written in the form:

$$W(\theta) = \frac{A^2 a^2 \sin^2\theta}{\lambda^2} \left\{ \frac{\sin\left[\frac{\pi a}{\lambda}\left(\frac{1}{\beta n} - \cos\theta\right)\right]}{\frac{\pi a}{\lambda}\left(\frac{1}{\beta n} - \cos\theta\right)} \right\}^2 \tag{3.73}$$

where a is the length of track, A a constant and θ the angle at which the light is viewed. The direction corresponding to the Čerenkov maximum is, as usual, $\theta_0 = \cos^{-1}(1/\beta n)$. The first factor in (3.73) is the intensity distribution for a single elemental dipole, while the second factor represents the diffraction pattern for the finite track length, taking into account the progressive phase shift. Equation (3.73) may be re-written

$$\frac{2\lambda^2 W(\theta)}{A^2 a^2 \sin^2\theta} = \frac{\lambda^2}{\pi^2 a^2 (1/\beta n - \cos\theta)^2} \left\{ 1 - \cos\left[\frac{2\pi a}{\lambda}\left(\frac{1}{\beta n} - \cos\theta\right)\right] \right\} \tag{3.74}$$

We are interested in how $W(\theta)$ varies with a and β; (3.74) is now simplified to:

$$S(y) = (1 - \cos 2y)/y^2 \tag{3.75}$$

where

$$y = \frac{\pi a}{\lambda}\left(\cos\theta - \frac{1}{\beta n}\right). \tag{3.76}$$

From (3.75) it is seen that θ is only real in the range $1 > (\lambda y/\pi a + 1/\beta n) > -1$. A plot of $S(y)$ is shown in Fig. 3.12 for the specific case when $a = 4\lambda$ and $1/\beta n = 0.5$. We see that the maximum of the curve only occurs at a real angle, if $\beta n > 1$ as in the Frank and Tamm theory, for an infinite track. There is however no discontinuity as βn passes through unity, the curve in Fig. 3.12 moving bodily to the right as βn decreases, so that when the main lobe of the distribution has passed into the region of imaginary angles, some radiation still remains in the

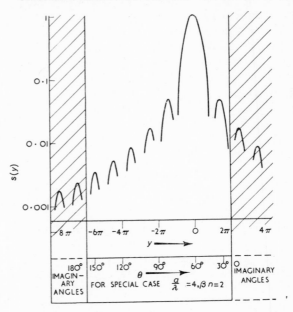

FIG. 3.12. The function $S(y)$ discussed by Lawson (1954); the real and imaginary regions shown for a particular case.

subsidiary lobes. When (a/λ) is small, $S(y)$ is constant throughout the real range and $W(\theta) \propto \sin^2 \theta$, as is shown in Fig. 3.11(a). As (a/λ) increases, $S(y)$ falls away more steeply with y, and the subsidiary peaks crowd closer together, until, when $(a/\lambda) \to \infty$, the transition at $\beta n = 1$ is sharp. In the example shown, the intensities of the first, second, etc., subsidiary peaks are $\sim 4.5\%$, 1.7%, 0.9%, etc. of the main peak.

In any practical case the clear diffraction pattern is of course blurred by the effects of scattering and dispersion (each frequency having its own polar diagram); nevertheless, a weak contribution to the radiation will still remain below the threshold.

Richards (1956) has reported radiation below the threshold for electrons in water which he attributes to the effects discussed above.

3.10 Čerenkov radiation and Bremsstrahlung

Reference has already been made to the fundamental difference between the two phenomena of Čerenkov radiation and Bremsstrahlung,* the former arising only from the macroscopic properties of the medium as a whole, and the latter involving interactions with individual atoms, i.e. the microscopic structure of the material. The significance of the differences is not always fully appreciated and it is appropriate therefore to discuss the matter further.

Let us first summarize the main features of the Bremsstrahlung process.

Since the interaction occurs with the Coulomb field of a "screened" nucleus (screened on account of the presence of the orbital electrons), it follows that the process will only take place when the particle approaches within a fairly well defined distance from the nucleus, which distance is usually referred to as the "impact parameter". Bremsstrahlung, in contrast to Čerenkov radiation, occurs as a result of a few collisions of relatively large energy transfer, and much of the emitted radiation has therefore a quantum energy comparable with that of the moving particle.

The radiated energy is proportional to e^2Z^2, where e is the charge of the particle and Z is the nuclear charge; the radiation is therefore more intense in heavy elements than in light. The radiation yield is also very sensitive to the *mass* of the moving particle. The radiation from a particle of mass M is weaker by a factor $(M/m)^2$ from that of a particle of mass m moving at the same *velocity*, if $M > m$. Thus the radiation from π- and μ-mesons, and protons, is negligible compared with that from electrons.

The spectrum of the radiation, to a first approximation, is of the form $(dW/dl) \propto$ const. $d\omega$, i.e. an equi-energy spectrum.

The distribution of intensity with angle, in the non-relativistic case, is similar to that from a dipole whose axis is at right angles to the direction of motion of the particle; at relativistic velocities the distribution is peaked forwards, with the width of the "lobe" given by θ r.m.s. $\sim (mc^2/E_0)$, where E_0 is the kinetic energy of the particle and mc^2 its rest energy.

With this brief résumé of the main properties of Bremsstrahlung, we will proceed to discuss a few points of detail in its relation to Čerenkov radiation.

* The term Bremsstrahlung is frequently used to cover a wide range of radiation processes involving the acceleration or deceleration of charges, such as for example the radiation of electrons in a magnetic field. For our purposes, however, the term will be used exclusively to refer to the radiation produced as a result of the interaction of a fast charged particle with the screened electrostatic field of an atomic nucleus; see for example Heitler (1944).

F

Relative Intensities

Although the *total* energy radiated by an electron in the Bremsstrahlung process is considerably greater than that emitted by Čerenkov radiation, the very different spectral distributions in the two cases result in the intensity of the Čerenkov radiation exceeding the Bremsstrahlung by a very large factor in the *visible* region.

Consider the two types of radiation emitted for instance by a 100 MeV electron traversing 1cm of water, over a wave-band of 4000–5000 Å. For the Čerenkov radiation the yield is ~ 100 photons or ~ 270 eV, or ~ 2700 eV if we consider the full Čerenkov bandwidth possible in this case, i.e. from $\omega = 0$ to $\omega \sim 10^{16}$ (cut-off by absorption at ~ 2000 Å). The total output of Bremsstrahlung over the whole band, up to the γ-ray energy maximum at 100 MeV is, on the other hand, $\sim 1{\cdot}9$ MeV, while the amount of energy in the same region of the visible spectrum is only 0·012 eV.

We thus see that under these circumstances

$$[W \, (\text{Brems})/W(\check{C})]_{\text{total}} \approx 700$$

whereas
$$[W \, (\text{Brems})/W(\check{C})]_{\substack{\text{visible} \\ (4000\text{–}5000 \text{ Å})}} \approx 4{\cdot}5 \times 10^{-5}$$

Spectral Distributions

We have seen that the spectral distributions of the two radiation processes are markedly different, $W(\text{Brems})$ varying as const. $d\omega$, and $W(\check{C})$ as $\omega \, d\omega$. A simple qualitative explanation of this difference may be gleaned from Fig. 3.13.

A single Bremsstrahlung event is shown in Fig. 3.13(a), in which an electron e has just passed the nucleus N of an atom whose impact parameter is indicated by the circle marked I.P. During the time τ that the electron is within the sphere of influence of the nucleus, it experiences a radial or transverse field. The radiation, produced by the *transverse* acceleration of the electron in this field E_ρ, may be represented by a pulse of width τ approximating to a δ-function. It is the Fourier analysis of this δ-function which gives rise to the equi-energy spectrum.

With Čerenkov radiation the situation is quite different, see Fig. 3.13(b). Consider the fast electron e passing some point S in the dielectric. When the electron is at a point e_1, owing to the retarded potential, the polarization vector P_1 will be directed at some point e_1'. A short time later, when the electron has reached another point e_2, P will have turned over and will be directed at some other point e_2'.

Resolving P into radial and axial components P_ρ and P_z, their variation with time will be as shown. The ρ-components will not contribute to the radiation since they are axially symmetrical and their resultant field, at a distance large compared with the distance of S from the z-axis, will be zero. Thus, in Čerenkov radiation it is the *axial* com-

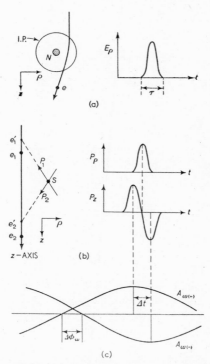

FIG. 3.13. To illustrate the fundamental differences between Čerenkov radiation and Bremsstrahlung.

(a) The transverse electric field in Bremsstrahlung.

(b) The transverse and longitudinal components of the Polarization field in Čerenkov radiation.

(c) Typical long-wave Fourier components of the positive and negative pulses of the longitudinal component of (b).

ponent of the electric field vector which is responsible for the radiation, and this is equivalent to two adjacent δ-functions of opposite sign, see Fig. 3.13(b).

Consider now a Fourier component of amplitude a and frequency ω for which the corresponding period T is $\gg \Delta t$, the separation of the two δ-functions, see Fig. 3.13(c). The phase difference $\Delta\phi_\omega$ between the two components of nearly opposite phase is

$$\Delta\phi/2\pi = \Delta t/T$$

or, since

$$T = 2\pi/\omega, \ \Delta\phi_\omega = \omega \,.\, \Delta t.$$

The resultant amplitude from the two components is thus:

$$A_\omega = a_\omega \sin \omega t - a_\omega \sin (\omega t + \Delta\phi_\omega)$$
$$= a_\omega [\sin \omega t \,(1 - \cos \Delta\phi_\omega) - \cos \omega t \sin \Delta\phi_\omega]. \qquad (3.77a)$$

Since the Fourier transform of each δ-function, taken separately, is an equi-energy spectrum (as in Bremsstrahlung), a is a constant independent of ω. With the condition
$\Delta t \ll T$, $\Delta\phi_\omega \ll 1$, $\cos \Delta\phi_\omega \to 1$ and $\sin \Delta\phi_\omega \to \Delta\phi_\omega$. Then (3.77a) becomes:

$$A_\omega \approx - a \,.\, \Delta\phi_\omega \,.\, \cos \omega t \qquad (3.77b)$$

and the resulting intensity for this Fourier component is therefore:

$$W_\omega \approx a^2\omega^2 \,.\, \Delta t^2 \,.\, \cos^2 \omega t. \qquad (3.78)$$

Neglecting the oscillatory factor $\cos^2\omega t$, and taking Δt constant for a medium of given dispersion, and for a given position of the point S, we see that

$$W \propto \omega^2$$

from which we find the spectral distribution

$$dW/d\omega \propto \omega \qquad (3.79)$$

as obtained by Frank and Tamm.

In the case of a non-dispersive medium, $\Delta t \to 0$, so that (3.79) is valid for all values of ω. If the medium is dispersive, the validity of (3.79) is limited to frequencies well removed from the resonance frequencies of the medium. In transparent media in which the resonances occur in the ultra-violet, (3.79) will apply in the optical and radio frequency regions, while deviations should be observable in the near ultra-violet.

Angular Distributions

There is also a distinct difference between the angular intensity distribution functions in the two processes. In Čerenkov radiation the angle of emission increases with the energy of the particle, while in Bremsstrahlung it decreases.

This difference arises essentially from two causes:

(i) In Čerenkov radiation the elemental dipoles causing the radiation do not move relative to the observer, so there is no relativistic transformation of their radiation pattern. In Bremsstrahlung, however, it is the fast-moving particle itself that radiates, and the radiation pattern is therefore subject to such a transformation.

(ii) In Čerenkov radiation one is concerned with frequencies for which the refractive index n of the medium is $> 1/\beta$ and the coherence condition determines the unique angle of emission. By contrast, in Bremsstrahlung, one is usually considering frequencies in the x-ray or γ-ray region for which $n < 1$ and no such coherence condition exists.

These points are illustrated in Fig. 3.11.

Consider, (a), the fictitious case of Čerenkov radiation in a thin film of dielectric, of thickness $\leqslant \lambda/2$. In this case there can be no coherence; nevertheless there will be radiation of a Čerenkov type, since the medium will still be polarizable. The radiation pattern will then have a $\sin^2\theta$ distribution as shown. If now the film thickness is increased to say $\sim 10\lambda$, the effects of coherence begin to be apparent, though the diffraction width will still be appreciable, see Fig. 3.11(b); the main lobe will now appear at an angle θ which is the Čerenkov angle. The $\sin^2\theta$ still persists as a multiplying factor in the distribution; indeed it is always present even with a thick radiator, for the factor $(1 - 1/\beta^2 n^2)$ in the normal intensity-equation of Frank and Tamm is in fact $\sin^2\theta$. Note that there are no relativistic effects.

In Bremsstrahlung, Fig. 3.11(c), where the effective dipole axis is perpendicular to the line of motion, the distribution in the nonrelativistic case will be of the form $\cos^2\theta$, with maxima ahead and behind.

In the relativistic case, owing to the motion of the particle, the distribution becomes modified and is peaked in the forward direction as in other relativistic radiation processes, and has a width $\sim (mc^2/E)$.

The above remarks concerning Bremsstrahlung are strictly only valid for collisions within an impact parameter corresponding to the screening radius of the nuclei. For very soft quanta and high particle-energies, radiation will arise from the integrated scattering of the particle along its path. If, furthermore, the emitted radiation is subject to the effects of the dielectric constant of the medium as a whole, there may well be a form of coherent Bremsstrahlung which will be barely distinguishable from Čerenkov radiation. At ultra-high energies, the Bremsstrahlung cross-section decreases however, for soft quanta; this arises from two causes which are discussed in detail by Feinberg and Pomerančuk (1956).

3.11 A point charge moving along the interface between two media

The radiation of a charge moving *in vacuo* close to a dielectric surface has already been discussed in section 3.4. Pafomov (1957) has recently solved the more general problem, that of the radiation from a point charge moving close to the plane interface between two dielectrics. He considers the case of an electron moving in a straight line, with velocity v, at a distance d from the interface of two media characterized by dielectric constants ϵ_1 and ϵ_2 both of which are real, i.e. there is no absorption. If the Čerenkov condition is fulfilled only in the second medium ($\epsilon_1\beta^2 < 1$; $\epsilon_2\beta^2 > 1$), all the energy is radiated into the second medium, and the distribution of intensity over all generatrices of the Čerenkov cone will be as follows:

$$\frac{dW}{dz} =$$

$$\frac{2e^2c^2}{\pi v^4} \int_{\epsilon_2\beta^2>1} \int_0^\pi \frac{\beta[(\epsilon_2\beta^2 - 1)(\epsilon_1 + \epsilon_2)\cos^2\phi + \epsilon_2(1 - \epsilon_1\beta^2)](\epsilon_2\beta^2 - 1)\sin^2\phi}{(\epsilon_2 - \epsilon_1)[(\epsilon_1 + \epsilon_2)\sin^2\phi + \epsilon_2\beta^2(\epsilon_2\cos^2\phi - \epsilon_1\sin^2\phi)]} \times$$

$$\times \exp\left\{-2d\frac{\omega}{v}[(\epsilon_2 - \epsilon_1)\beta^2 - (\epsilon_2\beta^2 - 1)\sin^2\phi]^{\frac{1}{2}}\right\}\omega d\omega d\phi \quad (3.80)$$

where ϕ is the azimuth angle. $\phi = 0$ corresponds to a plane parallel to the interface. The Čerenkov cone is defined, as in the homogeneous case, by the condition $n\beta\cos\theta = 1$, and since this is satisfied only under the interface, the cone is semicircular in section.

Equation (3.80) has the same form as those obtained by Linhart (1955) and Danos (1955), to the extent that there is an exponential decrease of intensity with increase of d. When however we put $\epsilon_1 = 1$ in (3.80), we do not obtain the equation (3.40) derived by Linhart; these differences arise from the approximations introduced in the other treatments. Returning to the main problem, if $\epsilon_1\beta^2 > 1$ and $\epsilon_2\beta^2 > 1$, Pafomov shows that the result depends on the relationship between ϵ_1 and ϵ_2. If $\epsilon_1 > \epsilon_2$, the energy distribution of radiation into the second medium has the form:

$$\frac{dW}{dz} = \frac{2e^2c^2}{\pi v^4} \int\limits_{\epsilon_2\beta^2>1} \int\limits_0^\pi \frac{A}{B^2}\ \omega d\omega\ d\phi \qquad (3.81)$$

with

$$A = \{(\epsilon_1\beta^2 - 1) + [\sqrt{[(\epsilon_1\beta^2 - 1) - (\epsilon_2\beta^2 - 1)\cos^2\phi]}\ .\ \sin\phi +$$
$$+ \sqrt{(\epsilon_2\beta^2 - 1)}\ .\ \cos^2\phi]^2(\epsilon_2\beta^2 - 1)\}(\epsilon_2\beta^2 - 1)\sin^2\phi,$$

$$B = \epsilon_1\sqrt{(\epsilon_2\beta^2 - 1)}\ .\ \sin\phi + \epsilon_2\sqrt{[(\epsilon_1\beta^2 - 1) - (\epsilon_2\beta^2 - 1)\cos^2\phi]}.$$

If, when $\epsilon_1\beta^2 > 1$ and $\epsilon_2\beta^2 > 1$, but at the same time $\epsilon_1 < \epsilon_2$, then in the region where $\cos^2\phi > (\epsilon_1\beta^2 - 1)/(\epsilon_2\beta^2 - 1)$, the expression under the integral in (3.81) must be replaced by that under the integral in (3.80).

The expression for the energy flow into the first medium is, in the general case, much more complex. When however $d = 0$, it is obtained directly from (3.80) and (3.81) by transposing ϵ_1 and ϵ_2.

An interesting point in connexion with this, and the vacuum-dielectric case, is that owing to the lack of symmetry of the medium around the trajectory of the particle, there is a force deflecting the electron from rectilinear motion.

The Čerenkov effect in composite media has also recently been discussed by Sayied (1958).

3.12 Effects in a superconductor

A study by Hayakawa and Kitao (1956) of the problem of the passage of a charged particle through a superconductor, leads to the conclusion that the threshold energy and Čerenkov radiation yield are a little higher than the corresponding values for the same material at room temperature. As an example, in the case of tin, the total energy loss (including ionization) for a relativistic particle is 1·4% higher near zero temperature than at normal temperature.

Modifications to the general theory arise because the dielectric constant (and refractive index) of the medium is slightly altered by the presence of the electrons taking part in the superconduction. Owing to the small interactions of these superelectrons, their effective mass m_s is considerably less than m_e, the mass of normal electrons; it is believed that $m_s \leqslant 10^{-3} m_e$.

Regarding the behaviour of an electron gas in a metal as equivalent to a plasma (see section 3.6), the characteristic frequencies of the normal and superelectrons are

$$\omega_e = \sqrt{(4\pi\, n_e\, e^2/m_e)}$$
$$\text{and } \omega_s = \sqrt{(4\pi\, n_s\, e^2/m_s)} \text{ respectively} \qquad (3.82)$$

where n_e and n_s are the corresponding electron densities. The ratio of these densities is such that $(\omega_s/\omega_e)^2 \leqslant 10^{-2}$, so that in the optical region the contribution to the dielectric constant from the superelectrons is very small.

The (complex) dielectric constant for a superconductor is expressed by Hayakawa and Kitao in the form:

$$\epsilon(\omega) = Re.\ \epsilon(\omega) - 4\pi/\Lambda\omega^2 + i\ Im.\ \epsilon(\omega) \qquad (3.83)$$

which differs from equation (3.46) in section 3.5 by the addition of another term. Λ is the characteristic constant of a superconductor and is equal to $4\pi/\omega_s^2$. The radiation output is obtained directly by inserting $\epsilon(\omega)$ from (3.83) in equation (3.48).

Although the relative enhancement of the radiation yield at low temperatures is negligible in the optical region, it may be considerable in the microwave region, for which Landau estimates that $\epsilon(\omega)$ may be as high at $10^7 - 10^{10}$. The absolute yield at these frequencies, for a single particle, will nevertheless still be small, see section 3.4.

CHAPTER 4

LATER EXPERIMENTAL WORK

WITH the rapid development of the photomultiplier immediately after the war, there followed a period during which there was a marked increase in experimental work on Čerenkov radiation. This work was essentially of an exploratory nature, centred on studies of the radiation itself rather than its applications; the techniques and instruments evolved for these experiments nevertheless paved the way for the development of the practical instruments described in Chapter 8.

A review of the main experiments of this exploratory type will now be presented, though space of course prevents anything but a brief summary of the results and the salient features of each experiment. The work has been arbitrarily grouped into classes, depending mainly on the source of particles used in the investigations. The experiments using artificially accelerated particles enjoy very high fluxes in beams that may be well collimated and which are in general variable in energy. In contrast, those using cosmic rays have particles of very high energy arriving at a relatively low rate, which cannot be collimated and which have a wide range of energy.

4.1 Experiments with artificially accelerated particles

Collins and Reiling (1938) were the first to repeat some of Čerenkov's experiments, using an intense and well collimated beam of mono-energetic particles. They had a 10 μA beam of 2 MeV electrons from an electrostatic generator, and used photographic recording to study the variation of the angle of light emission θ with the refractive index n, at a single energy. With thin foils of mica, glass and cellophane (with values of $n = 1\cdot59$, $1\cdot47$ and $1\cdot54$ respectively) they measured θ at 2 MeV. The observed values were $53° : 30'$, $45° : 15'$ and $50° : 0'$ respectively, agreeing well with the calculated values of $52° : 10'$, $46° : 30'$ and $49° : 22'$. They also studied the spectra of the radiations, confirming the continuous spectrum, and they measured the absolute light intensity, which agreed to within a factor of 2 with that predicted by Frank and Tamm. Their apparatus is shown in Fig. 4.1.

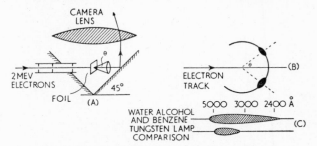

FIG. 4.1. The experiments of Collins and Reiling (1938).
(a) Apparatus.   (b) The appearance of the photographic images.
(c) The spectra as recorded on a photographic plate, for Čerenkov radiation,
and a tungsten lamp for comparison.

Wyckoff and Henderson (1943) carried out an experiment to check the relation between θ and β, with an apparatus and technique similar to that just described. They used mica foils (in the thickness range 0·00013–0·0025 cm) which they bombarded with $\sim 1 \mu A$ of electrons in the energy range 240–815 keV, obtaining the results shown in Fig. 4.2, in which the solid curve is that calculated from the Čerenkov

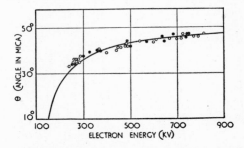

FIG. 4.2. The dependence of θ on E. (After Wyckoff and Henderson, 1943.)

relation. They realized that since mica has a crystalline structure there should be two cones of radiation (see section 3.3); these could not be resolved however with the existing resolution. Experiments of the same general type were also carried out by Harding and Henderson (1948), who investigated the variations of intensity and polarization of the light in the neighbourhood of the threshold, and arrived at the conclusion that the light was unpolarized at the threshold and rapidly became polarized as the energy of the electrons was increased.

Getting (1947) was the first to suggest the use of a photomultiplier to detect the light of Čerenkov radiation. He calculated the photon yield expected from a relativistic particle traversing a cylindrical block of Lucite 20 cm long. From considerations of the photoelectric efficiency of the cathode of the photomultiplier, and the rate of emission of dark current pulses, he estimated that the signal to noise ratio expected from such a system, with an amplifier of bandwidth 10 Mc/s, would be quite high. He then proposed optical systems (see Chapter 7) which, with collimated beams of particles, would concentrate into one

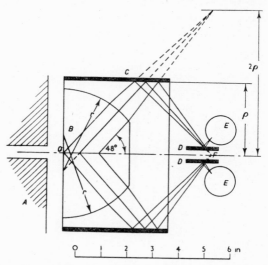

FIG. 4.3. The first Čerenkov detector of the focusing type, to use photomultipliers. (Marshall, 1951.)

direction all the light formed at a given Čerenkov angle in an extended radiator.

Shortly following Jelley's experiments with a water radiator (see section 4.2), Marshall (1951) was the first to use a Čerenkov detector with a photomultiplier, to detect artificially accelerated electrons. In these experiments, he used electrons generated in a thin ($\frac{1}{8}$ in.) radiator by the Bremsstrahlung γ-radiation produced in turn from 48 MeV electrons in a betatron. The electrons entered the apparatus from a collimator A, Fig. 4.3, and produced Čerenkov radiation in a radiator B made from Lucite or Plexiglas. This radiator was a figure of revolution generated by rotating a circle around an axis in its plane, but not through its centre. The radius of curvature r was so chosen as to focus the Čerenkov radiation into a sharp ring with a radius of approximately 2ρ, where ρ is the radius of a cylindrical reflector C. This in turn focused the light on the axis of the system at F where, in principle, the photomultiplier could be placed. To reduce the effective noise from the photomultiplier, Marshall found it better to split the beam by small mirrors D and then use two phototubes E run in coincidence; in addition this arrangement had the advantage that the beam of electrons did not pass through the multipliers themselves. By varying the position of the phototubes, different angles could be selected; the variation of output with angle is shown in Fig. 4.4. The Čerenkov angle θ calculated

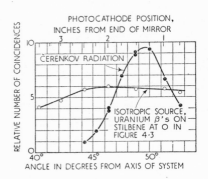

FIG. 4.4. Results obtained by Marshall, using fast electrons, with the counter shown in Fig. 4.3.

for $n = 1 \cdot 50$ and $\beta = 1$, is $48°$, quite close to the observed maximum at $49 \cdot 5°$. Shortly after these experiments, Marshall (1952) developed a whole range of instruments of the focusing type, the description of which are deferred to Chapter 8, while their optical features are discussed in Chapter 7.

4.2 Experiments with cosmic-ray particles

Dicke (1947) attempted to detect cosmic-rays with a device similar to that proposed by Getting, mounting the instrument above a Geiger counter in a coincidence arrangement. This experiment gave a negative result, the reason for which has not been explained.

Shortly after this, Weisz and Anderson (1947) tried to detect cosmic rays using the very simple apparatus shown in Fig. 4.5. They used light-sensitive Geiger counters of special construction which operated in the ultra-violet region of the spectrum, 2000–3000 Å, and which had quantum conversion efficiencies in the range $2\cdot10^{-4}$–$60\cdot10^{-4}$ counts/quantum. The experiment consisted of taking the counting rate

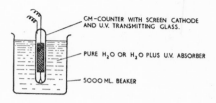

GM–COUNTER WITH SCREEN CATHODE AND U.V. TRANSMITTING GLASS.

PURE H_2O OR H_2O PLUS U.V. ABSORBER

5000 ML. BEAKER

FIG. 4.5. The apparatus used by Weisz and Anderson (1947), to detect Čerenkov radiation produced by the passage of cosmic-rays through water, using photo-sensitive Geiger counters.

with the counter immersed first in pure water and then in a solution containing 1% by weight of hydroquinone. Any contribution to the counting rate from Čerenkov radiation in the pure water would be eliminated in the case of the solution, which has strong absorption in the ultra-violet. The results, shown in Table 4A, suggest that cosmic rays were detected with this simple apparatus, though at low efficiency.

TABLE 4A

Run	Pure water counts/min	Hydroquinone counts/min	Possible contribution from Čerenkov effect counts/min	Fractional contribution of Čerenkov effect
	N_1	N_0	$(N_1 - N_0)$	$(N_1 - N_0)/N_0$
1	232 ± 5	210 ± 5	22 ± 7	$10 \pm 4\%$
2	254 ± 5	224 ± 6	30 ± 8	$13 \pm 5\%$
3	263 ± 7	224 ± 5	41 ± 9	$18 \pm 6\%$
				Mean $\sim 14\%$

This average contribution to the counting rate, from the ultra-violet radiation in pure water, $\sim 14\%$ of the total rate, compares favourably with a figure of $\sim 10\%$ calculated from the geometry and quantum efficiencies.

The first clear evidence that single fast particles could be detected at high efficiency with a photomultiplier, was obtained by Jelley (1951) who used the simple water detector shown in Fig. 4.6. This experiment was also the first in which particles other than electrons were used to produce Čerenkov radiation. The detector was first operated in coincidence with a tray of Geiger counters to select cosmic-ray particles

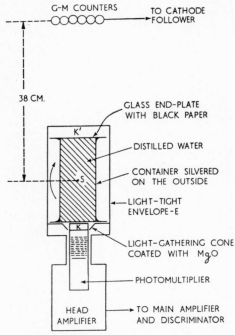

FIG. 4.6. The water detector used by Jelley (1951) to count single cosmic-ray μ-mesons.

near the zenith. Since nearly all the particles are travelling in a downward sense through the apparatus, it follows that the Čerenkov radiation will also be directed downwards. The coincidence rate would thus be expected to be higher when the photomultiplier was in the position K below the container than when it was above, in position K^1.

To investigate these coincidences, runs were done at different settings of the bias on a discriminator following the amplifier, with the phototube alternately in positions K and K^1; this was carried out by rotating the whole detector about its mid-point S. Allowance was made for chance-rate and effects due to the particles traversing the photo-multiplier; the latter were measured by repeating the runs with the container empty. Ratios of the counting rates (due to the water alone), for the phototube in position K and then in position K^1, of $3 \cdot 25 \pm 0 \cdot 32$, $4 \cdot 72 \pm 0 \cdot 35$ and $7 \cdot 7 \pm 1 \cdot 0$, were obtained at bias levels of 2, 5 and 15 V respectively. With this arrangement the absolute efficiency of the detector was found to be $\sim 50\%$ at a bias of 2 V. Confirmation that the observed directional feature of the light was genuine was obtained by replacing the water by a liquid scintillating medium which would give an isotropic light distribution. The corresponding ratio $N(K)/N(K^1)$ at 2 V bias was then found to be $1 \cdot 26 \pm 0 \cdot 06$. That the effects were mostly due to μ-mesons, the dominant component of cosmic-rays at sea-level, was shown by placing a 10 cm thick lead absorber above the apparatus, whereupon the rate dropped by $\sim 20\%$, which is approximately the electron contribution to the total cosmic-ray intensity at sea-level.

Jelley later found that at higher values of bias, at which the counting of dark-current pulses from the phototube was sufficiently reduced, the detector was sensitive to its orientation. It was then possible to detect particles with a good discrimination against background, without the necessity for the coincidence system, as revealed in the bias curves shown in Fig. 4.7. Curves (B) and (C) refer to the counting rates of the detector in the K and K^1 positions respectively, while curve (A) refers to the container empty. The ratio of the derived curves (D) and (E) for the water alone, shown inset, rises to an intensity ratio as high as 70/1 for the K and K^1 positions respectively. The directional characteristic of this simple cylindrical form of detector is shown in Fig. 4.8, where it is compared with the $\cos^2\theta$ distribution, the accepted law of variation of μ-meson intensity with zenith angle θ.

Bassi (1951) attempted to determine the energy of cosmic-ray particles by measuring light intensity rather than emission angle, from the relation $(dW/dl) \propto (1 - 1/\beta^2 n^2)$, equation (2.17). Using a detector similar to Jelley's, sandwiched between two Geiger counters, he obtained 100% efficiency for counting particles traversing the system. His efforts at measuring energies in this way were however defeated by statistical considerations. With a total flux of 3000 photons/particle (see equation 2.21) and a photocathode conversion efficiency of ~ 1 electron/100 photons, the fluctuations on the 30 available electrons amount to

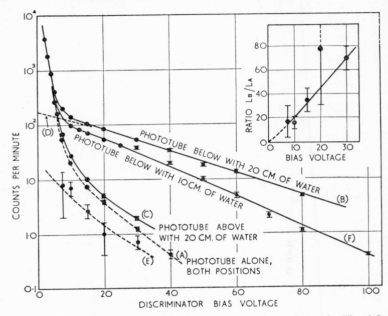

FIG. 4.7. Bias curves obtained by Jelley with the counter shown in Fig. 4.6, to illustrate the directional properties of the radiation.

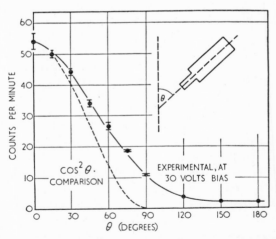

FIG. 4.8. The variation of counting rate with zenith angle, obtained by Jelley with his water detector, Fig. 4.6.

$\sim 20\%$, which in turn leads to a large error in β and an even larger error in the particle energy.

In a later series of experiments Bassi et al. (1952) investigated the light output of Čerenkov radiation produced in a Plexiglas converter, as a function of particle energy, using an anticoincidence system with lead absorbers. These results, which appeared to disagree with the

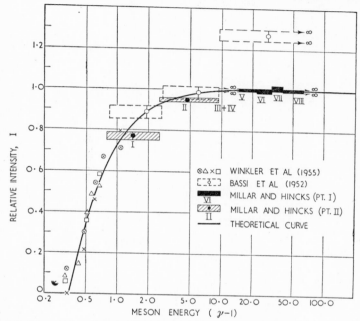

FIG. 4.9. The results of experiments by Millar and Hincks (1957) carried out to search for deviations of the Frank and Tamm theory at high energies. The results of other work are also included.

theory of Frank and Tamm, were, however, not inconsistent with the predictions of Budini (1953); nevertheless it must be admitted that their statistics were poor.

A very thorough examination into this question of the possible deviation of the Čerenkov yield from the Frank and Tamm theory, has recently been made by Millar and Hincks (1957). For this they used cosmic-ray μ-mesons, the energies of which were selected by lead absorbers in a scintillator telescope arrangement. Their results, which are shown in Fig. 4.9, reveal that with μ-mesons passing through their

G

Plexiglas radiator, there is no high-energy anomaly up to energies of 4·2 GeV for which $\beta = 0.99970\ c$. The results of other investigators are also reproduced in Fig. 4.9 in which the relative intensity I is plotted against $(\gamma - 1)$, where I is the ratio of the intensity at a velocity βc to the plateau intensity, i.e. $(1 - 1/\beta^2 n^2)/(1 - 1/n^2)$, and $\gamma = (1 - \beta^2)^{-\frac{1}{2}}$. The theoretical basis for a logarithmic rise in the Čerenkov yield at very high energies is mentioned in section 3.5.

4.3 Experiments with radioactive sources

A quite different approach to the study of Čerenkov radiation was made by Belcher in 1953, who carried out a thorough investigation into the faint luminescence observed from aqueous solutions of radioactive isotopes. In these experiments, unlike those of Mallet and Čerenkov, the sources of the exciting radiation (chiefly β and γ-ray emitters) were distributed uniformly in the media in which the Čerenkov radiation was generated. Belcher found that almost all the observed light may be attributed to the Čerenkov effect and that the relative and absolute intensities of the light were in general agreement with the theory of Frank and Tamm. He showed, in addition, that in the case of solutions of α-emitters, and β-emitters whose particle energies are below the Čerenkov threshold, there remains a very weak luminescence attributable to excitation of the solvent. Belcher's apparatus is shown diagrammatically in Fig. 4.10. Owing to the very low intensities of some

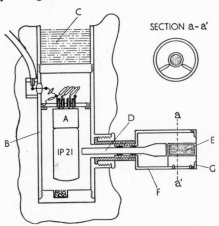

FIG. 4.10. The apparatus used by Belcher (1953) to study the Čerenkov radiation from aqueous solutions of radioactive isotopes.

of the radiations used, the light pulses were extremely weak, and it was necessary to cool the phototube to reduce the dark-current emission to a sufficiently low level, of less than 1 count/sec. The essential features are as follows: the radioactive solution was placed in a small Perspex or Dural cell E which faced a Perspex light-guide D mounted opposite the photocathode of the multiplier tube A (RCA type IP 21). The cooling was achieved by conduction from the heavy brass casing B to an upper container filled with liquid nitrogen C, and the whole apparatus was lagged with cotton wool.

The results of these experiments are shown in Fig. 4.11 where the

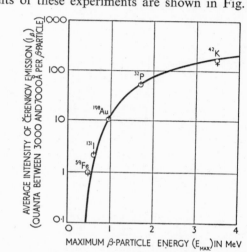

FIG. 4.11. Results of Belcher's experiment. (The continuous curve is constructed from the theory of Frank and Tamm.)

average intensity of the radiation, from each sample solution, is plotted against the corresponding maximum energy of the β-particles, in MeV. The isotopes used in this work are indicated beside the experimental points. The full line is that calculated from the theory of Frank and Tamm, taking into account the following factors for which corrections had to be applied: (a) the variation of β along the track of the particle, as it slows down, until its velocity is below the Čerenkov threshold, (b) the energy distribution of the β-particles, (c) the wall-effects, i.e. loss of particles emitted near the boundaries of the container, and (d) effects due to self-absorption of γ-rays when present. A value was obtained for the absolute intensity, which corresponded to an emission of ~ 90

photons between 3000–7000 Å for a 1 MeV electron brought to rest in the solutions. This represents an energy loss, in this wavelength region, of $\sim 0.20\%$ of the total energy dissipated by the particle in the medium.

Two α-emitting species were also used, polonium 210 and natural uranium. The radiations from these were of course far below the Čerenkov threshold, though a weak visible radiation was nevertheless observed. For instance, in the case of ^{210}Po, which is entirely free from β-radiation, this residual light emission amounted to ~ 0.5 photon for each α-particle brought to rest (for the same range of wavelengths).

It should be mentioned here that special interest is attached to the phenomena of luminescence in aqueous solutions of radioactive isotopes, from the biological point of view. For instance, Dee and Richards (1951) suggested that quantum emission might be responsible for the biological effects of nuclear radiations, and Dainton (1949) has discussed the possible rôle of the Čerenkov effect in the field of Radiation Chemistry.

Returning to the more usual arrangement, that in which the source of the exciting radiation and the medium are separated from each other, mention should be made of two experiments on the spectrum of the radiation carried out with radioactive sources. The first of these was performed by Greenfield et al. (1953) who studied the spectral distribution of the light from triple distilled water, in the spectral region 3130–4730 Å using the γ-rays from radium and the β-rays from ^{32}P. Rich et al. (1953) carried out a similar type of experiment over a much wider spectral range. With a 3400 c ^{60}Co source which was available, the resulting light intensity (0·1 foot-lambert) was such that they could obtain a direct spectrum over the range 3200–6000 Å using a large grating spectrograph, having a dispersion of 30 Å/mm. In this work, de-ionized water was used, and the spectrum was found to agree closely with that derived by Frank and Tamm, there being no evidence for fluorescence radiation from the water; see also section 11.8.

4.4 Čerenkov radiation in air

The work described so far has been exclusively concerned with generation of Čerenkov radiation in solids and liquids. Blackett (1948) was the first to point out that the Čerenkov effect should be observable in gases, though it was not until five years later that the radiation from single particles passing through gases was detected. In a gas the refractive index is so close to unity that the general features of the radiation appear rather different from those in solids and liquids. The light intensity is much lower, the threshold energy higher and the maximum angle of light emission smaller. For instance, in air at atmospheric pressure, $n = 1\cdot00029$, from which it is calculated through the usual relations, that (for electrons) $\theta_{max} = 1\cdot3°$, $E_{min} = 21$ MeV and $(dW/dl)_{\beta=1} = 0\cdot3$ photons/cm (4000–5000 Å). For comparison, the corresponding figures for electrons in water are: $n = 1\cdot33$, $\theta_{max} = 41°$, $E_{min} = 0\cdot26$ MeV and $(dW/dl)_{\beta=1} = 250$ photons/cm.

The first experiments to detect the radiation from gaseous substances were made by Ascoli Balzanelli and Ascoli (1953) who selected high energy cosmic-ray particles to pass through chloroform vapour; this was obtained by evaporating 0·4 to 0·8 ml of liquid chloroform per litre of air. In this way they obtained a refractive index in the region 1·01 to 1·02. The light pulses produced in the vapour were detected by a photomultiplier run in coincidence with the Geiger counter telescope used to select the particles. The observed coincidences, first without, and then with, a shutter interposed between the phototube and the vapour, revealed that at least some light was produced, though there was no evidence that it was due to Čerenkov radiation.

The same workers (1954) subsequently obtained undoubted evidence for Čerenkov radiation in pure air, using the apparatus shown in Fig. 4.12. Cosmic-ray particles were selected by the Geiger telescope I-II-III, and the light generated in the air inside the 80 cm long tube T (silvered on the inside) was reflected by a parabolic mirror P to the cathode K of the photomultiplier $F.M.$ In this arrangement the phototube is displaced to the side of the particle "beam", thereby reducing spurious counts previously observed when the particles passed through the dynode structure of the phototube. The apparatus could be rotated about the mid-point O and a shutter S interposed when required. Typical results obtained with this apparatus are:

		coincidences/hr
(a) Apparatus the right way up, without S		$1\cdot56 \pm 0\cdot20$
(b) Apparatus the right way up, with S		$0\cdot57 \pm 0\cdot20$
(c) Apparatus upside down, without S		$0\cdot765 \pm 0\cdot15$

The difference $[(a) - (b)] = 0\cdot99 \pm 0\cdot28/hr$, is evidence that the selected particles were producing light, while the difference $[(a) - (c)] = 0\cdot80 \pm 0\cdot25/hr$ suggests that this light was in fact due to Čerenkov radiation. An extension of their work has recently been published, Ascoli Balzanelli and Ascoli (1957).

In the experiments just described, the counting rates and pulse amplitudes were rather small, owing to the limited length of track and the relatively poor optical system. An experiment of the same general type was then carried out by Barclay and Jelley (1955), using the apparatus shown in Fig. 4.13(a). Considerable improvement was achieved on a number of counts. The track length was 6 m, and the counter telescope AB confined the particles so that almost all the

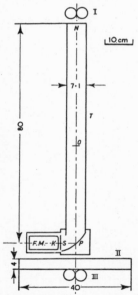

FIG. 4.12. The apparatus used by Ascoli Balzanelli and Ascoli (1954) in the first successful experiment to detect Čerenkov radiation from single particles in air.

Čerenkov light would be intercepted by the parabolic mirror M, see Fig. 4.13(b). The light was focused on the cathode of the photo-multiplier P, which was screened by the counters G to enable events produced by light alone to be distinguished from those in which the particles themselves had passed through the phototube. μ-Mesons were selected throughout, by interposing a 20 cm Pb filter above counter tray B; this ensured that only single particles were counted and at the same time gave some protection against electron showers and knock-o n electrons. A shutter H was used to obscure the light, for control runs. The results of this experiment are presented in Fig. 4.14 which shows the pulse height distributions obtained for events of type $(ABP\text{-}G)$ with the shutter open or closed; these events are due to genuine light flashes, in which the particle did not traverse the phototube. Histograms of events of type $(ABP + G)$, i.e. those for which the particle produced a pulse in the phototube directly and hence fired the G-counters, are also shown; these distributions, as we would expect, are the same

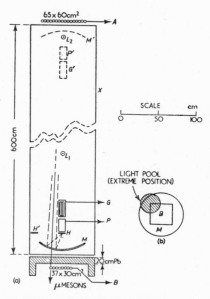

FIG. 4.13. Apparatus used by Barclay and Jelley (1955) for experiments on Čerenkov and other sources of light from fast μ-mesons in air.

whether the shutter was open or closed. An upper limit to the amount of light emitted isotropically and due to ionization or recombination in the air, was also estimated with this apparatus in the following way: The lead filter and the selecting trays A and B were left untouched while the remainder of the apparatus was bodily rotated through $180°$ about its mid-point, so that the mirror, phototube and G-counters took up positions M^1, P^1 and G^1 respectively. Pulse height distributions of the type $(ABP^1 - G^1)$ were again obtained with the shutter open and then

closed, the Čerenkov radiation having been eliminated since this would
still travel downwards. In this case the distributions were the same and
the counting rates very low; from these results it was deduced that the
output of isotropic visible radiation in air at N.T.P., from relativistic

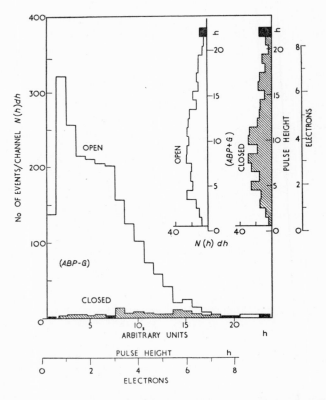

FIG. 4.14. Pulse height distributions obtained by Barclay and Jelley with the apparatus shown in Fig. 4.13.

μ-mesons, was $< 10^{-2}$ of that for Čerenkov radiation, or $< 4 \cdot 10^{-6}$ of
the total energy loss by ionization. This is a rather surprisingly low
figure which it would be well to confirm by a different type of experiment.

4.5 The generation of microwaves

The possibility of generating microwaves using the Čerenkov effect has already been discussed theoretically in section 3.4. The first experimental investigations were carried out by Danos *et al.* (1953) who used the apparatus shown in Fig. 4.15.

A current of 0·2 mA of electrons at an energy of 10 keV were "bunched" by a cavity driven from an oscillator at a frequency of 24 kMc/s. ($\lambda = 1 \cdot 25$ cm). The electron beam, of width 4 mm and thickness 0·3 mm, was directed over the face of a block of dielectric composed of polycrystalline TiO_2 having a dielectric constant of 105 at the above frequency. The Čerenkov radiation generated in the TiO_2 at the appropriate angle, was received by an electromagnetic horn coupled to a crystal and meter. In order to facilitate amplification, the

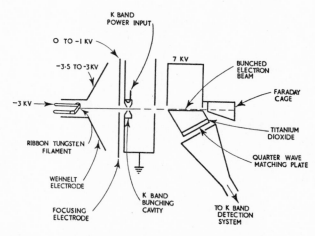

FIG. 4.15. Equipment used by Danos *et al.* (1953) in the first detection of Čerenkov radiation at microwave frequencies.

electron beam was modulated by switching the cavity on and off at a rate of 6 kc/s. Discrimination against possible direct interaction between the R.F. oscillator and the receiver was assured by "chopping" the electron beam at 20 c/s. The "bunching", discussed in section 3.4, causes a great enhancement of intensity, the electrons in each "bunch" radiating coherently.

With this apparatus in its earliest form, 10^{-7} W of radiation at this frequency was obtained, which is to be compared with a calculated figure of 10^{-6} W, the maximum possible output from this arrangement. As the distance between the electron beam and the dielectric was increased, the radiation output decreased rapidly, as predicted by theory.

CHAPTER 5

THE PHOTOMULTIPLIER

5.1 Introduction

The essential rôle of the photomultiplier in almost all Čerenkov counters suggests a consideration of some of its main properties, such as its extreme sensitivity as a detector of electromagnetic radiation, its versatility and its limitations. In the optical region of the spectrum, the photomultiplier is by far the most sensitive detector known. It has an energy sensitivity limited only by photo-cathode efficiency and thermal

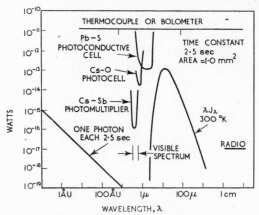

FIG. 5.1. Present attainable threshold sensitivities for the detection of electromagnetic radiation as a function of the wavelength. Black body emission at 300°K is also shown.

emission, while its effective bandwidth may run to a figure as high as $2 \cdot 5 \times 10^{14}$ c/s (4000–6000 Å). Figure 5.1 shows the absolute sensitivities of various types of detectors of electromagnetic radiation, reduced to the same integrating time constant of $2 \cdot 5$ sec, revealing that the photomultiplier is only surpassed by the radio receiver in sensitivity.

Most of the characteristics of a photomultiplier of interest in Čerenkov counters are also those relevant to scintillation counters. To avoid undue repetition, the reader is referred to the standard works on the scintillation counter, by Curran (1953) and Birks (1953), both of which contain detailed discussions on photomultipliers. A thorough account of the basic photoelectric phenomena may be found in the work of Hughes and du Bridge (1932), while the more comprehensive treatise on photomultipliers themselves by Rodda (1953) and Sommer (1951) are also recommended.

In these pages emphasis will only be laid on those aspects which are of particular importance to the use of photomultipliers in Čerenkov counters. The very low level of light intensity encountered in Čerenkov radiation, in general lower than that emitted in most scintillators, creates special interest in the dark-current and signal-to-noise characteristics. This low light intensity also has a direct bearing on the problem of fluctuations of the amplitude of the output pulse. In view of their importance, these three factors have been selected for detailed discussion, while most other features will only be mentioned very briefly. A fourth, and an also very important problem which receives special attention, is the question of the calculation of the absolute efficiencies of photocathodes for Čerenkov radiation.

The development of the photomultiplier may be traced historically as follows: After the discovery of secondary-electron emission, and particularly after it was realized that emission ratios in excess of unity could be obtained, there was an era during which much experimental work was carried out, and the early forms of multiplier evolved. Most of the designs appearing at that time, the early thirties, were reached in a semi-empirical way. A great stimulation occurred in 1938 when

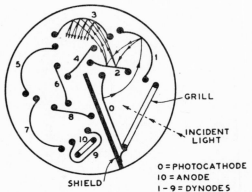

FIG. 5.2. The dynode structure of the RCA nine-stage photomultiplier type 931A.

Rajchman described in great detail the design and performance of a photomultiplier which used electrostatic focusing and had an extremely low noise level. This instrument proved to be the forerunner of some of the types of tube widely used at the present time. There are now a variety of basic designs which are commercially available, the main differences being in the geometry and layout of the dynode, or

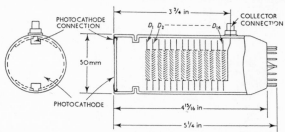

FIG. 5.3. The Venetian-blind dynode structure used in the EMI eleven and fourteen stage photomultipliers.

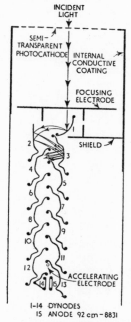

FIG. 5.4. The linear dynode structure used in the new fourteen stage RCA phototube type 6810.

electron-multiplying structure. Figure 5.2 shows the compact and successful arrangement of dynodes used by the Radio Corporation of America in their nine-stage Type 931A multiplier. The Electrical Musical Industries Ltd. use the linear system shown in Fig. 5.3 which is often referred to as the Venetian-blind type. A new and promising

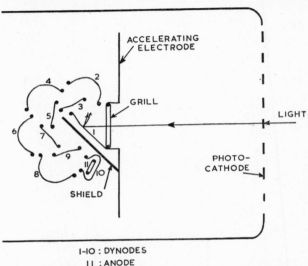

I-IO : DYNODES
II : ANODE

FIG. 5.5. The structure of the RCA photomultiplier type 6342 with focusing electrode.

tube is the type 6810 made by RCA and shown in section in Fig. 5.4. Each design has its own merits and there are a large number of factors to consider, in order to obtain optimum performance.

Besides variations in the design of the dynode system and the number of stages, etc., there are also available a number of different types of photocathode. It will be noticed for instance that the photocathode in the RCA type 931A, Fig. 5.2, takes the form of an internal opaque electrode. For most purposes, however, this is very inconvenient, and in recent years the evolution of the translucent or semi-transparent photocathode, deposited directly on the envelope of the tube, has led to its regular use; all the EMI and most of the RCA tubes now adopt this practice. Figure 5.5 shows the RCA type 6342 which has a focusing electrode; the potential of this is adjusted to obtain either maximum transfer of photoelectrons from the cathode to the relatively small opening into the dynode structure, or the maximum speed of response.

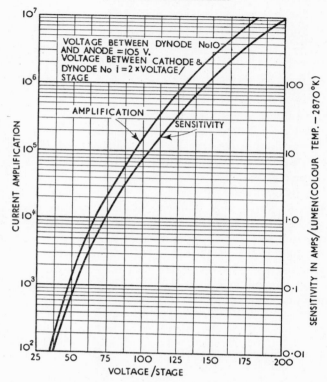

FIG. 5.6. Typical characteristics of a photomultiplier; curves relating the amplification and sensitivity to the interstage voltage, for Du Mont tubes types 6291, 6292, 6363, 6364 and 6467.

The overall current-gains of existing tubes range from $\sim 10^5$ to $\sim 10^9$. The amplication or gain G, is related to the gain per stage σ, and the number of stages m, by the relation $G = \sigma^m$, while σ is a function of the inter-stage voltage V. Over a reasonable range of voltage, it is found that $\sigma \approx kV$, where k is a constant for a given tube and dynode surface. We thus find that $G \approx (kV)^m$ or:

$$\frac{\Delta G}{G} \approx m \frac{\Delta V}{V} \tag{5.1}$$

This shows that the gain is very sensitive to the voltage. For instance, in an 11-stage tube, a 1% change of voltage would correspond to an 11% change of gain. It is usual to work at gains around 10^6 with subsequent amplification in thermionic valves; higher gains are being developed in applications for which extremely short response-times prohibit the use of amplifiers. The gain of a photomultiplier may be varied over quite a wide range, merely by adjusting the voltage across the dynodes; a typical gain vs. voltage curve is shown in Fig. 5.6 for the Du Mont types 6291, 6292, 6363, 6364 and 6467.

5.2 Statistical fluctuations

When successive pulses of light of equal intensity arrive at the cathode of a photomultiplier, so that on the average δ photoelectrons are emitted for each pulse, there will be fluctuations in the pulse amplitude at the output of the tube. These fluctuations may arise from three causes: (i) fluctuations in the number of photons per pulse (the number of photons is δ/η where η is the quantum conversion efficiency, see section 5.8); (ii) fluctuations in δ; and (iii) fluctuations in σ, the secondary emission ratio. Of these, (ii) is the most important; the effects of (i) are negligible when $\eta \ll 1$. Considering effects (ii) and (iii) together, Morton (1949) has shown that the fractional mean square deviation of the amplitude P of the output pulse of a photomultiplier is approximately:

$$\frac{\langle \Delta P^2 \rangle}{P^2} = \frac{1}{\delta} \cdot \frac{\sigma^{m+1} - 1}{\sigma^m(\sigma - 1)} \approx \frac{1}{\delta} \cdot \left(\frac{\sigma}{\sigma - 1} \right) \tag{5.2}$$

where m is the number of stages. Equation (5.2), though calculated on the assumption that the photo-electric and secondary-electron emissions both obey a Poisson distribution (see Appendix II), is however valid for a distribution deviating from the Poisson type.

For example, consider a Čerenkov light-flash of say 2000 photons, falling on the cathode of a phototube with a quantum efficiency of $\sim 10\%$. A typical 11-stage tube, e.g. EMI type 6097, operating at a gain of $\sim 10^7$, has a value of $\sigma = 4.4$. From (5.2) we find in this case $\Delta P/P = \pm 8\%$.

A very comprehensive treatment of the subject of the statistical problems involved in photomultipliers may be found in the work of Breitenberger (1955).

5.3 Calibration procedures

It is frequently desirable to know the overall gain of the system, photomultiplier plus amplifier, and to calibrate a discriminator directly in terms of the number of photoelectrons liberated at the cathode.

Two methods will be mentioned, both of which have the merits of simplicity and are found to give satisfactory results.

The first method, discussed by McIntyre and Hofstadter (1950), consists in measuring the fractional width of a pulse-height distribution curve obtained from a crystal, for example NaI(Tl), which is optically sealed to the photocathode and irradiated from a source emitting monoenergetic γ-rays. The 60 keV γ-ray line from ^{241}Am has been

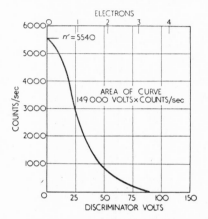

FIG. 5.7. A typical bias curve for single photoelectrons, used for calibration purposes. (After Morton, 1949.)

used by the writer, with satisfactory results. The calibration is then obtained directly, using equation (5.2) to find δ, while σ may be calculated sufficiently accurately from curves published by the manufacturer for the variation of gain with applied voltage.

The second method, described by Morton (1949), makes use of the integral pulse height distribution, or bias curve, obtained with the single-electron pulses of the normal "dark-current" of the tube. A typical bias curve, plotted on a linear scale, is shown in Fig. 5.7. Morton shows that the number of volts on the discriminator, corresponding to one electron from the photocathode, may be found simply by taking the area under the distribution curve, in volts-counts per second, and dividing this by n_0' the counting-rate extrapolated to zero bias. In the example shown in Fig. 5.7, the pulse-height corresponding to the emission of one electron, is found to occur at a bias of 27 V.

There is a more satisfactory variant of this method, which ensures

H

that all the pulses are in fact photoelectrons from the cathode. In this, a steady light source of very low intensity is used to obtain the bias curve, while the bias curve with the source switched off is subtracted before applying the Morton analysis.

5.4 Dark-current

This is the residual current that flows in a photomultiplier in the complete absence of light falling on the cathode. It is very important in many applications, particularly those in which the light signals are weak, that this dark-current should be as small as possible. The total dark-current is the sum of a number of separate components which have been classified by Rajchman as follows: (a) direct leakage over and through insulators, (b) ionization of residual gas, (c) field emission from sharp points on the electrode structure and (d) thermionic emission at the photocathode and from the first few dynodes. In the best multipliers now made, (d) is the only significant source of dark current at room temperature. The thermionic emission i from the cathode is sensitive to temperature, and indeed closely follows the form of the Richardson equation of thermionic emission, namely

$$i \approx AT^2 . \exp(- e\phi/kT) \tag{5.3}$$

where T is the absolute temperature, e the electronic charge, A a constant, and ϕ the effective thermionic work function. Note that with the composite surfaces used in modern photocathodes, such as Cs–Sb, this work-function is not the same as the photoelectric work-function, being somewhat higher. Considerable reduction in dark-current may thus be obtained by cooling a photomultiplier, say in dry ice or liquid mixtures containing dry ice; see Fig. 5.8. Great care however is required when using coolants to lower the dark-current, as it has been reported (Widmaier and Engstrom, 1955) that a Cs_3Sb cathode becomes an insulator at $- 200°C$, and the photosensitivity thus decreases with temperature.

The object of lowering the dark-current is to reduce the accidental rate when two or more multipliers are operated at low bias in a coincidence arrangement. A good tube with a 2-in. diameter cathode, when kept in the dark for a considerable time, has a dark-current corresponding to an emission of between 2000 and 4000 electrons per second, with a Cs–Sb cathode surface. In the majority of problems, difficulties due to the dark-current may be eliminated by recourse to

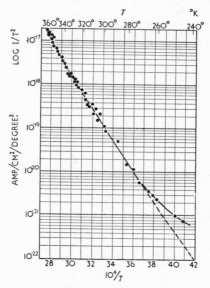

FIG. 5.8. The variation of dark-current with temperature, for a Cs–Sb surface. (After Rajchman, 1938.)

the coincidence technique referred to later (section 5.6). Except in extreme applications, such as the use of phototubes in a high mean light flux, as in the work described in Chapter 9, the problem of photoelectron "pile-up" does not arise. The "pile-up" which may sometimes occur at high counting rates, or in the presence of a general background of light, usually arises in the electronic circuits rather than in the multiplier itself.

5.5 Signal to noise ratio

Closely associated with the dark-current is the problem of signal to noise ratio, for the combined system of photomultiplier plus thermionic amplifier. Following the treatment of Sommer and Turk (1950), the main sources of noise in such systems are:

(a) Random fluctuations of electron emission from the photocathode, the dark-current already discussed;

(b) Thermal noise in the output load-resistor of the phototube;

and (c) Fluctuations in the thermionic emission from the cathode of the first amplifier valve.

With sufficient internal gain in the photomultiplier, it is easy to arrange that contribution (a) dominates over the other two, (b) and (c). Thus, when the gain is raised to such a point that the single-electron dark-current pulses stand out clearly above the amplifier noise, any further increase in gain will not improve the signal to noise ratio. The phototube gain G_{min}, required to achieve this condition, has been obtained by Williams (1938) for the combination of a photo-multiplier and amplifier. Williams obtains the expression:

$$G^2_{min} \geqslant \frac{2kT}{ei_cR} + \frac{2kT}{ei_cR^2} \cdot R_N \left(1 + \tfrac{1}{3} R^2C^2\omega^2\right) \tag{5.4}$$

where:

k is Boltzmann's constant,

T the absolute temperature,

e the electron charge,

i_c the dark-current from the photocathode,

R the load resistance in the output circuit of the phototube,

R_N the equivalent noise resistance of the first stage of the amplifier,

C inter-electrode and stray capacities from valve grid to earth,

and $\omega = 2\pi\Delta f$, where Δf is the bandwidth of the amplifier.

Inserting numerical values for e, k and T (room temperature), (5.4) becomes:

$$G_{min} \geqslant \sqrt{\left[\frac{5\cdot2 \times 10^{-2}}{i_cR} + \frac{5\cdot2 \times 10^{-2}}{i_cR^2} \cdot R_N \left(1 + \tfrac{1}{3} R^2C^2\omega^2\right)\right]} \tag{5.5}$$

With typical values of $i_c = 2\cdot2 \times 10^{-10}$ A, $R = 60\,\Omega$, $R_N = 1500\,\Omega$, $C = 5 \times 10^{-11}$ F and $\Delta f = 7$ Mc/s, (5.5) gives $G > 10^4$. It is usual, as already mentioned, to use a gain in excess of 10^5, so that the signal to noise ratio is then set entirely by the quantum conversion efficiency of the photocathode and the dark-current.

5.6 Other features

The arrival of an electron pulse at the collector of a photomultiplier is frequently accompanied by various forms of *feedback* to the photo-cathode and earlier dynode stages, which in turn give rise to *satellite pulses*. The main causes of feedback are (i) electrical, (ii) optical, with transit times of the order of 20 mμsec and (iii) ionic, with transit times that may go up to several milliseconds. The first of these is easily eliminated by suitable decoupling of the later dynode stages, and the second may be greatly reduced by careful design and internal optical screening. The feedback due to positive ions is more troublesome, particularly at the higher gains. The various effects and the origins of the satellite pulses have been discussed in detail by Davidson (1952), Harrison et al. (1952) and Wells (1952). As far as Čerenkov counting is concerned, the satellite pulses are troublesome in two types of application, those involving the detection of delayed particles and those in which very high counting rates are found.

The speed of response of a photomultiplier is limited by the *transit time* of the electrons down the tube, though it is the *spread* in this transit time which handicaps the realization of the intrinsic speed of a Čerenkov counter, which may be as short as $10^{-11} - 10^{-13}$ sec. for certain types of focused counter. The delays are determined not by the secondary-emitting process itself, but rather by the geometry of the electrode assembly and the applied potentials. As an indication of the performance of typical photomultipliers, Owen (1957, unpublished) has found that an EMI tube type 6097 operating at 3 kV had a transit time of ~ 40 mμsec, while the pulse rise-time was ~ 7 mμsec The corresponding figures for an RCA tube type 5819, operated at 1600 V, were ~ 40 mμsec and ~ 5 mμsec respectively.

Further discussion on the resolving times of photomultipliers may be found in papers by Post (1952), Law (1952) and Morton (1952).

The ultimate gain which may be achieved with a photomultiplier is limited by *saturation effects* due to space charge in the last stage. Under pulse conditions these effects give rise to a *non-linearity* between the amplitude of the output pulse and the incident light intensity. The gain at which these effects are observed, depends on such factors as the design of the later dynodes and the collector electrode, and on the spread in transit time, etc. Nevertheless, the range over which a multiplier behaves linearly is very large; in a typical tube it may be as much as 10^9 to 1, with an output pulse current as high as 10 mA. These space-charge effects have been discussed by Raffle and Robbins (1952) and many others.

External *magnetic fields* may influence the gain and performance of a photomultiplier; special care is required when setting up instruments in the proximity of large magnets.

With regard to associated *circuits*, most applications of Čerenkov counters require only conventional electronic techniques. However, when high resolving times are required, as in experiments on delayed particles, and frequently when coincidence counting is used, recourse must be made to millimicrosecond techniques, a very full account of which is given in the excellent book by Lewis and Wells (1954). The distributed-line amplifier, widely used at the present time, may eventually be abandoned if or when it is possible to attain the required overall gain in photomultipliers without the attendant saturation effects.

Owing to the very low light yield in Čerenkov radiation, the coincidence technique is of great value, and may be used to isolate pulses no larger than the individual dark-current pulses. The signal to noise ratio is then immensely enhanced, as will be seen in the following example: consider two typical photomultipliers running at room temperature and operated at a bias low enough to detect the separate dark-current electron pulses, which may be emitted at a mean rate of say 10^4/sec. With a fast coincidence unit of the type described say by de Benedetti and Richings (1952), the resolving time of which is $\tau = 2 \times 10^{-9}$ sec for each channel, the coincidence rate is then as low as 0·4 counts/sec.

With the coincidence technique, the efficiency of detecting a light pulse is close to unity only if $\bar{N}\eta \gg 1$, where $\bar{N}$ is the average number of photons collected by the cathode of each phototube, and η is here the product of the quantum conversion efficiency and the photoelectron transfer efficiency. Thus if η were say 5% and we set $\bar{N}\eta \geqslant 5$, it is necessary to have available, on the average, at least 100 photons falling on each multiplier, to obtain an overall coincidence efficiency approaching unity.

5.7 Some practical notes

There are a number of technical points to observe when assembling and using a photomultiplier system, some of which will now be mentioned.

(i) The high tension should never be applied to a photomultiplier in daylight or other bright light. It is always preferable to have a series resistance in the supply.

(ii) To obtain high gain-stability and low noise, it is best to operate the photomultiplier in absolute darkness, with the voltage on, for a considerable time before use, at least for several hours, or even a day or more, for the tube to settle down.

(iii) It is preferable to work with the cathode "earthy", to minimize breakdowns, damage to cathode, and instability. In some cases, wrapping thin metal foil round the cylindrical portion of the tube increases stability and reduces spurious pulses.

(iv) Decouple the last few stages of a multiplier to earth or the E.H.T., if the pulse current in the output is high.

(v) High stability resistors are recommended for the dynode chain; these should be wired directly on to the tube base. Unless there is a high d.c. current, the resistor values are not critical and are usually chosen in the range $100\text{k}\,\Omega - 1\,\text{M}\Omega$. Poor quality insulation for the tube base should be avoided; the PTFE bases now supplied by some tube manufacturers are excellent.

(vi) Care should be taken when using multipliers near magnets; mu-metal screening may be required. Even the earth's field may be found to be troublesome if the orientation of the tube is changed.

(vii) The manufacturers' recommendations on the grading of voltage across the dynode resistance chain should be followed carefully, unless of course there are special reasons for deviating from these. Special care should be given to this point when there is a focusing electrode between the cathode and the first dynode.

(viii) Cooling. When a low dark-current pulse rate is required and the tube must be cooled, a system should be designed to prevent dew frosting over the cathode, and moisture short-circuiting the pins on the tube base. In some cases the cooling may be achieved by conduction along the dynode supports. As already discussed, however, cooling to too low a temperature may result in loss of cathode sensitivity.

5.8 Photocathodes and quantum conversion efficiencies

Sommer (1951) has discussed the main types of photocathode, their sensitivities and spectral responses. At the present time most commercially available photomultipliers have either the caesium–oxygen–silver (Cs–O–Ag) surface, the bismuth–silver–caesium (Bi–Ag–Cs) surface as used in television pick-up equipments, or the caesium–antimony (Cs–Sb) combination. Of these three the third is the most common, and, for our purposes, by far the best. The Cs–Sb photosensitive surface combines a high quantum conversion efficiency with a response curve which is peaked in the blue and violet; at the same time it has a high thermionic work function which ensures a low dark-current. The response of the Cs–Sb surface extends into the ultra-violet, and some tubes are equipped with a quartz window to allow full use of this part of the spectrum.

Metal alkali cathodes are being studied at the present time on an experimental basis; the Na–K–Sb surface, in particular, shows great promise.

It should be mentioned that the preparation of the Cs–Sb surface is an "art"; various manufacturers have different recipes for it, and some lay down a substrate prior to the evaporation of the photoactive layers. This accounts for the differences between the shapes of the response curves for surfaces obtained by different makers.

Quantum Conversion Efficiencies

Since both the absolute intensity and the spectral distribution of Čerenkov radiation are well determined, it is possible, when designing certain Čerenkov counters, to make a reliable estimate of the number of photoelectrons emitted from the cathode of the multiplier for each event. One may then anticipate the effective signal to noise ratio and the gain required, etc. This is by no means easy in the case of a scintillator, for the fluorescence spectrum is complex, the light intensity is sensitive to impurities, and the effects of self-absorption of the light more serious.

To calculate the pulse size, it is necessary to know the quantum efficiency η of the photocathode. This may be found if, (i) the absolute sensitivity is known at a given wavelength and (ii) if the energy distribution of the Čerenkov radiation $\check{C}(\lambda)$ is combined with (iii) the spectral response curve $S(\lambda)$ for the photocathode, published by the manufacturer.

Great care must be exercised in using the photometric units, especially as the exact conditions under which photocathodes are tested are not always clearly defined. Some manufacturers quote the sensitivities of photocathodes in micro-amperes per lumen, the measurements being made with a standard light source. The standard is a tungsten lamp operated at a specified colour temperature; in England this standard colour temperature is 2848°K, and in America, 2870°K.

For those who use photomultipliers for Čerenkov and scintillation counter work, this way of measuring and quoting efficiency is not altogether satisfactory. In the first place, the spectral distributions of these sources are quite unsuited to the response curve of the Cs–Sb cathode, since most of the energy is concentrated in the red. Secondly, the introduction of lumens is unfortunate, for the measurements are then tied to the response-curve of the eye, the peak of which (at $\lambda = 5550$ Å) occurs at a wavelength very different from that corresponding to the peak of the sensitivity curve for the Cs–Sb surface.

Other manufacturers give the *shape* of the sensitivity curve, together with the absolute sensitivity (e.g. in micro-amperes per micro-watt) at a spot wavelength, usually the wavelength of maximum response (4100–4500 Å for a Cs–Sb cathode; usually 4400 Å).

Quantum-efficiency from Micro-amperes per Lumen

If $E(\lambda)$ is the energy distribution of the standard light source used for calibration purposes, $S(\lambda)$ the response curve of the photocathode to an equi-energy spectrum, and $V(\lambda)$ the visibility curve for the standard eye, then the quantum conversion efficiency η is obtained from the sensitivity expressed in micro-amperes per lumen, by:

$$\eta = K \frac{\int E(\lambda)\,S(\lambda)\,d\lambda}{\int E(\lambda)\,V(\lambda)\,d\lambda} \text{ photoelectrons per quantum} \qquad (5.6)$$

where K is a constant. To evaluate (5.6), the following two fundamental conversion factors are required:

(i) 1 W of luminous energy at the wavelength corresponding to that of maximum visibility, namely at $\lambda = 5550$ A, is equivalent to 685 lumens, and

(ii) from Table 5A (see page 114), a quantum efficiency of 100% at the peak of the response curve for a Cs–Sb cathode, i.e. at a wavelength of 4400 A, is equivalent to a photoelectric current of $0.357\ \mu A$ per 1 μW of luminous energy.

With these constants, a Cs–Sb *photocathode which has a sensitivity of 50 μA/lumen to a lamp source at a colour temperature of 2848°K, is found from (5.6) to have a quantum efficiency of 12% at a wavelength of 4400 Å.*

Figure 5.9 shows curves for the response $S(\lambda)$ of a typical Cs–Sb cathode (RCA type in a glass envelope) to an equi-energy spectrum, the energy distribution $E(\lambda)$ for a tungsten calibration source operating at a colour temperature of 2848°K, and the visibility curve $V(\lambda)$, all plotted on a wavelength scale; note that $E(\lambda)$ is here the energy emitted *per unit wavelength interval*.

Engstrom (1955) has published tables for the conversion of luminous sensitivity to radiant photoelectric sensitivity.

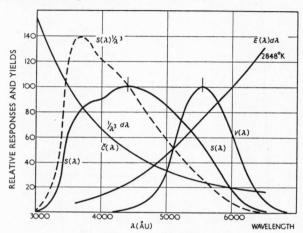

FIG. 5.9. Sensitivity and response curves.

$S(\lambda)$. Sensitivity curve for the RCA Cs–Sb cathode surface. (For an equi-energy spectrum.)

$E(\lambda)$. The energy distribution for a tungsten lamp running at a colour temperature of 2848°K.

$V(\lambda)$. The visibility curve for the standard eye.

$\check{C}(\lambda)$. The Čerenkov spectrum, and the product $\check{C}(\lambda)$. $S(\lambda)$.

Response of a Phototube to a Čerenkov Spectrum

If $S(\lambda)$ is the response curve of a photomultiplier to an equi-energy spectrum, then the response to a Čerenkov spectrum having an energy distribution $\check{C}(\lambda)$ is:

$$R_{\check{C}} \propto \int \check{C}(\lambda)\, S(\lambda)\, d\lambda \qquad (5.7)$$

If $R_{\check{C}}$ is expressed as an *energy* response, then we use the second of the equations (2.23) in Chapter 2, i.e. $\check{C}(\lambda) \propto (1/\lambda^3) . d\lambda$. The $(1/\lambda^3)$ distribution is shown in Fig. 5.9 and so is the product $(1/\lambda^3) . S(\lambda)$, (the $S(\lambda)$ for RCA or Du Mont tubes), illustrating the importance of choosing a phototube response peaked at short wavelengths.

If, as is usually the case, it is required to find $R_{\check{C}}$ as a yield of the *number of photoelectrons*, then the $(1/\lambda^2)$ distribution is used instead, i.e. the fourth of the equations (2.23).

The number of photons produced per unit path, neglecting dispersion and re-writing equation (2.21), may be expressed by:

$$\frac{dN_p}{dl} = \frac{2\pi}{137} \left[1 - \frac{1}{\beta^2 n^2} \right] \cdot \int \frac{1}{\lambda^2} \, d\lambda \text{ photons/cm} \qquad (5.8)$$

when λ is in cm.

Similarly, incorporating equation (5.7), the number of photoelectrons produced, per cm of path, at the cathode of the phototube will be:

$$\frac{dN_e}{dl} = \frac{2\pi}{137} \, \xi \eta_0 \left[1 - \frac{1}{\beta^2 n^2} \right] \cdot \int \frac{1}{\lambda^2} S(\lambda) \, d\lambda \qquad (5.9a)$$

where ξ is the optical efficiency for collecting the light at the cathode, η_0 is the absolute quantum efficiency of the photocathode at the peak of the response curve, and $S(\lambda)$ is the relative response, normalized to unity at the peak of the curve.

If now η_0 is replaced by S_0, the cathode efficiency expressed in μA/lumen (obtained with a standard source), we arrive at the following practical formula:

$$\frac{dN_e}{dl} = \frac{2\pi}{137} \, \xi S_0 F \left[1 - \frac{1}{\beta^2 n^2} \right] \cdot \int \frac{1}{\lambda^2} S(\lambda) \, d\lambda \text{ photoelectrons per cm}$$

$$(5.9b)$$

where $F = 0 \cdot 0024$ if we take the peak of the response curve to be at $\lambda = 4400$ Å (RCA and Du Mont tubes). This factor F arises by taking the figure quoted at the end of the last section, i.e. that 50 μA/lumen is equivalent to $\eta_0 = 12\%$ at this wavelength ($\therefore F = 0 \cdot 12/50 = 0 \cdot 0024$).

Grouping the numerical factors, (5.9b) may be expressed finally as

$$\frac{dN_e}{dl} = 1 \cdot 1 \times 10^{-4} \, \xi \, S_0 \left[1 - \frac{1}{\beta^2 n^2} \right] \cdot \int \frac{1}{\lambda^2} S(\lambda) \, d\lambda \qquad (5.9c)$$

in photoelectrons per centimetre path.

If the response curve is different from the one shown in Fig. 5.9, it is necessary to compute a different value for F, using Table 5A to find η_0 at the new peak wavelength, and also to normalize $S(\lambda)$ to unity at this new wavelength.

Table 5A is included for general use; it contains figures for the wave frequency $\nu = \omega/2\pi$, the photon energy $h\nu$ (in eV), and the photoelectric yield for a 100% quantum conversion efficiency (at various values of the wavelength λ), in micro-amperes per micro-watt.

A Numerical Example—What is the electron yield from the Čerenkov radiation produced by a 94 MeV π-meson traversing 1 cm of Perspex, when 30% of the available light is lost by reflexions at various surfaces, and the remainder is converted at the cathode of an RCA phototube for which the cathode efficiency is quoted as 40 μA/lumen?

For Perspex $n = 1.50$, and for a 94 MeV π-meson, $\beta = 0.8$, so that the factor $\left[1 - \dfrac{1}{\beta^2 n^2}\right] = 0.375$. $\xi = 0.7$, $S_0 = 40$, and a numerical integration between $\lambda = 3000$ and $\lambda = 6000$ Å gives:

$$\int (1/\lambda^2) \cdot S(\lambda)\, d\lambda = 1.03 \times 10^4 \text{ cm}^{-1}.$$

Inserting these figures in (5.9c), one arrives at:

$$N_e = 12 \text{ photoelectrons.}$$

TABLE 5A

Photoelectric Energy Relations

Wavelength, λ (Å)	Frequency, ν (10^{14}c/s)	Photon energy $h\nu$, $\left(\dfrac{12,336}{\lambda}\right)$ (eV)	Max. photoelectric yield, $Y = \dfrac{e \times 10^8}{h\nu c}$ (μ A/μ W)
1000	30·00	12·34	0·081
2000	15·00	6·17	0·162
2500	11·99	4·93	0·203
3000	9·99	4·11	0·243
3500	8·57	3·53	0·284
4000	7·49	3·08	0·324
4500	6·66	2·74	0·365
5000	6·00	2·47	0·405
5500	5·45	2·24	0·446
6000	5·00	2·06	0·486
6500	4·61	1·90	0·527
7000	4·28	1·76	0·567
8000	3·75	1·54	0·649
9000	3·43	1·37	0·710
10,000	3·00	1·23	0·811

From: Hughes and DuBridge, *Photoelectric Phenomena*, 1st Ed., 1932, p. 509.

5.9 Data for standard types of photomultiplier

The characteristics and performance of most of the commercially available phototubes have been grouped together in the accompanying tables and diagrams. Only those types are included which are suitable for use in Čerenkov detectors, and the diagrams have been selected to show but a few representative types.

The data refer to types available at the time of writing, March 1957, and is subject to revision as further development takes place and new types emerge and replace some of the existing ones.

TABLE 5B

EMI Photomultipliers

Tube type	No. of stages	Cathode diameter (mm)	Envelope diameter max. (mm)	Length seated ±3 mm (mm)	Min. overall sensitivity 160V per stage or less (A/lm)	Typical overall sensitivity at 160V per stage (A/lm)	Minimum photo-sensitivity (µA/lm)	Typical photo-sensitivity (µA/lm)	Dark current at minimum overall sensitivity (µA)	Window glass	Basic cathode type
6099B	11	111	130	230*	100	400	25	40	0·5	Pyrex	Cs–Sb
6099F	11	111	130	230*	25	—	35	45	0·5	Pyrex	Cs–Sb
6099C	11	111	130	230*	5	—	10	—	0·2	Pyrex	Cs–Sb
6097B	11	44	51	112	200	600	30	50	0·1	Pyrex	Cs–Sb
6097S	11	44	51	112	200	400	20	25	0·1	Pyrex	Cs–Sb(S)
6097F	11	44	51	112	50	—	40	55	0·1	Pyrex	Cs–Sb
6097C	11	44	51	112	10	—	10	—	0·04	Pyrex	Cs–Sb
9514B	13	44	51	121	2000	6000	30	50	1·0	Pyrex	Cs–Sb
9514S	13	44	51	121	2000	4000	20	25	1·0	Pyrex	Cs–Sb(S)
9514C	13	44	51	121	100	—	10	—	0·4	Pyrex	Cs–Sb
6094B	11	10	50	94	200	600	30	50	0·01	Pyrex	Cs–Sb
6094C	11	10	50	94	10	—	10	—	0·004	Kodial	Cs–Sb
9502B	13	10	50	108	2000	6000	30	50	0·1	Kodial	Cs–Sb
9502C	13	10	50	108	100	—	10	—	0·04	Kodial	Cs–Sb
6255B	13	44	51·5	121*	2000	6000	30	50	1·0	Kodial	Cs–Sb
6256B	13	10	51·5	108*	2000	6000	30	50	0·1	Quartz	Cs–Sb
6095B	11	44	51	112	200	300	20	30	0·1	Quartz	Cs–Sb
6095F	11	44	51	112	50	—	30	—	0·1	Pyrex	Bi–Ag–Cs
6095C	11	44	51	112	10	—	10	—	0·04	Pyrex	Bi–Ag–Cs
6098B	11	21	28·5–(1⅛″)	112	100	—	20	—	0·05	Pyrex	Bi–Ag–Cs
6260B	11	44	50	112	200	500	20	25	0·1	Lime soda	Cs–Sb(S)
6262B	14	44	50	125	10,000	30,000	20	25	5·0	Kodial	Cs–Sb(S)

* ±6 mm

The Type 6260 is recommended for replacement purposes only, since the Type 6097 which is electrically similar and commonly has a rather higher average gain, is more convenient as all its connexions are made to the base pins.

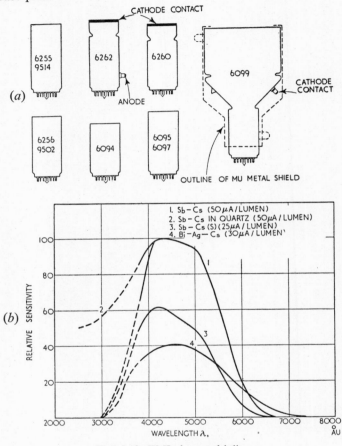

FIG. 5.10. EMI photomultipliers.

(a) Physical forms.   (b) Response curves.

A magnetic shield for the Type 6099 is available.

All these tubes have semi-transparent cathodes deposited on a flat end-window, and are manufactured by:

E.M.I. Electronics Ltd., Hayes, Middlesex, England.

TABLE 5c

RCA Photomultipliers

Type	No. of stages	Spectral response †	Wavelength of max. response (Å)	Anode supply voltage	Anode sensitivity		Current amplification	Max. equiv. anode dark current (lm)	Equiv. noise input (lm)	Cathode area (cm²)	Remarks
					Radiant (μA/μW)	Luminous (A/lm)					
*1P21	9	S 4	4000	1000	80,800	80	2×10^6	5×10^{-10}	5×10^{-13}	1·9	
*1P28	9	S 5	3400	1000	61,800	50	$1·25 \times 10^6$	$1·25 \times 10^{-9}$	$7·5 \times 10^{-13}$	1·9	Quartz window, for use in the ultra-violet.
2020	10	S 11	4400	1250 1500	4800 22,400	6 28	$1·2 \times 10^5$ $5·6 \times 10^5$	$2·25 \times 10^{-9}$ —	7×10^{-12}		Low resistance cathode; otherwise similar to 6342.
5819	10	S 11	4400	1000	20,000	25	5×10^5	2×10^{-9}	7×10^{-12}	14·2	
6199	10	S 11	4400	1000	21,600	27	6×10^5	$2·5 \times 10^{-9}$	4×10^{-12}	7·75	
6342	10	S 11	4400	1250 1500	6000 28,000	7·5 35	$1·25 \times 10^5$ 6×10^5	2×10^{-9} —	7×10^{-12} —	14·2	With focusing electrode. A particularly useful tube.
6372	10	S 11	4400	1000	16,000	20	6×10^5	1×10^{-8}	1×10^{-10}	80	Cathode deposited on bulb wall.
6655	10	S 11	4400	1000	20,000	25	5×10^5	2×10^{-9}	7×10^{-12}	14·2	With focusing electrode.
6810	14	S 11	4400	2300	6×10^5	750	$1·25 \times 10^7$	5×10^{-10}	6×10^{-12}	14·2	Linear dynode structure; high gain and high speed.
C7170	14	S 11	4400	3400	—	Cathode 50μ A/lm	6×10^6	—	—	100	Large area, high gain.
C7204	9	S 11	4400	—	—	Cathode 40μ A/lm	1×10^5	—	—	1·6	

* These tubes have internal opaque cathodes. † The S11 response corresponds to that shown in Fig. 5.9.

These tubes are manufactured by the Radio Corporation of America, 415 South Fifth Street, Harrison, N.J., U.S.A.

TABLE 5D

Du Mont Photomultipliers

Type	*Average cathode sensitivity ($\mu A/lm$)	Radiant sensitivity at $\lambda =$ 4400 Å ($\mu A/\mu W$)	Number of stages	Anode sensitivity (A/lm)	Current amplification	Anode dark current (μA)
6365	50	0·056	6	0·15 (150 V/stage)	3×10^3 (150 V/stage)	1·0
6467	60	0·056	10	13 (105 V/stage) 120 (145 V/stage)	$2·15 \times 10^5$ $2·0 \times 10^6$	< 0·05
6291	60	0·056	10	120 (145 V/stage)	$2·0 \times 10^6$	< 0·05
6292	60	0·056	10	120 (145 V/stage)	$2·0 \times 10^6$	< 0·05
6363	60	0·056	10	120 (145 V/stage)	$2·0 \times 10^6$	< 0·05
6364	60	0·056	10	120 (145 V/stage)	$2·0 \times 10^6$	< 0·05
K1328	30	—	12	—	5×10^5 (105 V/stage)	3·0
K1258	40	—	12	—	1×10^6 (105 V/stage)	1·0
K1384	—	—	12	In developmental stage		—
K1386	—	—	12	In developmental stage		—

* The cathode sensitivities are measured with a tungsten lamp operated at a colour temperature of 2870°K.

† P indicates that the focusing shield is internally connected, so that focusing is pre-set, while V indicates that the focus electrode is brought out to a separate pin, so that its potential is variable.

All the above tubes have an S 11 response, peaked at $\lambda = 4400 \pm 500$ Å, with the response down to 10% of its maximum value at wavelengths of 3250 ± 250 Å and at 6125 ± 275 Å.

These tubes are manufactured by:

Allen B. Du Mont Laboratories Inc.,
Clifton, New Jersey, U.S.A.

TABLE 5D (*continued*)

Du Mont Photomultipliers

Ext. diam. of bulb (in.)	Diam. of photocathode surface (in).	Price March 1955 ($)	†Focusing shield	Remarks
$\frac{3}{4}$	$\frac{1}{2}$	25	P	A useful tube for small counters if sufficient gain can be obtained.
$1\frac{1}{4}$	1	55	P	—
$1\frac{1}{2}$	$1\frac{1}{4}$	55	V	—
2	$1\frac{1}{2}$	55	V	The most suitable tube for general use.
3	$2\frac{1}{2}$	115	V	—
$5\frac{1}{4}$	$4\frac{3}{16}$	150	V	A generally satisfactory size for counters of the non-focusing type.
16	14	500	V	A valuable instrument for exceptionally large Čerenkov counters.
16	14	1000	V	A valuable instrument for exceptionally large Čerenkov counters.
$12\frac{1}{2}$	$11\frac{1}{4}$	—	V	Tentative data only.
$20\frac{1}{2}$	≈ 18	—	V	Tentative data only.

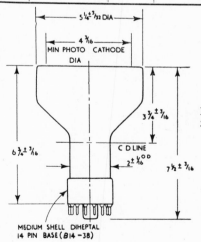

FIG. 5.11. The Du Mont 5-in. photomultiplier type 6364.

I

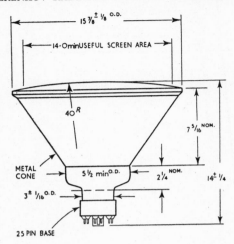

NOTE: DIRECTION OF LIGHT INTO
END OF BULB

FIG. 5.12. The large Du Mont photomultipliers, types K 1258 and K 1328.

TABLE 5E

A.F.I.F. Photomultipliers

Type	Diam. of cathode (mm)	Dynode number	Current gain at max. voltage	Max. voltage	Dark current at cathode (A)	Cathode sensitivity (μA/lm)
I	50	12	10^6–10^7	3000	10^{-14}	30–50
II	50	17	10^8–10^9	3600	10^{-14}	30–50
III	30 (i)	12	10^6–10^7	3000	10^{-14}	30–50
IV	260 (ii)	12 (iii)	10^5	3000	10^{-12}	30–50

These tubes all have Cs–Sb cathodes and Cu–Be dynodes.

(i) Photocathode directly on quartz window.

(ii) A report on this tube may be found in a paper by N. Schaetti in *Acta Electronica*, Vol. I, No. 2, April 1956.

(iii) A species with 15 dynodes is in preparation.

These tubes are manufactured by:

Abteilung für industrielle Forschung des Institutes
für technische Physik der E.T.H.,
Gloriastrasse 35, Zürich 7, Switzerland.

TABLE 5F

Radiotechnique Tubes

Type	Photocathode	Diam. of tube (mm)	Diam. of cathode (mm)	Cathode sensitivity* (μA/lm)	Number of stages	Maximum overall voltage	Inter-electrode capacities		Wave-length of max. response ($\text{\AA}$)	Anode sensitivity at 1800 V (A/lm)	Anode dark current (A)
							Anode to last dynode	Anode to all other electrodes			
51 AVP	Semi-transparent flat, end window	38 ±1·5	32	50	11	2250	3pF	5pF	4800 ±500	min. 60 av. 125	25×10^{-9} —
53 AVP	Semi-transparent flat, end window	55	44	50	11	2250	3pF	5pF	4800 ±500	min. 60 av. 125	50×10^{-9} —

* The cathode sensitivity is measured with a tungsten filament lamp operating at a colour temperature of 2870°K.

These tubes are manufactured by:

S. A. la Radiotechnique,
130 Avenue Ledru-Rollin,
Paris 11e, France.

The Russian Photomultiplier Type FEU-12

This tube, developed by G. S. Wildgrube and his collaborators, has been described by Nemilov and others: *Atomnaya Energiya* 1, (4), 51 (1956), a translation of which appears in *Journal of Nuclear Energy* 4, (3), 358 (1957). Some of the essential characteristics are listed below.

The tube has 12 dynodes in a venetian blind structure.

Diameter of photocathode 50 mm.

Current gain: 10^5– $4 \cdot 10^6$ with 1600 V uniformly distributed, or 10^6–10^7 with 2000–2500 V uniformly distributed.

Output linear up to mean currents of at least 50 mA.

Pulse rise-time $1 \cdot 5$–2×10^{-8} sec.

Photocathodes. Two types available: Cs–Sb and Bi–Ag–Cs.

Sensitivities—30–80 μA/lumen. Eighty per cent of 25 specimens had sensitivities > 45 μA/lumen (measured with a tungsten lamp at a colour temperature of 2848°K).

Sensitivity uniform to within 10%, for the whole cathode area, or to within 5% over 0·7 of the total area, in the central region.

Wavelength at maximum response—4600 Å.

The response curves are such that the sensitivity on the long-wavelength side is down to 10% of the peak value at 6200 Å for the Cs–Sb surface, and at 7300 Å for the Bi–Ag–Cs surface. On the short-wavelength side, the response is still 80% of the peak value at 4000 Å. There is no data on the dark-current.

Photovoltaic Barrier-layer Cells

Eel cells—Useful in certain very limited applications such as those mentioned in sections 11.8 and 11.11. The following information concerning standard sizes of "EEL" cells, was kindly provided by:

Evans Electroselenium Ltd.,
Harlow, Essex, England.

Cells of different size produce currents approximately in proportion to their sensitive areas at low illumination and low circuit resistance. Fatigue of "EEL" cells is reduced to a minimum by a special ageing process and does not occur in the great majority of cases (see *Phil. Mag.* 33, March (1942), p. 226, and *Phil. Mag.* 31 (1941), p. 490). The temperature coefficient of "EEL" cells varies slightly with the size of cell, but it is of the order of $-0 \cdot 3$% per °C; they should not be operated

TABLE 5G

Unmounted Cells

Cell size	Sensitive surface	Sensitive area (cm²)
Circular		
25 mm dia.	21 mm dia.	3·5
32 mm dia.	28 mm dia.	6·1
35 mm dia.	30 mm dia.	7·0
45 mm dia.	40 mm dia.	12·5
55 mm dia.	50 mm dia.	19·5
67 mm dia.	61 mm dia.	29·2
Rectangular		
4 × 8 mm	4 × 6 mm	0·24
11 × 18 mm	11 × 16 mm	1·4
16 × 37 mm	16 × 33 mm	5·3
17 × 43·5 mm	13 × 39·5 mm	5·1
22 × 40 mm	17 × 35 mm	5·45
37 × 50 mm	33 × 50 mm	1 ·8

at temperatures in excess of 50°C. The cells can also be supplied mounted and, further, may be hermetically sealed, if this is specified. There is no information on the possible effects produced by irradiation in γ-ray or neutron fields. The spectral response and sensitivity of these cells is shown in Fig. 5.13.

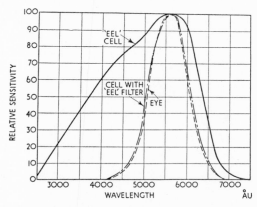

FIG. 5.13(a). The response curves and sensitivities for "EEL" photovoltaic cells, made by Evans Electroselenium Ltd.

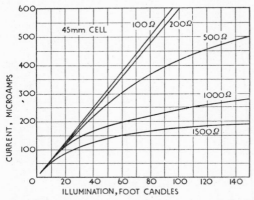

FIG. 5.13(b). The response curves and sensitivities for "EEL" photovoltaic cells, made by Evans Electroselenium Ltd.

Luxtron photovoltaic cells—The following information on standard types of Luxtron photovoltaic cells, was kindly provided by the manufacturers:

Bradley Laboratories Inc., 168 Columbus Avenue,
New Haven 11, Connecticut, U.S.A.

TABLE 5H

Circular Cells (unmounted)

Model No.	Diameter	Active area	Diameter contact ring	Diameter rear contact
1-A	1·772 in.	1·85 in²	1·625 in.	1·562 in.
4-A	1·00 in.	0·518 in²	0·906 in.	0·875 in.
6-A	0·375 in.	0·049 in²	0·312 in.	0·343 in.

Rectangular Cells (unmounted)

Model No.	Dimensions	Active area	Contact sides	Dimensions rear contact
7-A	0·880 in. × 0·281 in.	0·20 in²	short	0·880 in. × 0·281 in.
10-A	1·458 in. × 0·650 in.	0·70 in²	short	1·375 in. × 0·562 in.
20-B	1·690 in. × 0·880 in.	1·12 in²	long	1·625 in. × 0·812 in.

The temperature coefficient varies with the type of cell, but is of the order of + 0·1% per °C at low values of external resistance, and of the order of -0.4 to -0.7% per °C at higher values of external resistance, up to 10 kΩ.

The spectral response and sensitivity of these cells is shown in Fig. 5.14.

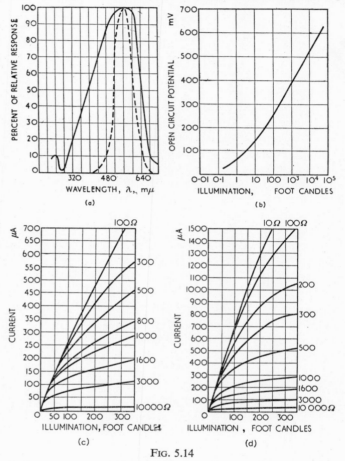

FIG. 5.14

(a) The spectral response of Luxtron barrier-layer cells, as compared to the response of the human eye.

(b) The open circuit potential as a function of the illumination of a typical Luxtron cell.

(c) and (d) Photocurrent characteristics of Luxtron cells with several values for the external resistances.

(c) Rectangular cell type 10-A, (d) circular cell type 1-A. These characteristics are obtained with a lamp operating at a colour temperature of 2850°K.

CHAPTER 6

ČERENKOV DETECTORS AND THEIR APPLICATIONS

6.1 General considerations

In developing practical radiation counters from the foregoing experimental and theoretical work, there are two techniques available for detecting and measuring the light output, namely photography and the use of photomultipliers. The photosensitive Geiger counter has both a low intrinsic efficiency and possesses no discrimination against direct detection of the particles passing through the counter itself. The photographic method may be used only when the intensity of the particle beam, and hence the light output, is sufficient to obtain images of adequate contrast with tolerable exposure times. A possible alternative in such cases is to use a photovoltaic cell or vacuum photocell coupled to an amplifier.

For most applications photomultipliers have superseded other forms of light detector. They have an unparalleled sensitivity, high gain, adequate stability and a relatively low background. Moreover, they are compact, easy to operate and the associated electronic circuits are in general straightforward and conventional. The most important feature however is their great speed of response combined with a negligible paralysis time.

In most, but not all, of the practical applications of Čerenkov counters to problems in nuclear and cosmic-ray physics, direct advantage is taken of the unique features of the radiation.

With these points in mind, the practical applications of Čerenkov counters may be listed under the following general headings.

(i) *Fast counting of charged particles*—Short response times, high efficiencies and high counting rates may be obtained.

(ii) *The direct determination of the velocity* of a charged particle over a limited range above the threshold. This in turn implies a direct determination of the energy of the particle if its mass is known.

(iii) *Threshold discrimination*—This may be achieved in any of three ways.

126

(a) Discrimination between particles of different mass having either the same momentum, or the same range in an absorber.

(b) Selection of a component of high-energy particles against an intense background of particles of lower energy. For this it is necessary that a medium be found which has a threshold that falls between the energies of the two different components. The two groups of particles here may have the same or different mass.

(c) The isolation of a weak component of low energy from a more intense background of particles of higher energy. This is achieved by using a Čerenkov counter in an anticoincidence arrangement with other counters.

(iv) *Velocity selection*—With a suitable optical system, it is possible to arrange a single counter to give a pulse only when the velocity of the incoming particle falls in a well defined range, which can be set by the geometry of the system. The same effect can also be achieved using two threshold detectors, one behind the other, if materials with suitable refractive indices can be found.

(v) *"Antidirectional" indication*—One can determine in which *sense* an ultra-relativistic particle is travelling. This is useful in certain applications (particularly in the cosmic-ray field) in which the track of the particle is defined but doubt exists as to in which of the two possible directions it is moving.

(vi) *Determination of charge*—The rate of production of light in the Čerenkov effect is proportional to e^2 where e is the charge on the particle.

(vii) *Spectrometry by total absorption*—The energies of γ-rays and electrons may be measured directly, from the light output from deep Čerenkov counters in which most or all of the energy of the incident radiation can be contained within the radiator of the counter. This, the total absorption method, is only applicable in the high energy region, i.e. when $E > \sim 20$ MeV.

(viii) *Counting over large areas*, particularly useful in the cosmic-ray field, may be achieved with detectors which have a response sensibly uniform over areas ~ 1 m² or more.

(ix) *Measurement of particle density*—Čerenkov counters may be used to obtain information on the *number* of particles that traverse a given area simultaneously, irrespective of their energy, provided this is well above the threshold.

(x) *Direction selection*—Suitable optical systems may be devised so that a pulse is obtained only from particles entering the counter within a well-defined solid angle; in this way it is possible to discriminate against a background of particles travelling through the counter in directions outside this zone.

(xi) *Neutron detection*—Neutrons in the low energy region may be detected by the Čerenkov radiation emitted from the secondary electrons produced by γ-rays following neutron capture in an element having a high cross-section, such as cadmium. This element may be loaded into the Čerenkov medium which can also serve as a moderator. This scheme, however, is not as satisfactory as that in which a loaded scintillator is used, in which case correlation between recoil protons and the capture γ-rays enhances the discrimination against general γ-ray background. Neutron detection at ultra-high energies is however feasible, when the recoil protons in a hydrogenous medium have themselves sufficient energy to produce Čerenkov radiation.

The *direct* detection of fast neutrons, through the "magnetic" Čerenkov radiation arising from their magnetic moment (see section 3.1), is quite out of the question on grounds of intensity.

The scope of usefulness of the Čerenkov counter is amply illustrated by the list of headings above, but what of its limitations? The first of course is that it cannot be used for low energy radiations; the thresholds in Perspex for example ($n = 1.50$) are, approximately, 175 keV, 36 MeV, 48 MeV and 322 MeV, for electrons, μ-and π-mesons, and protons respectively.

A second and more serious limitation is the very weak light yield available from radiators of reasonable dimensions; the intensity is in general considerably less than that to be had from most scintillators of comparable size. This is particularly serious when it is necessary to use very thin radiators, as sometimes arises for reasons to be discussed later. The discrimination between the weak light pulses and the "dark-current" pulses from the phototube, may be improved by using two tubes connected in a coincidence arrangement and "looking" at the same radiator. There are, however, two factors which to some extent compensate for the low light output in Čerenkov counters: one is the directional character of the light, which may be used to concentrate the radiation at the light detector, and the other is the absence of self-absorption of the light in the radiator. It should be mentioned here that some scintillators, those incorporating "wave-shifters" (see section 7.6), also have quite low self-absorption for their light.

When it is necessary to load a large radiation detector with substances such as cadmium or lead, the Čerenkov counter has a distinct advantage over the scintillator, because these substances are often found to quench the radiations in the scintillation process.

Returning to the eleven general groups listed above, it must be admitted that at least some of the applications may be tackled as well or better by the scintillation counter. Most of the features under (i) are shared by the scintillation counter, while the e^2 dependence in (vi) is found in *all* "proportional" detectors that depend intrinsically on the ionization process; i.e. photographic emulsions, cloud chambers, ionization chambers, as well as proportional and scintillation counters. The applications under headings (ii), (iii), (iv), (v) and (x) are however unique to the Čerenkov counter, while those in groups (vii), (viii), (ix) and (xi) may use the scintillation counter as an alternative. In some cases, however, there are certain specific reasons for preferring to use a Čerenkov detector. The differences in behaviour of the two types of instrument will become apparent in due course.

A further important consideration, in the case of large counters, is expense. Some scintillators require liquids of great purity, whereas the Čerenkov counter will operate satisfactorily with ordinary materials provided the impurities do not produce serious light absorption.

6.2 The classification of Čerenkov detectors

There are a number of criteria by which it is possible to classify Čerenkov detectors into groups of different types. A useful scheme, and the one adopted throughout this book, is to group the various types under the two general headings of focusing and non-focusing counters, which will be denoted in this section by F and NF respectively. Almost all forms of instrument are found to fall within one of these two categories, though there are a few exceptions.

A focusing counter is one in which an optical system is used to concentrate the Čerenkov radiation on a small area where the light detector is placed. A non-focusing counter has no such optical system; moreover, steps are often deliberately taken to diffuse the light, so that the intrinsic directional feature of the radiation is obliterated. Since the optical considerations are so important for a successful design of either type of counter, they will be discussed in detail separately; see Chapter 7.

The choice of which type of Čerenkov counter to use in a particular application depends on the function it has to perform. There is a fairly definite correlation between the two, which has been summarized in Table 6A. The numbers in the first column refer to the list of headings

TABLE 6A

No. in section 6.1	Application	Type of counter
(i)	Fast counting the main requirement.	F for extreme speed but NF usually adequate with existing photomultipliers.
(ii)	Direct determination of velocity, by measurement of the angle θ.	F only; careful design essential for the best performance and resolution.
(iii)	Threshold discrimination.	Either type.
(iv)	Velocity selection.	Usually F-type, but of simple design.
(v)	"Antidirectional" indication.	Either. F-type of simple design, if particles selected over a small area and/or a small range of solid angle. NF-type provided no diffusing surfaces used.
(vi)	Determination of charge.	THIN counter; usually NF-type with maximum optical efficiency.
(vii)	Energy determination by the method of total absorption. (high energy spectroscopy)	DEEP counter; usually NF-type with good light collection. Use radiators loaded with a material of high atomic number.
(viii)	Counting over large areas.	Always NF-type, with diffusing surfaces to obtain uniformity of response across the area of the counter.
(ix)	Particle-density measurements.	THIN counter; same remarks as for (vi).
(x)	Direction selection.	F-type only; as in (ii) for the best resolution in angle.
(xi)	Neutron detection.	NF-type with cadmium-loaded radiator, for slow neutrons. For ultra-high-energy neutrons, use a DEEP counter of the NF-type, with a hydrogenous radiator.

F. Focusing-type optical system.   NF. Non-focusing type of counter.

in section 6.1 above, with their abbreviated titles in the second column. The third column indicates, with notes, which type of counter is used.

The main features relevant to the design of the type F counter, and the simpler versions of type NF, will be found in Chapter 7. Two rather specialized instruments, which we shall call the "Thin" counter, and the "Deep" counter respectively, both in the NF category, are discussed separately, see sections 6.4 and 6.5.

6.3 Choice of photomultiplier

Although there are no hard and fast rules by which to decide the exact type of phototube for a given type of counter, a careful choice is required for optimum performance. A universal requirement is that the cathode sensitivity should be as high as possible; in addition, the spectral response should be peaked in the blue and extend as far down in wavelength as absorption in the radiator and optical elements permit. In almost all cases it is best to use tubes with the semi-transparent cathode deposited on the glass envelope. The main characteristics by which tubes may be selected are cathode area, uniformity of sensitivity across the cathode, and the speed of response, while secondary features are internal gain, linearity, output pulse-size, after-pulses and signal to noise ratio.

6.4 The "thin" counter

Thin Čerenkov counters are used whenever it is important that they should cause the least disturbance to the incoming particles. The three applications for which such a counter is useful are the following:

(i) To count a fast particle with the minimum chance of disturbing its direction of motion.

(ii) To measure particle density, e.g. the number of electrons traversing the radiator simultaneously.

(iii) To determine the charge (Ze) of the incoming particles. This is a particularly useful application for studies of the primary cosmic radiation at the top of the atmosphere.

Different factors limit the depth of radiator in each of these three applications. In (i) the thickness should be small compared with the mean free path for scattering, in (ii) small compared with the radiation length, to avoid electron multiplication, and in (iii) small compared with the mean free path for nuclear collisions. These criteria determine the maximum depth.

The minimum thickness of radiator permitted is invariably set by the resolution required. With most existing photocathodes, with quantum efficiencies around 10%, the width of the pulse-height distribution arises almost entirely from statistical fluctuations in the number of primary photoelectrons in the multiplier. If cathode efficiencies of $\sim 100\%$ are eventually obtained, the width will instead arise from the fluctuations in the number of photons. With the relatively weak light available from thin radiators, it is therefore imperative in such counters to collect as much as possible; it is thus usual to seal the radiator optically direct to the photocathode.

Of the three applications mentioned, the third presents the least difficulty, for the following reason: Let us assume we have a mixed beam in which there are particles with charges e, $2e$, $3e$, etc. Since the output of Čerenkov radiation is proportional to $(Ze)^2$, where Z is the charge number, the various pulse-height distributions will be spread out by increasing intervals on a pulse-height scale, namely V, 4V, 9V, etc., while the widths of these distributions will be increasing only linearly, as V, 2V, 3V, etc.

The Scintillator v. the Čerenkov Counter

The resolution of a scintillation counter, in general different from that of a Čerenkov counter having a radiator of the same thickness, is determined primarily by statistical fluctuations in the ionization processes. The fluctuations in the photoelectric emission are usually negligible in this case, for the light yield is so much greater from a scintillator; for instance, a typical liquid scintillator will produce one useful photon for 150 eV spent in ionization (at the minimum in the curve for specific ionization), see Curran (1953, p. 146). The light yield from this scintillator is then ~ 30 times as great as that from a Čerenkov medium of comparable density and average refractive index.

These fluctuations in ionization apply not only to scintillators, but to other radiation detectors based on the ionization process.

In scintillators using thin radiators, for which the energy loss Δ is small compared with the kinetic energy E of the particle, the distribution of energy loss, $\phi(\Delta)$, is both broad and asymmetrical, of the form obtained by Landau (1944), see Fig. 6.1. In a typical case, the full width of this distribution at half-height is $\sim 30\%$ of Δ_0, the most probable energy loss. When however $\Delta \approx E$, the distribution is narrower and the high-energy tail is absent.

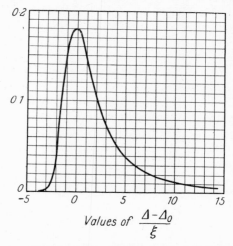

Values of $\dfrac{\Delta - \Delta_0}{\xi}$

FIG. 6.1. The Landau distribution. The probability ϕ of an energy loss Δ, as a function of the most probable energy loss Δ_0 and the parameter ξ defined by equation (6.2). (After Landau, 1944.)

For Δ_0, Landau obtains the expression:

$$\Delta_0 = \xi \left[\ln \frac{3\cdot10^3 \, \xi\beta^2}{Z^2(1-\beta^2)} + 1 - \beta^2 \right] \ \text{eV} \tag{6.1}$$

where Z is the atomic number of the material, and

$$\xi = \frac{2\pi N e^4 \rho}{mv^2} \cdot \frac{Z}{A} \cdot x = \frac{1\cdot54 \times 10^5 \, \rho}{\beta^2} \cdot \frac{Z}{A} \cdot x \ \ \text{eV} \tag{6.2}$$

where N is Avogadro's number, ρ the density of the material, m the electron mass, v the particle velocity and A the atomic weight. Blunck and Leisegang (1950) have shown that for materials of large Z, the width of the distribution may even exceed that of the Landau distribution. For further information on the ionization mechanism, the reader is referred to the review articles by Cranshaw (1952) and Price (1955).

Let us see, for comparison, what widths may be expected in the case of a thin Čerenkov counter. Consider for instance an ultra-relativistic particle traversing a 2 cm thick Perspex radiator, i.e. 2·4 g/cm². The available light within a reasonable bandwidth is in this case ~ 500 photons, corresponding to a pulse of ~ 50 photoelectrons for a quantum efficiency of 10%. The full width of the distribution, assumed to be primarily due to fluctuations in this number of electrons, will then be $\sim 14\%$, about half of that obtainable with a scintillator of the same depth.

Most of the contributions to the width of the Landau distribution arise from collisions in which only small amounts of energy are transferred to the secondary electrons, or δ-rays. Much of the light emitted in a scintillator therefore comes from δ-rays of quite low energy. In a Čerenkov counter the conditions are very different, since most of the light comes directly from the particle itself; there may be *some* Čerenkov light from the few δ-rays that have energies above the threshold (e.g. 260 keV for water). The fraction of light arising from the δ-rays depends

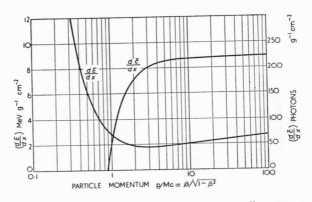

FIG. 6.2. To illustrate the difference in behaviour between a Čerenkov detector and an ionization detector.

(i) The curve for specific ionization (dE/dx) is valid for all particles heavier than an electron; i.e. radiation losses are excluded. The curve is calculated for media of $Z \sim 6$ and is therefore applicable, for example, to air or Perspex.

(ii) The Čerenkov radiation curve $(d\check{C}/dx)$ is calculated for protons in Perspex $(n = 1.50,$ specific gravity $1.19)$ and a spectral band 3500–5500 Å.

on (i), the energy of the particle relative to its own threshold (which will be considerably higher than the electron threshold if the particle is a meson or proton), (ii) the maximum transferable energy E_{max}, and (iii) the energy spectrum of the δ-rays. $E_{max} \approx 4\, E_0/\mu$ where E_0 is the kinetic energy of the particle, and μ is the mass of the particle, in electron masses (if $\mu \gg 1$).

Some of these points have been discussed in greater detail by Linsley and Horwitz (1955), and corrections for contributions to the light yield from knock-on electrons were made in the experiment of Duerden and Hyams (1952).

The essential difference in the behaviour of the two instruments may be seen from Fig. 6.2 which shows the curves for both specific ionization, $(dE/dx)^*$, and the Čerenkov light output $(d\check{C}/dx)$, as a function of electron energy. While the former is rising steeply at the lower electron (or δ-ray) energies, the latter is decreasing, falling to zero at the threshold.

The ideal material for the radiator of a thin Čerenkov counter is one of high refractive index combined with low density and low atomic number.

Returning once more to thin scintillators, the pulse-height distributions are narrower for the organic than for the inorganic phosphors. This arises from the non-linearity between ionization density and light output in the organic family, the output falling as the specific ionization increases.

6.5 The "deep" counter (Total absorption spectrometer)

When a single γ-ray photon or electron of high energy enters a block of material, it will give rise to a shower of further photons and electrons. Such a shower is called a photon–electron cascade (see for example Rossi, 1952; Rossi and Greisen, 1941; and Heitler, 1944). The development of the shower proceeds through a succession of pair production and Bremsstrahlung processes, so that the initial energy of the primary electron or photon is shared out among the secondary particles. The number of particles (and photons) continues to increase with depth in the medium, until such time that the energies of the particles have dwindled to values at which the pair production and Bremsstrahlung interactions fail in competition with other processes. The pair-production process falls off in competition with Compton scattering, and the Bremsstrahlung with ionization losses. The numbers-*versus*-depth distribution has therefore a maximum, the decay beyond this maximum being rather slower than the growth before the maximum.

The cross-sections σ_π and σ_{rad} for the two processes, and the corresponding critical energies† ϵ_e and ϵ_γ, depend on the atomic number Z

---

* At energies well below that at which minimum ionization occurs, the specific-ionization follows the form $(dE/dx) \propto Z^2 e^2/\beta^2$ for a particle having a charge number Z and a velocity βc.

† The critical energy is usually defined as that energy for which the radiation and ionization losses are equal to each other.

K

and the atomic weight A. In most media σ_π and σ_{rad} are comparable with each other, so that it is sufficient to use single symbols σ and ϵ.

Kantz and Hofstadter (1954) were among the first to realize that deep scintillation or Čerenkov counters could be used to measure high energy γ-rays and electrons. In the ideal case, the radiator in such counters should be deep enough to contain the *whole* of the cascade, though in practice it is often adequate to have depths sufficient to include the maximum of the shower; in this case, however, overall linearity cannot be assumed and an energy calibration is desirable.

It is convenient in these problems to use the concept of "radiation length" in place of cross-section. A radiation length X_0 is defined as that distance in an absorber in which an electron loses, on average, $1/e^{\text{th}}$ of its energy by radiation (Bremsstrahlung). Thus, an electron of energy E_0 will give rise to one electron and one photon after one radiation length of passage, and in the second radiation length this secondary electron produces a further electron–photon pair, and the secondary photon an electron–positron pair. σ is proportional to $1/X_0$.

Under the assumption, which is necessary in the simplest treatment of shower theory, that $E_0 \gg \epsilon$, the total number of particles after t radiation lengths will be $n \approx 2^t$ and the energy of each will be $E \approx E_0 \, 2^{-t}$, until the energy of the electrons has been reduced to ϵ. The maximum number of particles occurs at a thickness $\approx \log_e (E_0/\epsilon)$ and the total number of shower particles at the maximum is $\approx (E_0/\epsilon)$.

When $E_0 \gg \epsilon$ and the whole shower is contained in the radiator, the energy spent must be proportional to E_0. It is now necessary to see whether the Čerenkov light output is also proportional to E_0. The requirement here is simply that $\epsilon \gg E_{\min}$ where $E_{\min}$ is the threshold energy at which the Čerenkov radiation starts, the light production $(d\check{C}/dx)$ rising very rapidly from zero to its maximum value. In practice, this condition is amply satisfied, e.g. in water $E_{\min} = 0.26$ MeV (electrons) while $\epsilon = 84$ MeV. Thus, with $E_0 \gg \epsilon$ and $\epsilon \gg E_{\min}$, there will be a linear relationship between the light output and the energy of the primary electron (or photon).

With the vital assumption $E_0 \gg \epsilon$, X_0 is obtained from:

$$\frac{1}{X_0} = 4a \left(\frac{N}{A}\right) Z^2 r_0^2 \log_e 183 \, Z^{-\frac{1}{3}} \tag{6.3}$$

where a is the fine structure constant $= e^2/\hbar c$, r_0 the classical electron radius $= e^2/mc^2$, and Z and A the atomic number and weight respectively, of the medium. N is Avogadro's number and X_0 is expressed in g/cm².

If the medium is composed of several elements, for example glass, the effective radiation length X_{eff} is computed from:

$$1/X_{eff} = p_1/X_1 + p_2/X_2, \text{ etc.,} \tag{6.4}$$

where p_1, p_2, . . ., are the fractions, by weight, of each component element.

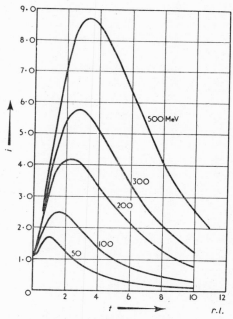

FIG. 6.3. Universal transition curves. The number of electrons i (of energy > the critical energy) to be found at different depths (expressed in radiation lengths) for various primary energies between 50 and 500 MeV.

Values of X_0 expressed in g/cm² for a number of common substances will be found in Table H in Appendix I, while Fig. 6.3 shows universal curves for the numbers of electrons i of energy > ϵ at various depths t (in radiation lengths) in an infinite medium, for showers initiated by a single electron of energy E_0. Although it is difficult to make a precise estimate of the performance of a deep counter in advance, use of Fig. 6.3 and Table H are in general sufficient for design purposes. If, instead of an electron the initiating radiation is a γ-ray photon, of energy E_0, it is a sufficiently good approximation to add one extra radiation length to the depth of the radiator already chosen for an electron of energy E_0.

We have mentioned that in principle the scintillation or Čerenkov process may be used in the total-absorption counter. There are however two points in favour of the use of the Čerenkov effect for this type of instrument. It is evident from (6.3) that materials of high Z and high density are required, and it is found very difficult to add suitable substances to solid and liquid scintillating media which do not poison or impair their fluorescing properties. It is however relatively straightforward to add suitable materials to a Čerenkov counter (e.g. solutions of salts in a liquid counter or impurities to glass) without serious deterioration of the light transmission. The second point is that the directional characteristics of the Čerenkov radiation may be utilized, so that the light is collected at the far end of a large cylindrical radiator, along the axis of which the shower is developing. Suitable materials for the construction of deep counters are discussed in section 6.7, and typical instruments described in section 8.4.

The main criteria for the radiator material of a deep counter is that it should have a short effective radiation length and good optical transmission.

6.6 Total internal reflexion counter

Whilst the property of total internal reflexion has often been used in Čerenkov counters, its full potentialities have not been really explored. An interesting counter of a new type has recently been proposed by Porter (unpublished) in which it is in principle possible to combine a large collecting area with good directional characteristics. The essential features of this instrument will now be described.

Consider a counter which is rectangular in plan and section, see inset in Fig. 6.4(a), and suppose a particle is incident orthogonally with the largest face. Since $\cos \theta = 1/\beta n$, and the condition for total internal reflexion is $\theta > \sin^{-1}(1/n)$, such reflexion will occur at the lower face, for an ultra-relativistic particle, provided $\sin \theta > \cos \theta$; i.e. when $\theta > 45°$, or $n > \sqrt{2}$. Light reflected at the lower face will also be reflected at the upper face. Thus, if the particle is incident exactly perpendicular to the face, the light will all be maintained within the block.

Light from an ultra-relativistic particle incident at an angle a will also be totally reflected at the faces, provided

$$a < \left\{ \cos^{-1} \frac{1}{\beta n} - \sin^{-1} \frac{1}{n} \right\} \qquad (6.5)$$

though some light will always be lost at the sides, however, if $a \neq 0$. If absorption in the medium is neglected, all the light maintained within the counter may be collected by covering one end of the rectangular block completely with photomultipliers. This follows because all possible trajectories must intersect each side at least once in every rotational traversal about the centre of the counter (neglecting the limiting case of $a = 90°$ which is possible at only one exact angle).

The sides of the counter may be silvered, but in general the efficiency is then lower than in the counter with unsilvered sides; the directional characteristics are also more marked if the sides are unsilvered.

The fraction of light retained in a counter with specular reflecting side walls (assuming 100% efficiency) and made of Perspex ($n = 1.49$) has been calculated for different values of β over a range of values of a; the results are shown in Fig. 6.4(a). These theoretical curves are valid for particles incident in any plane, and for a counter of any relative dimensions, *providing* that all the light undergoes at least one

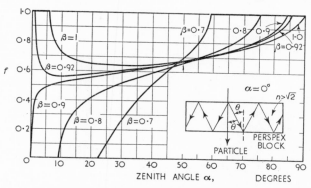

FIG. 6.4(a). To illustrate the calculated directional and threshold characteristics of Porter's total internal reflexion counter.

f is the fraction of light produced which is retained within the block and which can be collected. The axis $a = 0°$ corresponds to tracks perpendicular to the largest face. Drawn for the case in which the sides are silvered (reflectivity assumed 100%); in these calculations β is assumed to be constant, and scattering has been neglected.

reflexion at the lower face; i.e. for a block of thickness t, the point of incidence of the particle must be at a distance greater than $t \times \tan (\theta + \alpha)$ from the side at which the light is collected. The response for

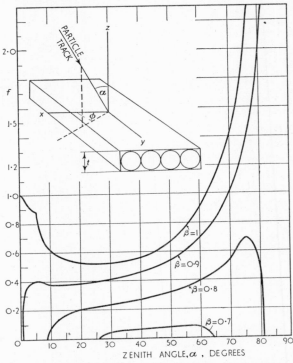

FIG. 6.4(b). To illustrate the calculated directional and threshold characteristics of Porter's total internal reflexion counter.

Curves strictly valid only for $\phi = 0°$ or $180°$, or for $\phi = 90°$ and α in the positive quadrant. For $\phi = -90°$ use Fig 6.4(a). The curves are a good approximation for practically all planes of incidence provided the dimensions x and y are both greater than about five times the thickness of the slab, except for regions where the particle strikes within a distance $\sim t$ from the phototubes; in the latter case the errors will be $\sim 50\%$.

particles closer to the side than this may be up to 50% greater than the theoretical value at the given value of α.

Figure 6.4(b) shows the relative amount of light retained in the block for a counter made of Perspex with unsilvered sides, as a function of the angle α and the velocity β. These curves are strictly valid only for particles incident in the plane parallel to the side at which the light is collected, but, provided the thickness is much less than the length and width, they will be a reasonable approximation for all planes of incidence.

Bradley (unpublished) has constructed a Perspex counter 45 cm long and 5×5 cm in section, and having a single EMI photomultiplier at one end, of cathode area ~ 10 cm². Using cosmic-ray μ-mesons selected with a Geiger counter telescope, the qualitative validity of the theory has been established. The uniformity of response with aluminium reflecting walls was found to be poor, but with unsilvered walls it was $\sim 20\%$ over the counter length, except for the region within 5 cm of the photomultiplier. The zenith angle dependence has not yet been verified in detail.

Three possible applications of this instrument are:

(i) Directional studies of extensive cosmic-ray air showers.

(ii) Velocity threshold selection up to $\beta \approx 0.85$ if α can be defined to $\sim 5°$, or up to $\beta \approx 0.90$ if α is defined to $\sim 1°$.

(iii) Measurement of velocities of particle beams in the region $\beta \sim 0.7$ to 0.9 under non-axial but angle-defined conditions.

It is probable that further information could be obtained by collecting the light that escapes from the block in addition to that trapped inside; this should lead to greater sensitivity and better discrimination.

6.7 Choice of materials, practical considerations and technical data

The ideal medium for most Čerenkov counters would be one having a high refractive index, low light absorption, low density and low atomic number; an additional requirement in focusing counters is that the medium should possess a low dispersion. Unfortunately these requirements are not in general compatible with one another and it is necessary to make compromises. For instance, a high refractive index, desirable for high output of light, is usually associated with a high dispersion and is frequently coupled with poor transmission characteristics, particularly at the shorter wavelengths. Similarly, low density and low atomic number, both of which are important for minimum energy-loss and scattering, are usually associated with the lower refractive indices.

There are in addition various practical considerations which are important, such as the ease with which the material may be worked, its availability and cost, whether the material exhibits fluorescence, and whether its optical and chemical properties are disturbed when it is alloyed with other substances.

Although glass is a natural choice for a radiator material, some of the plastics have been found to be more suitable; of these special mention should be made of polymethyl mythacrylate resin, which comes under the various trade names of Perspex, in England, and Lucite and Plexiglas in America. This material combines an average value of refractive index with a low dispersion, and has excellent transmission characteristics over the wavelength range of main interest. In addition, it has a low density, its constituents are of low atomic number, and, most important of all, it is a material which is easy to work and polish. Other points in its favour are that it is available and cheap, and possesses a negligible fluorescence.

For its pre-eminence in these respects, it is the ideal radiator material for all small counters, particularly those having surfaces that must be optically worked; i.e. those classified as focusing counters. It is likewise a much used material in "thin" counters, threshold detectors and velocity discriminators.

For larger counters, particularly those in the non-focusing class, and those for which the shape of the radiator is less important, it is often more convenient to use liquids. The manufacture of large single blocks of solid materials, such as glass or plastic, is usually very expensive, and it is furthermore difficult to obtain samples free from cracks and flaws.

The regrettable feature of the more common materials is that the range of refractive indices in the optical band is so small, very few solids and liquids having indices outside the range $1 \cdot 3$–$1 \cdot 8$. It is this small latitude, corresponding to a range of threshold velocities from $0 \cdot 77c$ to $0 \cdot 56c$, which somewhat restricts the applications of the Čerenkov counter.

The essential data relevant to most of the materials of interest will be found in the accompanying tables. Refractive indices, dispersion and transmission characteristics will be found in Tables 6B to 6G, while properties of some special materials suitable for total-absorption counters are listed in Tables 6H to 6J. The characteristics of Čerenkov radiation produced by the elementary particles in the more common substances have been drawn up in the various graphs reproduced in Appendix II. The data on reflectivities in Tables 6K and 6L may also be useful in special problems.

TABLE 6A

Characteristics of Optical Materials

SPECTRAL LINES

Optical materials are specified by their refractive indices for the series of wavelengths listed below.

Fraunhofer line	A′	b	C	D_1	d	e	F	g	G′	h
Element	K	He	H	Na	He	Hg	H	Hg	H	Hg
Wavelength Å	7682	7065	6563	5896	5876	5461	4861	4358	4340	4047

REFRACTIVE INDICES AND DISPERSION

Data on refraction and dispersion are usually given in the following way: refractive index for the helium d line (n_d) is stated (replacing n_{D_1}), the mean dispersion between the hydrogen C and F lines (n_C-n_F) and the **reciprocal dispersive power** V calculated from these figures, thus

$$V = (n_d - 1)/(n_F - n_C)$$

Partial dispersions ($n_b - n_C$), ($n_C - n_d$), etc., are stated, and also the relative partial dispersions ($n_b - n_C$)/($n_C - n_F$), ($n_C - n_d$)/($n_C - n_F$), etc.

For brevity, b is written for n_b, C for n_C, etc.

TABLE 6B

Optical Properties of Plastic Materials

Material	V	A′	C	D	e	F	g	Transmission range
Polystyrene 15°C	31·0	1·581	1·587	1·592		1·606	1·617	
35°C		1·578	1·584	1·589		1·603	1·614	0·34μ–2μ
55°C		1·575	1·581	1·586		1·600	1·612	
Poly*cyclo*hexyl-methacrylate 15°C	56·9	1·501	1·504	1·507		1·513	1·518	
35°C		1·499	1·502	1·504		1·501	1·516	
55°C		1·496	1·499	1·501		1·508	1·513	
Polymethyl-methacrylate 20°C	57·8		1·489	1·491	1·493	1·497	1·501	0·34μ–2μ

Temperature coefficient of refractive index for above three polymers is $- 14 \times 10^{-5}$ per °C.

See *Proceedings of the London Conference on Optical Instruments* (1950), Chapter 21, page 243. "Plastic Glasses" by H. C. Raine.

I.C.I. "Perspex", Polymethyl Methacrylate

Specific gravity at 20°C 1·19

	Plasticized	Unplasticized
Refractive Index n_D	1·495	1·490
Relative Dispersion V	53·7	58·0
Critical angle, "Perspex"/air boundary		42°

Transmission characteristics, shown in Fig. 6.5.
The chemical composition is very close to that of the formula

$$-\underset{\underset{CO-O-CH_3}{|}}{\overset{\overset{CH_3}{|}}{C}}-CH_2- \qquad \text{i.e. } C_5H_8O_2$$

because the organic impurities present (such as a small amount of monomer) do not disturb the C, H, O proportions, and the amounts of heavier atoms such as Fe, Al, Zn, Cu and Cr are in small fractions of one part per million.

This data was kindly provided by the Plastics Division of the Imperial Chemical Industries, Limited, Black Fan Road, Welwyn Garden City, Herts, England.

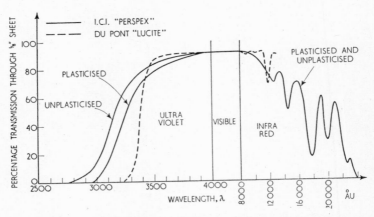

FIG. 6.5. The transmission characteristics of Perspex and Lucite.
(These curves have not been corrected for reflexion losses at the two surfaces.)

Du Pont " Lucite " Polymethyl Methacrylate

Refractive index n_D 1·489 to 1·493
Dispersion V 49
For transmission characteristics, see Fig. 6.5.
This information was kindly provided by the Research Division of the Polychemicals Department of E.I. du Pont de Nemours and Company, Wilmington 98, Delaware, U.S.A.

Optical Cement

Canada balsam $n_D = 1·530$

TABLE 6C

Crystals, Natural and Synthetic

Refractive indices at 18°C for various wavelengths

Wavelength (Å)	Calcspar		Fluorite	Quartz		Fused silica	Rock salt	Sylvine
	ord.	ex.		ord.	ex.			
6708	1·6537	1·4843	1·4323	1·5415	1·5505	1·4561	1·5400	1·4866
6563	6544	4846	4325	5419	5509	4564	5407	4872
6438	6550	4847	4327	5423	5514	4568	5412	4877
5893	6584	4864	4339	5443	5534	4585	5443	4904
5461	6616	4879	4350	5462	5553	4602	5475	4931
5086	6653	4895	4362	5482	5575	4619	5509	4961
4861	6678	4907	4371	5497	5590	4632	5534	4983
4800	6686	4911	4369	5501	5594	4636	5541	4990
4047	6813	4969	4415	5572	5667	4697	5665	5097
3034	7196	5136	4534	5770	5872	4869	6085	5440
2144	8459	5600	4846	6305	6427	5339	7322	6618
1852			5099	6759	6901	5743	8933	8270
Temperature coefficient per °C × 10⁵	+ 0·5	+ 1·4	− 1·0	− 0·5	− 0·6	− 0·3	− 4·0	− 4·0

TABLE 6D

Glass Manufactured in Great Britain

A. STANDARD CHANCE OPTICAL GLASS

See Chance Catalogue O.S.6 (1950)

Glass type	n_d	V	C–F	$\frac{b-C}{(b-C)/}$ $(C-F)$	$\frac{C-d}{(C-d)/}$ $(C-F)$	$\frac{d-e}{(d-e)/}$ $(C-F)$	$\frac{e-F}{(e-F)/}$ $(C-F)$	$\frac{F-g}{(F-g)/}$ $(C-F)$	$\frac{g-h}{(g-h)/}$ $(C-F)$	Density g/cm^3
Fluor Crown (FC)	1·48503	70·2	0·00 690	0·00 124 0·180	0·00 214 0·310	0·00 165 0·239	0·00 311 0·451	0·00 365 0·529	0·00 299 0·434	2·44
Borosilicate Crown (BSC)	1·50970	64·4	791	139 0·176	243 0·307	188 0·238	360 0·455	423 0·535	348 0·440	2·49
Hard Crown (HC)	1·51899	60·4	859	149 0·173	262 0·305	205 0·239	392 0·456	465 0·541	386 0·449	2·53
Light Barium Crown (LBC)	1·54065	59·5	908	158 0·174	277 0·305	217 0·239	414 0·456	493 0·543	406 0·447	2·87
Zinc Crown* (ZC)	1·50759	61·2	830	147 0·177	255 0·307	198 0·239	377 0·454	446 0·537	368 0·443	2·49
Medium Barium Crown (MBC)	1·56938	55·8	1021	176 0·172	309 0·303	243 0·238	469 0·459	560 0·548	468 0·458	3·12
Dense Barium Crown (DBC)	1·61230	58·5	1046	181 0·173	318 0·304	249 0·238	479 0·458	569 0·544	472 0·451	3·56
Soft Crown (SC)	1·51507	56·4	914	156 0·171	278 0·304	218 0·239	418 0·457	500 0·547	422 0·462	2·58
Telescope Flint (TF)	1·53033	51·2	1036	177 0·171	313 0·302	247 0·238	476 0·459	573 0·533	482 0·465	2·70

Glass																	
Barium Light Flint (LBF)	1·57427	52·0	1104	188	0·170	333	0·302	262	0·237	509	0·461	614	0·556	515	0·466	3·21
Extra Light Flint (ELF)	1·54769	45·6	1201	200	0·167	358	0·298	285	0·237	558	0·465	678	0·565	578	0·481	2·95
Barium Flint (BF)	1·60483	43·8	1380	228	0·165	410	0·297	327	0·237	643	0·466	787	0·570	671	0·486	3·48
Light Flint (LF)	1·57860	41·1	1407	231	0·164	417	0·296	333	0·237	657	0·467	807	0·574	693	0·493	3·23
Dense Flint (DF)	1·61323	36·9	1661	268	0·161	489	0·294	393	0·237	779	0·469	965	0·581	836	0·503	3·55
Extra Dense Flint (EDF)	1·70035	30·3	2313	365	0·158	671	0·290	547	0·236	1095	0·473	1381	0·597	1218	0·527	4·33
Double Extra Dense Flint (DEDF)	1·74842	27·8	2687	421	0·157	775	0·288	635	0·236	1277	0·475	1620	0·603	1438	0·535	4·76

Special Glasses

Glass																	
Double Extra Dense Flint (DEDF)	1·92707	21·0	4412	672	0·152	1250	0·283	1037	0·235	2125	0·482	2768	0·627			6·11
Borate Flint (BoF)	1·61200	44·9	1363	232	0·170	410	0·310	324	0·238	629	0·461	762	0·559	646	0·474	3·18
Special Barium Crown (SBC)	1·65100	58·6	1111	193	0·174	338	0·304	265	0·239	508	0·457	604	0·544	498	0·448	3·97
Special Barium Flint (SBF)	1·71700	47·9	1497	253	0·169	449	0·300	356	0·238	692	0·462	834	0·557	705	0·471	4·45

* Low thermal expansion ($5·0 \times 10^{-6}$ per °C between 0°C and 100°C).

B. LIGHT TRANSMISSION, CHANCE OPTICAL GLASS

The figures given below are extinction coefficients multiplied by 100.

Extinction coefficient $K = (\log_e I_0 - \log_e I)/t$, where $I_0 =$ initial light intensity, $I =$ transmitted light intensity, $t =$ glass thickness, inches.

Glass Type	BSC	HC	MBC	DBC	LF	LBF	DF	EDF	SBC	SBF	DEDF
d	1·5090	1·5189	1·5682	1·6157	1·5792	1·5683	1·6230	1·6516	1·6451	1·7205	1·7525
V	64·7	59·9	55·6	55·3	41·1	55·0	36·0	33·6	57·8	47·6	27·7
Wavelength, mμ											
365	4·60	7·82	31·7	—	14·8	25·4	39·2	49·5	—	—	—
400	1·37	—	5·4	13·3	4·4	—	6·70	12·9	—	—	—
404·8	—	2·48	—	11·8	—	5·21	—	9·67	16·6	36·4	48·1
420	—	—	—	7·0	—	—	—	7·28	—	—	—
435·8	1·32	3·67	3·8	6·2	2·3	4·54	4·45	5·21	7·06	17·3	10·9
440	—	—	—	5·92	—	—	—	5·30	—	—	—
460	0·87	—	1·75	4·61	1·17	—	2·48	4·05	—	—	—
480	—	1·88	—	3·29	—	2·49	—	2·78	—	—	—
491·6	—	—	—	—	—	—	—	2·71	—	—	—
500	0·49	—	0·9	2·18	0·69	—	—	2·29	—	—	—
520	—	—	—	2·04	—	—	—	1·66	—	—	—
540	—	1·35	—	1·92	—	1·44	1·41	1·48	1·77	6·08	1·52
546	0·35	—	0·6	1·96	0·51	—	—	1·40	—	—	—
560	—	1·69	—	1·81	—	1·78	1·54	1·28	2·25	5·80	1·71
579	—	—	—	2·26	—	—	—	1·21	—	—	—
580	0·49	—	0·76	2·32	0·60	—	—	1·20	—	—	—
600	—	—	—	2·88	—	—	—	1·90	—	—	—
620	0·67	3·04	0·87	3·20	0·74	2·85	2·12	2·22	2·39	4·62	1·78
640	0·87	—	0·8	3·44	0·6	—	—	2·35	—	—	—
680	—	—	—	3·46	—	—	—	2·17	—	—	—
700	—	—	—	3·32	—	—	2·02	1·83	—	—	—

Figures supplied by kind permission of Chance Pilkington Optical Works, Pilkington Bros. Ltd., Smethwick,

TABLE 6E

Some Glasses Manufactured in the U.S.A.

Corn'g   Corning Glass Works.
EK   Eastman Kodak Company.
Hay   Hayward Scientific Glass Corp.
NBS   National Bureau of Standards.

Origin		Type	V	A′	Indices of refraction			
					C	D	F	G′
NBS	..	610/620	62·0		1·6067	1·6096	1·6165	1·6220
NBS	..	639/597	59·7		1·6363	1·6395	1·6470	1·6531
NBS	..	656/582	58·2		1·6522	1·6555	1·6634	1·6698
EK	..	EK–110	56·2	1·68877	1·69313	1·69680	1·70554	1·71255
NBS	..	673/562	56·2		1·6697	1·6733	1·6817	1·6885
Hay	..	651/558	55·8		1·64757	1·65100	1·65924	1·66590
NBS	..	682/553	55·3		1·6782	1·6819	1·6906	1·6976
NBS	..	705/540	54·0		1·7011	1·7049	1·7142	1·7216
NBS	..	714/531	53·1		1·7103	1·7143	1·7238	1·7315
Hay	..	671/520	52·0		1·66724	1·67100	1·68018	1·68772
EK	..	EK–210	51·2	1·72482	1·72979	1·73400	1·74413	1·75235
Corn'g	..	8313	47·8		1·69639	1·70065	1·71104	
EK	..	EK–330	47·2	1·74499	1·75043	1·75510	1·76643	1·77571
EK	..	EK–310	46·4	1·73491	1·74033	1·74500	1·75638	1·76577
EK	..	EK–320	45·8	1·73432	1·73978	1·74450	1·75603	1·76557
EK	..	EK–450	41·8	1·79180	1·79814	1·80370	1·81738	1·82880
EK	..	EK–448	41·1	1·86714	1·87420	1·88040	1·89564	1·90827

See *Proceedings of the London Conference on Optical Instruments* (1950), Chapter 20, page 241. "New types of Optical Glasses available in the United States" by I. C. Gardner.

TABLE 6F

Refractive Indices of Liquids

Values at or near 20°C.

Liquid	n_D	V
*Fluorochemical FC 75	1·276	
Water	1·333	56
Paraldehyde	1·405	
Menthyl acetate	1·450	
Carbon tetrachloride	1·46	49
Glycerol	1·47	
Liquid paraffin	1·48	
Toluene	1·497	
Benzene	1·501	30
Ethyl salicylate	1·523	
Chlorobenzene	1·525	30·6

* This material, whose empirical formula is $C_8F_{16}O$, is manufactured by the Minnesota Mining and Manufacturing Company, 900 Bush Avenue, Saint Paul 6, Minnesota, U.S.A.

TABLE 6F—*continued*

Liquid	n_D	V
Methyl salicylate	1·538	
Ethyl cinnamate	1·559	20
Benzyl benzoate	1·568	
Aniline	1·586	
Quinoline	1·627	20
a-Monobromonaphthalene	1·660	
Mercury potassium iodide	1·717	
Methylene iodide	1·737	
Methylene iodide and sulphur (saturated)	1·78	
Barium mercuric iodide aq.	1·793	
Potassium iodide and mercuric iodide aq.	1·82*	
Solution 35% by weight CH_2I_2 ⎫		
Solution 31% by weight SnI_4 ⎪		
Solution 16% by weight AsI_3 ⎬	1·868	
Solution 8% by weight SbI_3 ⎪		
Solution 10% by weight S ⎭		
Hydrogen disulphide	1·885	
Phosphorus in carbon disulphide	1·95*	
Yellow phosphorus, 8 parts by weight ⎫		
Yellow sulphur, 1 part by weight ⎬	2·06	
Methylene iodide, 1 part by weight ⎭		
Mercuric iodide in aniline or quinoline	2·2*	
Oil, paraffin	1·44	
Oil, olive	1·46	
Oil, turpentine	1·47	
Oil, cedar	1·516	
Oil, cloves	1·532	
Oil, cinnamon	1·601	

* Maximum value obtainable.

Refractive index of water at 20°C *for various wavelengths*

Wavelength Å	12,560	6708	6563	6438	5893	5461
Refractive index	1·3210	1·3308	1·3311	1·3314	1·3330	1·3345
Wavelength Å	5086	4861	4800	4047	3034	2144
Refractive index	1·3360	1·3371	1·3374	1·3428	1·3581	1·4032

Temperature coefficient—$8·0 \times 10^{-5}$ per °C.

The absorption and transmission properties of various samples of natural water are shown in Fig. 6.6, page 155.

TABLE 6G

Refractive Indices of some Liquefied Gases

Liquid	Temperature	n_D at $\lambda = 5893$ Å
O_2	$-181°C$	1·221
N_2	$-190°C$	1·205
NO	$-\ 90°C$	1·330
H_2	$-253°C$	1·097
H_2S	$-\ 62°C$	1·374
Cl	$-\ 35°C$	1·385
He I	$4·22°K$	1·0206, $\rho = 0·125$ g/ml
He I	$2·26°K$	1·0269 $\quad$ 0·147 g/ml
He II	$2·18°K$	1·0269 $\quad$ 0·147 g/ml

TABLE 6H

Special Materials for High-energy γ-ray and Electron Spectroscopy with "Deep" Counters

Chance Glass Type EDF 653335

Density 3·9 g/ml
Refractive index 1·689 at $\lambda = 4047$ Å
Radiation length X_0 2·56 cm (1·01 in.)
Approximate critical energy ϵ 16·2 MeV
Chemical composition

	Weight %			Weight %
SiO_2	40·9		Si	19·1
K_2O	4·5		K	3·7
Na_2O	1·7		Na	1·3
PbO	52·7		Pb	49·0
As_2O_3	0·2		As	0·15
			O	26·8

Transmission (without reflexion loss); %

λ (Å)	Thickness = X_0	Thickness = 10 X_0
3200	0	0
3300	0·4	0
3400	4	0
3500	27	0
3600	53	0·2
3700	71	3
3800	80	10
3900	87	25
4000	92	45
4200	96	62
4400	97	70
4600	98	79

The values quoted for the thickness of 10 X_0 have been extrapolated from measurements at the X_0 thickness, and are only intended to give an indication of the likely transmission at this thickness.

L

The above glass is made by the optical glass process, that is, the glass is stirred whilst molten. However, isolated fine striae and bubbles may be present in Čerenkov blocks made from melts of this glass. This, nevertheless, is of little consequence in its application to counters of this type.

This information was kindly supplied by Chance-Pilkington Optical Works, Pilkington Brothers Ltd., at the Glass Works, Smethwick, Birmingham, 40, England.

Corning Glasses

Corning Code 8392
Density 3·89 g/ml
Refractive index 1·64 for the sodium D-line
Dispersion value (V) 33·8
Radiation length X_0 2·81 cm (1·11 in.)
Critical energy ϵ 13 MeV

Average photon track length (200–500 MeV) 2·6 cm
Ionization energy loss $\sim 1·36$ MeV/cm (relativistic velocities)
Čerenkov radiation production ~ 954 eV/cm for $\beta = 1$.
Chemical composition (by weight)

PbO	52%
SiO_2	42
K_2O	3
Na_2O	3

Transmission (without reflexion loss) for a thickness of 17·8 cm, that of a standard block.

λ (Å)	% transmission (5% accuracy)
6707	80
5890	80
4916	80
4358	80
4046	10
4000	0
3650	0

This glass has so far been available in a standard size block, a cylinder of 12·25 in. diameter and 7 in. length (17·8 cm).

For optical seals between two or more blocks, and between the last block and the phototubes, it is recommended that Dow Corning 200 silicone compound be used. This material is clear and colourless, and has a viscosity of $2·5 \times 10^6$ centistokes, a refractive index of 1·4 and a light transmission of more than 95% in the visible region.

Corning Code 9766
This glass provides a performance significantly superior to that formerly available in Corning 8392. It is available in sizes up to 12 in. diameter by 14. in. thick. Its physical properties are indicated below.

Density	4·6276 g/ml
Refractive Index (Sodium D)	1·7240
Radiation length	1·933 cm

Transmission (corrected for reflexion) for 10 radiation lengths (19·33 cm).

Wavelength λ (Å)	% Transmittance	Absorb. coeff. cm^{-1}
7000	93·4	0·00355
6000	97·0	0·00159
5000	96·3	0·00194
4400	92·4	0·00409
4000	82·8	0·00975
3800	55·1	0·03850

The above information has been kindly supplied by the Corning Glass Works, Corning, New York, U.S.A.

Thallous Chloride Crystals

A single sample grown by Moffat and Stringfellow (1958) had the following properties:

Dimensions   A cylinder 12 cm long and 9·3 cm in diameter
Density   7·0 g/ml
Refractive index   2·2
Radiation length X_0, 0·94 cm
Critical energy ϵ, 8·3 MeV
Transmission characteristics:

TABLE 6I

Filter	Effective wavelength λ (Å)	% transmission through the whole sample	Absorption coefficient cm^{-1}
Wood's glass	3650	0	—
Violet	4100	66	0·034
Blue	4400	76	0·023
Green	5200	88	0·011
Orange–yellow	5900	94	0·005

Lead Perchlorate Solutions

Fidecaro (1956) has described experiments with saturated solutions of Pb $(ClO_4)_2$. These solutions were made from pure lead nitrate and perchloric acid, according to the method used by Kassner (1930). The properties of this solution are as follows:

Density   2·77 g/ml
Refractive index $n = 1·51$
One radiation length $X_0 = 4·1$ cm
Transmission (for one radiation length in depth):

TABLE 6J

λ (Å)	3100	3250	3375	3500	3750	4000	4500
T %	0	20	50	70	84	90	95

TABLE 6K

Reflectivities

OPAQUE METAL FILMS ON POLISHED GLASS

Percentage reflexion for light incident normally on metallized surface, except where indicated by "BACK"

Wavelength Å	1863	1886	1936	1990	2000	2144	2196	2265	2313	2510	2573
Chemically deposited silver		22			25					34·1	
Evaporated aluminium	70		87	87		84	86	86	91		89

Wavelength Å	2749	2880	2981	3050	3160	3261	3380	3404	3570	3610	3850
Chemically deposited silver		21·2		9·1	4·2	14·6	55·5		74·5		81·4
Evaporated aluminium	90		90			91		83		84	90

Wavelength, μ	0·42	0·45	0·46	0·50	0·54	0·55	0·58	0·60	0·62	0·65	0·66
Evaporated aluminium		91		92				92			
Sputtered gold platinum silver										89·1 63·8 94·6	
Chemically deposited silver silver BACK mercury BACK	86·6	90·5 85·7 72·8	90·5 81·0	92·0 84·0 70·9	93·0 86·2	92·7 88·2 71·2	94·8 88·5	92·6 88·1 69·9	95·0 90·2	93·5 89·1 71·5	95·2 91·9

Wavelength, μ	0·70	0 80	1·0	1·5	2·0	3·0	4·0	5·0	9·0	11·0	12·0	14·0
Evaporated aluminium	90	88	95									
Sputtered gold platinum silver			93·6 70·4 95·5	94·8 75·3	94·9 79·8 96·8	95·6 88·5 97·4	96·0 91·6 97·6	95·7 90·8 97·3	96·1 93·1 98·1	96·5 92·7 98·8	97·2 94·9 98·1	96·7 94·7
Chemically deposited silver silver BACK mercury BACK	95·0 93·0 72·8	96·3 89·0	96·6 92	97·9 94		98·1 95	98·5 96	98·1 96	98·5			98·8

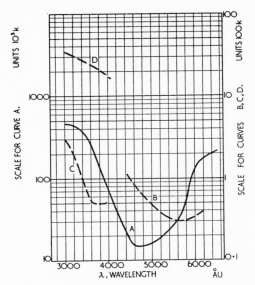

FIG. 6.6. The transmission characteristics of water. The attenuation is expressed in terms of the quantity k in the equation $I = I_0 \exp(-kx)$. I represents the intensity of a parallel beam of light, of initial intensity I_0, after passing through a depth of x cm of the water in question. Unit $k = 1$ cm^{-1} at room temperature.

Curve A. Pure water. Sawyer, W. R. (1931). *Cont. Canad. Biol.* (N.S.) **7**, (8), 75.

Curve B. Gunflint Lake, Minn. (U.S.A.). Erikson, H. A. (1933). *J. Opt. Soc. Amer.* **23**, 170.

Curve C. Tap Water. Hodgman, C. D. (1933). *J. Opt. Soc. Amer.* **23**, 426.

Curve D. Melted Snow. Hodgman, C. D. *Ibid.*

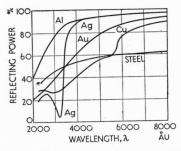

FIG. 6.7. The reflecting power of freshly prepared metal surfaces at normal incidence. (After Jenkins and White, 1937.)

POLISHED GLASS SURFACES

Percentage reflexion from a thin glass plate: both surfaces and internal reflexions taken into account. Calculated for yellow light corresponding to n_D.

Refractive index	1·50	1·55	1·60	1·65	1·70
Angle of incidence	Percentage reflexion				
0°	7·8	8·8	10·2	11·3	12·6
10°	7·8	8·8	10·2	11·3	12·6
20°	8·0	8·9	10·3	11·4	12·7
30°	8·0	9·1	10·4	11·4	12·8
40°	8·6	9·8	11·1	12·2	13·4
50°	10·4	11·6	12·7	13·9	15·1
60°	15·2	16·3	17·4	18·4	19·4
70°	27·3	28·1	28·9	29·6	30·2

See Habell and Cox, *Engineering Optics* (Pitmans).

The reflected light is materially reduced by covering the surface with a "non-reflecting" film; the surface is then said to be "bloomed". For light of a given wavelength at normal incidence, the optical thickness of the film is one-quarter that wavelength, and the refractive index of the material of the film is equal to the square root of that of the glass on which it is deposited. Efficiency of the film depends on the extent to which these conditions are fulfilled, and in practice is such that for a single surface light reflexion is reduced to about 1%. The material most commonly used is magnesium fluoride ($n_D = 1·390$).

Reflexion and Refraction at Dielectric Surfaces

If a plane polarized wave of amplitude E is incident on a dielectric surface, the amplitudes of the reflected, R, and the refracted, D, components are related by the Fresnel formulae

$$R_\perp/E_\perp = \frac{-\sin(i-r)}{\sin(i+r)}, \qquad R_\parallel/E_\parallel = \frac{\tan(i-r)}{\tan(i+r)}$$

$$D_\perp/E_\perp = \frac{2\sin r \cos i}{\sin(i+r)}, \text{ and}_\parallel \; D/E_\parallel = \frac{2\sin r \cos i}{\sin(i+r)\cos(i-r)}$$

where i is the angle of incidence, r the angle of refraction and $\parallel$ and $\perp$ refer, respectively, to the cases for which the plane of polarization of the incident wave is either parallel or perpendicular to the plane of incidence. The intensities are obtained by squaring the amplitudes.

White Reflecting Materials

For counters which rely on diffuse reflexion of the light, it is essential to use materials with the highest possible reflectivity. The choice of material depends largely on whether it is in contact with air or the Čerenkov medium itself. Most published information on the performance of different materials is very vague, and it is difficult to arrive at a figure of merit, since the geometries of the various systems are different, and the light absorbing properties of the Čerenkov media also vary. In view of this we present merely a list of a number of typical examples of materials used in detectors employing light diffusion, with references and brief comments, see Table 6L. In some cases the detectors are scintillators but the essential requirements are the same for Čerenkov counters.

Broadly speaking, it would appear that the very best reflectivities are obtained with fresh MgO or TiO_2 powder, but such surfaces deteriorate with age, cannot be used in contact with a liquid and are bound only lightly to the surfaces on which they are deposited. For these reasons the tendency has been to develop paints loaded with such substances; these are robust, easy to apply, durable and are found to be satisfactory for most applications.

Other suitable materials, not mentioned in Table 6L, include water glass, porcelain and etched aluminium.

A method for measuring the reflectivities of such materials is described in section 7.6.

The Plastic "Darvic"

This is a form of polyvinyl chloride manufactured by I.C.I. which contains 15% by weight of TiO_2. In sheet form it has a glossy surface for which the total reflectivity has been measured to be 83%. This was measured with reference to standard illuminant "A" (i.e. a tungsten lamp run at a colour temperature of 2848°K). Most of this reflectivity is contained in the specular component, and consequently the reflectivity at different angles deviates markedly from a cosmic law. If the glossy surface is suitably destroyed, then the intensity of the specular component is reduced. Immersion of the sheet in a liquid will also reduce the intensity of the specular component, depending on the relative refractive indices of the liquid and the Darvic ($n_D = 1.54$). It is probable however that the *total* reflectivity *increases* when immersed.

This information was kindly supplied by the Plastics Division of the Imperial Chemical Industries Limited, Welwyn Garden City, Herts, England.

TABLE 6L

	Detector	References	Diffusing material
1.	Liquid scintillator	Jelley, J. V. and Whitehouse, W. J. (1953)	MgO powder
2.	Large liquid scintillator	Cowan et al. (1953) Reines and Cowan (1953)	White Tygon paint; sodium silicate—titanium dioxide reflecting surface
3.	Čerenkov (water)	Harris and Ogilvie (1956) Ogilvie (1955)	Waterproof reflecting paint Type NRP 448
4.	Large plastic scintillators	Clark et al. (1957)	Commercial white titanium dioxide paint. Glidden ultra-white "Japalac"
5.	Čerenkov (water)	Duerden and Hyams (1952) Barker et al. (1955)	$MgCO_3$ surfaces
6.	Čerenkov (water and kerosene) 300 gal	Porter (1956 and 1957)	I.C.I. product "Darvic" polyvinyl chloride sheet, loaded with titanium dioxide (see below)
7.	Liquid scintillator	Brennan and Landecker (1956)	MgO dusted on to a white paint

TABLE 6L—*continued*

Remarks
Freshly prepared MgO layer deposited on the inside of a hemispherical dome filled with air, above the scintillator liquid which was in a sealed container with glass lid. The MgO prepared by burning Mg ribbon 2–3 in. below the clean surface of the dome.
Liquid in contact with the surface.
Developed in the paint research laboratories of the National Research Council of Canada. The paint contains a zinc oxide pigment and its reflectivity was found to be 94% between wavelengths of 4250–7000 Å.
With plastic discs 16 in. diam., and 2½ in. thick fitted in a can painted with this material, a figure of 65% was obtained for the reflectivity. This figure *includes* effects due to absorption, and refers to the product $(1 - \mu) \times p$ discussed in section 7.6.
In the first reference, the interior of the counter was coated with a waterproof $MgCO_3$ surface; in the later work $MgCO_3$ powder was packed into a separate double-walled Perspex box not in contact with the water. The overall optical efficiency of the detector was found to be 15%; this *includes* absorption in the water and the geometrical factor.
Two types in use: (i) Unplasticized tough sheet ⅛ in. thick, used in a water counter. Reflectivity measured to be 91% in the visible region. In this counter 20% of the light is lost in water absorption. (ii) Soft plasticized loaded p.v.c. of thickness 0·020 in., used in a kerosene counter. The liquid slowly dissolves the plasticizer so that the material hardens with age. Reflectivity measured to be 85% and light absorption 50%. The growth of algae presented an obstinate problem in the case of the water counter, particularly with the plasticized material.
The scintillating liquid lies in an open tray at the bottom of the light diffusing container; the vapour but not the liquid is in contact with the MgO.

CHAPTER 7

OPTICAL CONSIDERATIONS

7.1 Introduction

The distinguishing feature of Čerenkov radiation, namely its directional characteristic, requires the development of optical systems of a type different from those encountered in other fields. Since the emission of light is symmetrical about the axis of the particle, it is usual to arrange this to coincide with the axis of the optical system. This at once points to the essential difference between Čerenkov and conventional optics, that the source lies along the axis while the image is required in a plane perpendicular to the axis.

Optical considerations in the design of Čerenkov counters fall broadly under two headings, first those concerning the focusing type of counter, to which the above remarks apply, and, secondly, those associated with counters of the non-focusing class. It should be emphasized at the outset that the optics of Čerenkov counters are in general very crude by normal optical standards. For example, in focusing systems, the limits of resolution are not usually set by the purely optical effects such as spherical and chromatic aberrations; one is concerned, for instance, with angular resolutions of the order of minutes of arc at best, compared to fractions of a second of arc required, say, in telescope design.

7.2 The optics of counters of the focusing type

The main considerations here are (i) response time, and (ii) energy resolution. All that need be said with regard to (i) is that the extremely short times of response inherent in focusing counters follow immediately from the fundamental Principle of Least Time common to all optical systems. The energy resolution of counters (i.e. their property of velocity discrimination) is determined by a large number of factors to be discussed later, following a survey of the principal types of instrument.

Optical Systems with Fixed Focus

Although there are only a few fundamental designs, there are an unlimited number of variants of these, some of which will be described

160

in Chapter 8. The first proposal for a focused counter was due to Getting (1947) who considered the simple design shown in Fig. 7.1(a). In this arrangement the particle travels along the axis of a solid conical radiator R, the semi-apex angle ϕ of which is made precisely equal to half the Čerenkov angle θ. The light generated by the particle is reflected off the curved surface of the cone, at angles larger than the critical angle, and emerges normal to the end-face, after which it is brought to a focus F by the lens L. The advantage of this simple design is that there is no loss of light except that due to partial internal reflexion at the base of the cone, and absorption in the medium, both of which are small; there are, furthermore, no corrections due to refraction. The serious disadvantage is that a given cone is strictly only suitable for a fixed value of θ, and the instrument has therefore very limited applications. Čerenkov light generated in the lens itself, and some formed near the base of the cone (where it cannot reach the curved surface) will not reach the detector, though there is of course no objection to cutting away the central portion of the lens. Further, to avoid the particles traversing the detector, the light may be reflected by a plane mirror, before or after the lens, so that the focus point is displaced from the axis. Note that the *useful* length of the Getting cone, L_{eff}, is less than the actual length L. If R is the radius of the base of the cone, then

$$L_{\text{eff}} = (L - R \cot \theta) \qquad (7.1)$$

Chromatic aberration, intrinsic in Čerenkov radiation, is easily eliminated by a suitable design of compound lens for L.

In Getting's second design, Fig. 7.1(b), a much longer and cylindrical radiator is used, whereby more light may be produced; this is conducted by internal reflexion into the conical section which serves the same purpose as in the earlier design. This type is only suitable when $\theta < \theta_{\text{max}}$, for when $\beta \sim 1$ the light is incident at the cylindrical surface at an angle close to the critical angle, and may be lost, in the limiting case. If required, the cylindrical surface may be coated with a metallic layer which will give specular reflexion, obviating this difficulty.

A third form proposed by Getting is shown in Fig. 7.1(c). This is claimed to have three advantages over the other types.

(i) By suitable choice of the angle ψ, the light emerges at Brewster's angle (the electric vector always in the radial plane), so that there

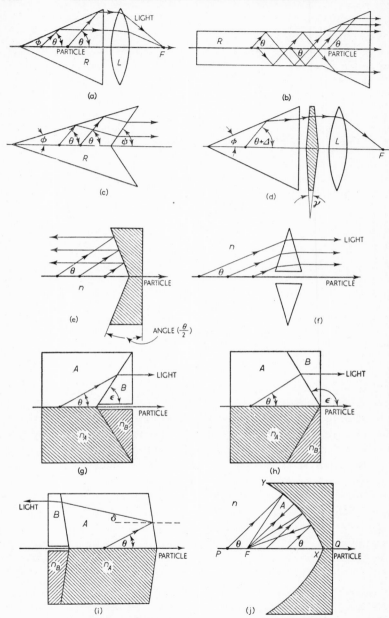

FIG. 7.1. Basic optical systems for counters of the fixed focus type.

is no loss of light as it leaves the radiator. This seems to be a trivial point however, since, in the first design, the loss is very small, only 4% for $n = 1\cdot5$. For the geometry of this design, if B is Brewster's angle, so that tan $B = n$, it is seen that:

$$\psi = \left(\frac{\pi}{2} - B\right) \text{ and } n = \frac{\sin B}{\sin [B - (\theta - 2\phi)]} \qquad (7.2)$$

For example, with fast electrons ($\beta = 1$) in Perspex ($n = 1\cdot50$), $\theta = 48°: 10'$, $B = 56°: 18'$, $\phi = 12°: 45'$ and $\psi = 33°: 42'$.

(ii) The smaller is ϕ, the smaller the colour dispersion.

(iii) In this design no part of the radiator is producing light that is not collected.

Returning to the question of the inflexibility of these designs, the range may be somewhat extended by the addition of thin conical lenses as shown in Fig. 7.1(d). If Δ is the deviation from the normal Čerenkov angle for which the cone was originally designed, the angle γ between the two surfaces of the lens required to regain focus, is related to the refractive index n (the same for cone and lens) by the equations:

$$n \approx \left(\frac{\gamma}{\gamma - \Delta}\right), \text{ or } \gamma \approx \left(\frac{n}{n - 1}\right) . \Delta \qquad (7.3)$$

valid when Δ and γ are small. In a typical case, when $n = 1\cdot50$, $\gamma = 3\Delta$.

Two very simple arrangements, particularly adapted to gas counters (see Chapter 10) are shown in Figs. 7.1(e) and 7.1(f). Owing to the very small light yield in gases, it is preferable to avoid lenses, in which stray radiation generated may easily swamp the light from the gas; this favours the mirror arrangement of Fig. 7.1(e).

Some achromatic variants of the simple conical radiators have recently been discussed by Frank (1956). His main aim in these systems is to obtain the shortest possible duration of light pulse over a wide band of wavelengths; this can only be achieved with achromatic systems, so that the light of different wavelengths arrives at the same time.

In Frank's first model, Fig. 7.1(g), two optical cones A and B, having refractive indices n_A and n_B respectively, are sealed together, and it is arranged that the particle travelling from left to right along the axis only produces Čerenkov radiation in the element A; the production of radiation in B is avoided by a tunnel along its axis for the particle to escape. In this case, for $n_B > n_A$, the relation between θ and ϵ, for the light to emerge parallel to the axis, is:

$$\frac{n_B}{n_A} = \frac{\cos(\epsilon - \theta)}{\cos \epsilon} = \cos \theta + \sin \theta \tan \epsilon \qquad (7.4)$$

A necessary condition, for ϵ to be $> \theta$, is

$$\frac{n_B}{n_A} > \frac{1}{\cos \theta} = \beta n_A, \text{ or } n_B > \beta n_A^2 \qquad (7.5)$$

In another version, Fig. 7.1(h), when $n_B < n_A$, the corresponding condition is:

$$\frac{n_B}{n_A} < \cos \theta = \frac{1}{\beta n_A}, \text{ or } n_B < \frac{1}{\beta} \qquad (7.6)$$

Writing (7.4) in the form

$$\tan \epsilon = \left(\frac{\beta n_B - 1}{\tan \theta}\right) \qquad (7.7)$$

and differentiating with respect to the frequency ν, the following condition for achromatism is obtained for the first design:

$$\frac{dn_B}{d\nu} = \frac{\beta n_B - 1}{\beta n_A \sin^2 \theta_\nu} \cdot \frac{dn_A}{d\nu} = \frac{\beta n_A (\beta n_B - 1)}{\beta^2 n_A^2 - 1} \cdot \frac{dn_A}{d\nu} \qquad (7.8)$$

A third model of this type is shown in Fig. 7.1(i). For light emerging from B parallel to the axis, the angle δ replaces θ in (7.5) so that $\frac{n_B}{n_A} > \frac{1}{\cos \delta}$, and, when $d\delta/d\nu = d\theta/d\nu$ the following condition for achromatism is derived:

$$\frac{dn_B}{d\nu} = \left[\frac{n_B}{n_A} + \frac{\frac{n_B}{n_A}\cos \delta - 1}{\sin \delta \sqrt{(\beta^2 n_A^2 - 1)}}\right] \cdot \frac{dn_A}{d\nu} \qquad (7.9)$$

In the above designs the procedure has been to collimate the light into a parallel beam and then to focus it with conventional mirrors or lenses. It is possible of course to figure the optical surfaces so that the Čerenkov radiation may be brought to a direct focus at a single stage of reflexion or refraction. One example of this is shown in Fig. 7.1(j) where radiation produced in the medium in front of the mirror (for example a gas) is focused to a single point on the axis. The required figure of revolution in this case is obtained by rotating a parabola about a point off its own axis. If PQ is the path of the particle, θ the Čerenkov angle and F the point on PQ at which the focus is required, then a parabola YAX whose axis lies along AF, where $\widehat{AFQ} = \theta$, will focus all the Čerenkov light in this plane, to the point F. The complete figure of revolution is obtained by rotating the parabola about FX, where X is thus always a point of discontinuity. In the general case YA will not equal AX. The equation of the curve in polar co-ordinates ρ and Θ with respect to the point F is:

$$2f = \rho \left[1 - \cos(\Theta - \theta)\right] \tag{7.10}$$

where f is the focal length. When θ is small, as in gas counters, (7.10) tends to the form for a normal parabola. A figure of revolution of this type would be extremely difficult to work in practice.

Optical Systems with Adjustable Focus

In the systems described so far, the focus condition is satisfied for only one value of θ, so that different cone angles must be used to obtain sharp images for radiation produced by particles of different velocity.

Marshall (1951) was the first to develop the versatile focusing counter, in which a single instrument would cover a wide range of Čerenkov angles. This fundamental improvement in design was achieved by introducing optical systems with spherical lenses and cylindrical mirrors, the basic types of which are shown in Fig. 7.2. Some of the designs proposed and tried by Marshall and others are discussed in greater detail in Chapters 4 and 8. In his first instrument (Marshall, 1951), Fig. 7.2(a), the figure of the lens L is obtained by rotating a circle around an axis in its plane, the axis coinciding with the track of the particle, with the centre C of the circle displaced from the axis. The radius of curvature r is so chosen as to focus the light into a sharp ring image F' of radius 2ρ. The cylindrical mirror M, of radius ρ, is used to bring the light to a focus F on the optic axis.

In his second design, Fig. 7.2(b), a long cylindrical radiator is used, which is optically sealed to a hemispherical lens. For a material such as Perspex, for which $n = 1.5$, the focal length of the lens is very short, twice its radius of curvature. The spherical aberration in such a lens is considerable by normal optical standards, and therefore the best performance is obtained when the diameter of the lens is large compared

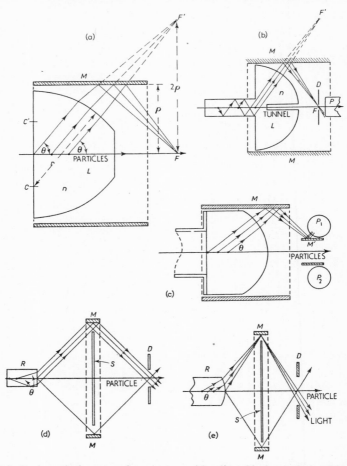

FIG. 7.2. Basic optical systems for counters with adjustable focus. (After Marshall, 1951, 1952 and 1954.)

with the diameter of the radiator. Neglecting this aberration, F will be a point focus, and the aperture D behind which the photomultiplier P is placed may be small. Different Čerenkov angles are then selected quite simply by moving D along the axis and finding the position at which the maximum light is collected by the phototube. It is desirable, in this design, to avoid the production of light in the lens itself; this may be achieved by cutting a tunnel down the centre of the lens as shown, whereby the particle emerges from the radiator portion without further interaction with the medium. This has the additional advantage that the light is divided into two parts, which is convenient when the coincidence technique is used, as in the example cited in section 8.1.

In spite of its obvious spherical aberration, the design shown in Fig. 7.2(c) was found by Marshall (1952) to be highly successful; the radiator and lens have been combined into a single unit which slides inside the mirror for selecting the Čerenkov angle.

A particularly simple design of variable-focus counter, also proposed by Marshall (1952), uses only a cylindrical radiator R (with flat end), a cylindrical mirror M, a diaphragm D and a stop S, see Fig. 7.2(d). This instrument has recently been developed and used in a practical application discussed in section 8.3. A variant of this form, Fig. 7.2(e), in which the end of the radiator has a convex surface, is claimed to reduce the effects of image spread caused by finite beam width of the particles, see section 7.3 below.

There are already countless varieties of focusing counter, and no doubt many others will appear in future; owing to their greater flexibility, we shall expect most of these to be of the variable focus type.

Just recently Hutchinson (unpublished) has developed a proton counter with anti-astigmatic spherical optics, the velocity-gate of which is set by the relative proportions of water and glycerine used for the radiator.

7.3 The energy resolution of focusing counters

The following factors contribute, in varying degrees, to limit the overall resolution of Čerenkov counters of the focusing type.

1. Finite width of the particle beam.
2. Diffraction.
3. Multiple Coulomb scattering.
4. Dispersion, or chromatic aberration.
5. Spherical aberrations and coma.
6. Slowing-down of the particles in the radiator.
7. Intrinsic angular spread among the particles.
8. Intrinsic energy spread among the particles.

Effects (1), (7) and (8) are directly connected with the properties of the beam of particles, while effects (2) to (6) inclusive arise within the radiator and therefore can never be completely eliminated.

M

Finite Beam Width

In discussing the various optical systems, we have so far assumed all the particles to be travelling along the optic axes. In practice, of course, the beam of particles will have finite width. From fundamental considerations, Marshall (1952) has shown that it is never possible to focus all the light to a point from a beam of finite width, even for a single Čerenkov angle. This is a general theorem for all optical systems having cylindrical symmetry, and is embodied in the well known Abbe's Sine Rule encountered in geometrical optics. It will be assumed in the following treatment that particles in the beam are travelling parallel to the optic axes, though some are laterally displaced from it.

Suppose a particle is travelling parallel to the axis of a cylinder of dielectric material, but displaced from this axis by a distance d. Since the Čerenkov light is emitted at quite a large cone angle θ from all parts of the track, it follows that most of the light travels in paths skewed with respect to the axis. Consequently the photons have angular momentum around the axis. This angular momentum, in any optical system, is conserved, and can never be changed no matter how often the light is reflected or refracted at cylindrically symmetrical boundaries. This sets a limit on the sharpness of focus. For the most-skewed ray inside the dielectric, the angular momentum of a photon about the axis of the system is d (sin θ) $h\nu n/c$, where h is Planck's constant, ν the frequency of the photon, c the velocity of light in free space and θ the angle between the path of the photon and the axis. The same photon, when it emerges from the dielectric, will have an angular momentum D (sin θ') $h\nu/c$, where θ' is the angle of divergence of the light outside the medium (or convergence if a mirror is used, as for example in Marshall's detectors) and D is the closest approach the photon makes again with the axis, which ideally is in the focal plane. The conservation of angular momentum leads to the condition:

$$D = nd \, (\sin \theta / \sin \theta') \qquad (7.11)$$

D can never be much smaller than d and in general is larger. If D is set by the dimensions of the photocathode of a multiplier, it follows that an upper limit is set to the width d of the radiator of a Čerenkov detector for efficient collection of the light. It should be noted that if the radiator is optically sealed to the detector, so that the light never leaves the medium, the factor n in (7.11) disappears. As an example of the application of (7.11), consider Marshall's detector shown in Fig.

7.2(b). In this case $\theta = \theta'$ and hence $D = nd$. Thus the light from a Perspex radiator of diameter 2 cm, bombarded by a beam of mono-energetic particles of width > 2cm, may be brought to a focus within a circular area of diameter 3 cm (for $n = 1\cdot50$), which will then be the optimum size of the diaphragm in front of the phototube. Somewhat better conditions may be achieved with the system shown in Fig. 7.2(d). In this case $\sin \theta' = n \sin \theta$ so that, from (7.11), $D = d$.

The effects of *Diffraction* and *Scattering* have already been discussed in detail in section 3.8. For an approximate estimate of the energy resolution set by the second of these two effects, the r.m.s. angle of scatter $\langle \theta^2 \rangle^{\frac{1}{2}}$ is first obtained, using equation (3.68), and Table H in Appendix I for the radiation length of the radiator material. The resolution in *energy* resulting from a given resolution in *angle* is obtained as follows:

From the Čerenkov relation, differentiating with respect to β, one obtains:

$$d\theta = \frac{1}{(\beta^2 n^2 - 1)^{\frac{1}{2}}} \cdot \frac{d\beta}{\beta} \tag{7.12}$$

If W is the *total* energy of the particle, measured in terms of its rest energy, so that $W = (1 - \beta^2)^{-\frac{1}{2}}$, then, differentiating again with respect to β:

$$\frac{dW}{W} = (W^2 - 1) \cdot \frac{d\beta}{\beta} \tag{7.13}$$

From (7.12), and remembering that $\cos \theta = 1/\beta n$ we find:

$$\frac{dW}{W} = (W^2 - 1) \tan \theta \cdot d\theta \tag{7.14}$$

To obtain (dW/W) for the effects of scattering, it is only necessary to put our $\langle \theta^2 \rangle^{\frac{1}{2}}$ equal to $d\theta$ in (7.14).

Dispersion

Some of the optical systems already described are corrected for chromatic aberration, but for those simpler arrangements where there are no such corrections, the effects on the energy resolution may be obtained as follows:

Writing the Čerenkov relation in the form $\cos \theta = 1/\beta n(\lambda)$ and taking

$\bar{n}$ for the average refractive index over the spectral region covered by the photomultiplier, one obtains by differentiation:

$$\frac{d\beta}{d\theta} = \bar{n}\beta^2 \sin \theta \qquad (7.15)$$

and

$$\frac{d\theta}{d\lambda} = \frac{1}{\bar{n}} \cdot \cot \theta \cdot \frac{dn}{d\lambda} \qquad (7.16)$$

from which, again using $W = (1 - \beta^2)^{-\frac{1}{2}}$

$$\frac{dW}{d\beta} = \frac{\beta}{(1 - \beta^2)^{\frac{3}{2}}} \qquad (7.17)$$

Writing $\dfrac{dW}{d\lambda} = \dfrac{dW}{d\beta} \cdot \dfrac{d\beta}{d\theta} \cdot \dfrac{d\theta}{d\lambda}$, one then finds

$$dW = \frac{\beta^2}{(1 - \beta^2)^{\frac{3}{2}}} \cdot \frac{dn}{\bar{n}}, \text{ or } \frac{dW}{W} = \frac{\beta^2}{(1 - \beta^2)} \cdot \frac{dn}{\bar{n}}. \qquad (7.18)$$

If dispersion effects are serious, it is best to adopt some form of achromatic arrangement. The alternative is to use a filter, to reduce the bandwidth, but the resultant loss of light cannot in general be tolerated. Gelatine dye filters have poor transmissions, while interference filters usually require that the light arrives normal to the surface of the filter.

The effects of *Spherical Aberration* cannot be calculated easily and it is recommended that ray-tracing be carried out graphically for some of the extreme situations, and an average value derived.

The effects of *Slowing-down* can best be estimated from the kinetic energy loss dE suffered by the particles in passing through the radiator. (dW/W) will then be $\propto (dE/E)$. Values of dE may be obtained from the various curves in Appendix II. Two methods have been proposed to compensate for the effects of slowing-down. J. Marshall (1956) has proposed the use of a tapered radiator, see Fig. 7.3(a). If the radiator has a conical or pyramidal form, of small opening angle, it can be shown that the rate of change of the angle θ is given by:

$$\frac{d\theta}{dx} = -\frac{\alpha \tan \theta}{d} = -\frac{\tan \theta}{x} \qquad (7.19)$$

where θ is the angle between the light ray and the axis of the radiator, d the width of the "pipe" at the position x measured from the apex of the cone. If the change of angle of reflexion in such a tapered radiator is adjusted to be the same as the change of Čerenkov angle, complete compensation will be achieved. The design of such a pipe is carried out using relations (7.14) and (7.19) and the curves in Appendix II. To minimize the spread of angles of the light emerging from the end of the radiator, its diameter must be small compared with its length. Since this would seriously reduce the sensitive area of the counter, it was proposed that the radiator be built up from a honeycomb of thin tapered elements, as shown in Fig. 7.3(b). As an example, the average full-angle of taper for a radiator 5 mm wide used with protons of energy 350 MeV is $\bar{\alpha} = 1 \cdot 8°$, in the case of Perspex.

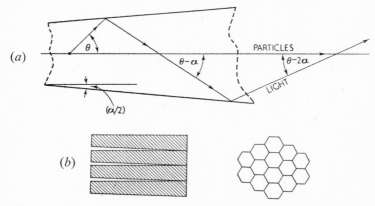

FIG. 7.3. The use of tapered radiators to compensate for slowing down of the particles. (J. Marshall, 1956.)

The second method, suggested by Lundby (1956), for compensating for the slowing-down, is to use a medium whose refractive index varies along the track. It is doubtful, except in special applications, whether the adoption of either of these ideas warrants the trouble involved, in view of all the other sources of spread in image size.

The *Intrinsic Angular Spread* among the particles in the beam is converted directly to the equivalent energy spread, by use of equation (7.14).

Since most of the above sources of energy spread are independent of one another, the *overall* resolution (dW/W) will be equal to the square root of the sum of the squares of the individual contributions.

7.4 The optics of counters of the non-focusing type

This has been discussed in great detail by Mandò (1954) who classifies such counters in three groups:

(i) Those having specular reflecting walls,

(ii) Those which have diffusing walls only, and

(iii) Those which rely partly on specular reflexion and partly on diffusion.

The most important of the non-focusing counters fall in group (ii), and will be discussed in detail below. The others, relying wholly or partially on specular reflexion, have but few rather limited applications and will not be considered. The following general remarks however will serve to indicate the properties and limitations of the various types.

The important factors in the design of successful non-focusing counters are:

(a) Effective sensitive area,

(b) Uniformity of response over this area,

(c) Light collection time (i.e. speed of response), and

(d) "Anti-directional" properties,* ADP for short.

It is found that for a given effective area, the maximum efficiency and best uniformity are obtained with a counter having only diffusing walls. Such counters however are relatively slow and have no ADP. Counters relying entirely on specular reflexion have excellent ADP and are faster, but have poor uniformity and low efficiency, particularly when their area exceeds that of the photocathode of the multiplier. Counters having mixed walls retain the feature of good ADP but still have rather low efficiency, though the uniformity can be preserved.

Counters relying on Diffuse Reflexion

We will consider, for our prototype, an integrating sphere S of radius R, coated inside with a matt-white scattering material, and filled to capacity with some suitable Čerenkov medium. Somewhere, flush with the surface of the sphere, is situated the photosensitive cathode of the multiplier P, see Fig. 7.4. The following symbols are introduced:

μ the absorption coefficient at any single point of reflexion on the surface; $(1 - \mu)$ is then the reflexion coefficient.

---

* The term "anti-directional property" is used to mean that one can deduce which way a particle is moving, without specifying the energy of the particle or the angle of emission of the light. "Good ADP" means a *large* ratio of the light intensity in the direction of motion to that in the backward direction.

A_k area of the photocathode.

A_s total area of scattering material; in the case of a sphere

$$A_s = (4\pi R^2 - A_k) \approx 4\pi R^2.$$

ρ the ratio of the area receiving light to that scattering light. i.e. $\rho = (A_k/A_s)$.

η optical efficiency of the counter, i.e. the ratio of the light collected to that produced.

t_m the average time between successive reflexions.

τ the characteristic time of build-up of the light pulse, as detected by the phototube.

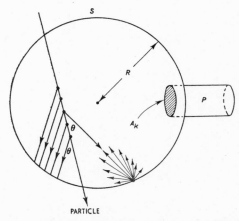

FIG. 7.4. The basic form of a non-focusing counter; a photomultiplier protrudes inside an integrating sphere filled with a refracting medium.

In order to obtain a relatively simple expression for η, the following assumptions are made:

1. Light absorption in the medium is neglected.
2. The photocathode behaves as a sink for photons impinging on it.
3. The coefficient of reflexion is close to unity, i.e. $(1 - \mu) \approx 1$, or $\mu \ll 1$.
4. $A_k \ll A_s$ so that $\rho \ll 1$.
5. At any diffuse reflection the cosine law is obeyed.*

* Although Mandò's equations were obtained assuming the cosine law, it is clear that almost any law of diffusion with a sufficiently broad distribution will yield very similar results.

The interpretation of (5) is that the probability dP, that a photon impinging on an area $d\sigma$ shall be scattered so as to strike a second surface element $d\sigma'$ distant r from $d\sigma$, is given by:

$$dP = \left(\frac{\cos \epsilon \cos i}{\pi r^2}\right) . d\sigma' \qquad (7.20)$$

where ϵ and i are the angles between the perpendiculars to $d\sigma$ and $d\sigma'$, and the line joining them.

Light Efficiency

With the above assumptions, it is easily shown that after an infinite number of reflexions:

$$\eta_\infty = \left(\frac{\rho}{\rho + \mu}\right) \qquad (7.21)$$

As $\mu \to 0$, so $\eta_\infty \to 1$, and the higher the reflectivity of the walls, the closer does the response approach complete uniformity.

Speed of Response

If (c/n) is the velocity of light in the medium, it can be shown for a sphere, that:

$$t_m = \frac{4Rn}{3c} . \qquad (7.22)$$

If now Q is the quantity of light present at a time t, $dQ = -(\mu + \rho) . Q . dt/t_m$ from which, given

$$\tau = t_m/(\mu + \rho) \qquad (7.23)$$

we get $Q = Q_0 e^{-t/\tau}$ where Q_0 is the total light initially produced. The efficiency at a time t is then:

$$\eta(t) = \left(\frac{\rho}{\mu + \rho}\right) (1 - e^{-t/\tau}). \qquad (7.24)$$

Naturally, for $t \gg \tau$, (7.24) tends to (7.21) while, for $t \ll \tau$

$$\eta(t) \approx \rho(t/t_m). \qquad (7.25)$$

The spherical counter has distinct disadvantages in many experiments, and it is preferable to consider such shapes as a cube or squat cylinder; the latter form is particularly useful in cosmic-ray work when particles, arriving predominantly in a vertical direction, are to be counted over a large area, each traversing approximately the same depth in the medium. Equations (7.21) and (7.24), though strictly only valid for a sphere, are quite adequate for counters of other shapes provided their dimensions do not differ widely from one another. It is essential to *avoid elongated forms* if uniformity is required.

The non-uniformity that arises when elongated forms are used, has been carefully studied by Mandò, who found for instance that light generated at a particular point by a particle passing across the axis of a cylinder of radius R was mostly confined within a distance $\sim 3R$ along the counter each side of the point in question.

To illustrate the use of the above relations, let us consider a typical large counter designed for cosmic-ray work. Suppose it has the form of a pill box, of area 2000 cm^2 and depth 30 cm, and that it is filled with pure water and viewed by a single EMI 5 in. photomultiplier; we will further assume a realistic reflectivity of 85% for a suitable white paint, take a photocathode quantum efficiency of 10% and a Čerenkov production yield of 200 photons/cm for a relativistic particle. With this data, we find $A_k = 125$ cm^2, $A_s = 8575$ cm^2 and deduce $\rho = 1\cdot45 \times 10^{-2}$. $(1 - \mu) = 0\cdot85$ so that $\mu = 0\cdot15$. From (7.21) it is then found that $\eta = 0\cdot088$. Each fast particle will generate 6000 photons, so that with this value of η, the light collected will be ~ 530 photons. The primary photoelectron yield will be ~ 53, which will therefore lead to a spread in pulse height $\sim \pm 14\%$ of the mean height.

The speed of response of the counter is obtained as follows: With a width-to-height ratio of 50/30, the form of this counter is fairly symmetrical and we may consider it equivalent to a sphere of diameter 40 cm. R is then 20 cm, and (c/n) in water $= 2\cdot10^{10}$ cm/sec, so that t_m (from 7·22) $= 1\cdot16 \times 10^{-9}$ sec. With the above values for μ and ρ, from (7.23), $\tau = 7\cdot1 \times 10^{-9}$ or $\sim 10^{-8}$ sec. A differentiating time constant in the amplifier of $\sim 10^{-7}$ sec would therefore result in a negligible reduction in the height of the pulses.

Light Absorption in the Medium

An extension of Mandò's theory, important in some of the largest diffusing counters coming into use in cosmic-ray work, has been made by Porter (unpublished) who takes account of light absorption in the medium. If $\bar{x}$ is the average distance between successive reflexions (equivalent to t_m in (7.22) for the time), and λ is the mean free path for absorption of photons in the medium, he shows that the efficiency of the counter is then

$$\eta_\infty = \frac{\rho}{\rho + \mu + \rho\mu + [\exp(\bar{x}/\lambda) - 1]} . \tag{7.26}$$

When $\lambda \gg \bar{x}$, and (as before) μ and ρ are each $\ll 1$, (7.26) tends to the simpler form, (7.21). Equation (7.26) only applies when λ refers to pure absorption. The effects of scattering of light in the medium (i.e. "elastic" scattering of photons without change of wavelength) may be taken into account by estimating the effective increase in the average distance between successive reflexions at the boundary of the sphere. That is, we use equations (7.22) to (7.25) but introduce a correction to t_m.

The Measurement of Reflectivities

In designing large non-focusing counters of the diffusion type, it is often necessary to know the reflectivity $(1 - \mu)$ of the walls of the vessel, in order to use equation (7.21) for estimating the pulse size and hence the resolution of the counter.

There are a number of ways of doing this, which include optical methods using an Ulbricht sphere or a spectrophotometer. Probably the most suitable method for our purpose, and one which has the merits of simplicity, and of providing an overall figure for the reflectivity which *includes* the effects of light absorption in the medium, is that described by Clark *et al.* (1957) who used it during the development of large plastic scintillators for cosmic-ray work.

They measure the average pulse height h from cosmic-ray particles traversing the detector, as a function of the fraction F of the total reflector area covered with black velvet. The velvet was laid fairly uniformly, in strips over the reflector, so that the fraction of surface covered was nearly independent of the distance from the photo-multiplier. Assuming $h \propto \eta$ and re-writing (7.21) in the form $(1/h) = \frac{1}{\rho}\{\rho + 1 - (1 - \mu)\}$, the effect of introducing the velvet strips is to replace $(1 - \mu)$ by $(1 - \mu) \times (1 - F)$. Thus, for μ and F both $\ll 1$, one obtains a linear plot between $1/h$ and F. When this is carried out, the slope and intercept of the plot leads to a direct determination of the product of $(1 - \mu)$, and a factor p, which represents absorption in the medium, and is the average probability that a photon will not be absorbed between successive reflexions.

References to information on various suitable reflecting materials for diffusion counters will be found in Table 6L in section 6.7.

Other advantages of Clark's method is that the determination of $(1 - \mu)$ is carried out with a Čerenkov spectrum and in the geometry of the counter itself.

7.5 Light guides

As in scintillation counting, it is often necessary or desirable that the photomultiplier be some distance away from the radiator, in which case some form of light guide or optical "pipe" is required. The use of light guides for Čerenkov counters requires rather more care than for scintillation counters; in the first place the available light is less, so that it is important that the transfer efficiency of the guide shall be as

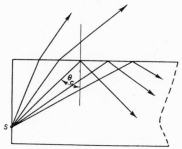

FIG. 7.5. To illustrate the light-gathering efficiency at the entrance of a light guide.

high as possible, and secondly, the directional features of the Čerenkov radiation (if these are preserved, as in the focusing counter) will set certain conditions on the reflexions within the guide. A third point to consider is that some substances such as polystyrene commonly used for light guides are themselves very weak scintillators; it is therefore sometimes preferable to use quartz or Perspex which are much better media in this respect.

The properties and limitations of light guides are often misunderstood and it is hoped the following notes may clarify some of the points. The use of guides in focusing counters have already been covered in section 7.2.

The first problem is to determine what fraction of light from an isotropic source S falls outside the critical angle θ_c at its *first* reflexion in the guide; see Fig. 7.5 for the case of a cylindrical guide having a flat end. If we assume optical contact between the source and the guide (to avoid corrections introduced by refraction), the fraction f of radiation emitted isotropically, and making an angle less than $\left(\dfrac{\pi}{2} - \theta_c\right)$ with respect to the axis of the guide, is:

$$f = \frac{1}{4\pi} \int_0^{\theta_c} 2\pi \sin \theta \, d\theta = \tfrac{1}{2}(1 - \cos \theta_c) \tag{7.27}$$

For instance, in Perspex, for which $n = 1 \cdot 5$ and $\theta_c = \sin^{-1}(\tfrac{1}{n}) = 42 \cdot 2°$, $f = 0 \cdot 129$, i.e. only 13%. Thus, for very short guides, it is often better to use diffusely reflecting walls coated with say MgO, TiO_2 or etched aluminium.

Equation (7.27) only determines the fraction of the light which is led satisfactorily into the guide. The main interest is to find what proportion of this fraction f may be collected at the far end, taking into account that the receiver placed there may have a different shape or area from that of the input of the guide. Basing his considerations on thermodynamical arguments, Garwin (1952) has given a very lucid account of the properties, designs and limitations of light guides. The fundamental point is that it is always possible to conduct all the light along a guide of any cross-sectional shape into another guide of any other shape, *so long as the cross-sectional areas of the two light pipes are the same.* The only requirement is that the transition shall be adiabatic, i.e. the angles of taper shall be small enough so that sampling of all walls is achieved. Thus it is possible to conduct all the light from say a square hole in the side of a non-focusing diffuse-reflecting Čerenkov counter, to the circular cathode of a photomultiplier, *if* the area of this hole is the same as that of the cathode. But it is *not* possible to lead the light from say a large aperture in an integrating sphere to the smaller area of a multiplier cathode, without loss of efficiency.

Garwin shows that if a light ray makes an angle θ with respect to the longitudinal axis of a light guide, at a point where its cross-sectional area is A, then its inclination further on, at a point distant z from the first point, is given by $A(z) . \sin^2\theta(z) = \text{const}$. Thus a ray with inclination θ_0 when $A = A_0$ will have an inclination $\theta_1 = \sin^{-1}(A_0 \sin^2\theta_0/A_1)^{\frac{1}{2}}$ at A_1 if the taper is slow enough that full sampling of the walls is achieved. Therefore a pipe of area constant with z will maintain θ

constant and will neither reject light falling into it nor lose light through imperfect total internal reflexion, counting of course only that light originally inside the critical angle. Conversely, if we couple a source, for instance an aperture in an integrating sphere, of area A_0, to a photocathode of smaller area A_1, then only a fraction (A_1/A_0) of the light can be received by the phototube, even of that which initially falls within the critical angle.

7.6 Wavelength shifters

Since much of the energy of Čerenkov radiation occurs in the ultraviolet, where most photomultipliers are insensitive, it would appear feasible to use fluorescing materials to convert some of this energy into radiation in the visible region. The idea is particularly attractive in liquid counters where weak aqueous solutions of well-known fluorescing substances may be used.

Counters in which the light is intensified in this way will of course lose most of their directional characteristics; this is usually of no consequence since these "boosters" are mainly intended for non-focusing counters where deliberate efforts are made to bring about isotropy.

Further, if, in addition to fluorescing, the medium at the same time behaves as a scintillator, the threshold feature of the Čerenkov detector will also be lost.

Heiberg and Marshall (1956) carried out tests with solutions of a number of fluorescing substances in water, and found two compounds which gave a reasonable gain of overall light yield. With a simple water-detector operating on cosmic-ray μ-mesons, they found a 30% increase in pulse height (relative to water) with a 10 mg/l solution of 2-amino-6, 8-naphthalenedisulphonic acid, disodium salt. The second solution was also of strength 10 mg/l and contained 2-naphthol-3, 6-disulphonic acid, disodium salt; this gave a light increase of 20% relative to water. (The Du Pont classifications of these two materials are MDD-3169 and MD-3168 respectively.)

Porter (1957) has recently carried out similar tests, using three water-soluble materials, fluorescein, β-methyl umbelliferone (see de Ment 1942) and the commercial product Uvitex. No increase in light intensity was observed with the fluorescein or Uvitex, but a slightly alkaline solution of the β-methyl umbelliferone gave an increase of as much as 100%. The effect was almost independent of the concentration between 0·005 g/l and 0·1 g/l, but above this level the intensity decreased again.

Both Heiberg and Marshall, and Porter, have evidence that there is negligible direct scintillation effect with their solutions. These figures quoted are likely to depend markedly on the geometry of the system used in the tests. Since the improvement obtained with these "boosters" does not exceed a factor of two, it would seem more profitable to seek improvement in the performance of counters in other directions, such as increased photocathode efficiencies and the use of phototubes of larger cathode area, etc.

The wavelength-shifter POPOP, which has been used extensively in large scintillators, has also been adapted to a total absorption Čerenkov counter by Jones et al. (1957, see section 8.4) which employs CCl_4 as the dielectric medium. POPOP, or diphenylhexatriene, is available from the Pilot Chemical Co., Waltham, Massachusetts, U.S.A., and from the Arapaho Chemical Co., Denver, Colorado, U.S.A. The addition of POPOP to the CCl_4 was found by Jones et al. to increase the pulse height from their instrument by a factor two, and the resolution by $\sim 30\%$. Using 6 MeV protons (Čerenkov threshold for protons in CCl_4 is 319 MeV) they detected no measurable scintillation effects from the counter.

Other similar materials which have been tried by Clark et al. (1957), among others, are BBO (2,5-diphenylyloxazole) and TPBD (tetraphenylbutadiene). As far as the author is aware, these two wavelength shifters have so far only been used in scintillators.

CHAPTER 8

DESIGNS OF SOME PRACTICAL COUNTERS

DESCRIPTIONS will now be presented of a number of Čerenkov counters that have been used in various problems in nuclear and cosmic-ray physics. The applications are so numerous that a reference to each is impossible. The aim here has therefore been to describe a few instruments in detail, a representative selection in each group.

8.1 Accurate determination of particle velocities

Mather (1951) developed a photographic instrument of great precision, simplicity and elegance, which was used for the direct determination of the energy of protons in the external beam of the 184 in.

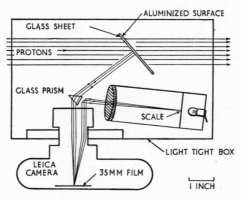

FIG. 8.1. A precision photographic instrument developed by Mather (1951) for accurate measurements of proton velocities.

synchrocyclotron at Berkeley, California. In this instrument, Fig. 8.1, the protons pass through a thin sheet of dense flint glass ($n = 1\cdot88$) of thickness 0·67 mm in which the Čerenkov radiation is generated. The sheet is ground optically flat on both sides and its rear surface is aluminized. It is tilted with respect to the axis of the proton beam, so that a portion of the light-cone striking the reflecting surface would emerge normal to the front surface, thus eliminating first order refraction effects. Reflecting the light in this way also enables the camera, used to record the image, to be placed close to the glass plate while keeping it well out of the proton beam.

To overcome dispersion, Mather ingeniously introduced a small prism whose angle α is chosen so that its dispersion cancels the first-order dispersion of the Čerenkov radiation. If ψ is the ray direction as

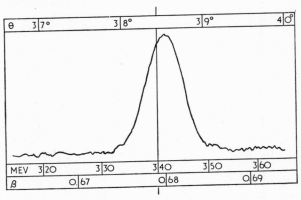

FIG. 8.2. Microphotometer trace of an image obtained with the instrument shown in Fig. 8.1.

seen by the camera, Mather obtains the following conditions for achromatization of the system and the desired prism angle:

$$\frac{d\psi}{d\lambda} = \frac{d\psi}{dn} \cdot \frac{dn}{d\lambda} = \left[\frac{1}{\sqrt{(n^2\beta^2 - 1)}} - \frac{2 \sin \frac{1}{2}\alpha}{(1 - n^2\sin^2\frac{1}{2}\alpha)} \right] \cdot \frac{dn}{d\lambda} = 0 \quad (8.1)$$

where

$$\sin \tfrac{1}{2}\alpha = 1/[n_o^2 + 4(n_o^2\beta^2 - 1)]^{\frac{1}{2}} \quad (8.2)$$

and n_0 is the refractive index corresponding to the "effective" wavelength of the overall system.

Built into the optical system is an illuminated scale and collimator, for convenience of accurate measurements of the position of the Čerenkov images. Figure 8.2 shows a microphotometric trace of an image obtained with this apparatus, together with the corresponding scales of θ, β and the proton kinetic energy E; it will be seen that the overall resolution is $\sim 1\%$; the estimated contributions to this error are presented in Table 8A.

TABLE 8A

		$\Delta\beta$	ΔE(MeV)
Error in θ	$\pm$ 2·5′	$\pm$ 0·00040	$\pm$ 0·6
Error in n	$\pm$ 0·0003	$\pm$ 0·00012	$\pm$ 0·2
Error in reading	$\pm$ 1·6′ in θ	$\pm$ 0·00025	$\pm$ 0·4
Total		$\pm$ 0·0005	$\pm$ 0·8

The values of E are obtained from the measured values of n and θ, from the relations $\cos\theta = 1/\beta n$ and $E = Mc^2 [(1 - \beta^2)^{-\frac{1}{2}} - 1]$, where M is the rest-mass of the proton, so that:

$$E = Mc^2 \left[\frac{n \cos\theta}{(n^2 \cos^2\theta - 1)^{\frac{1}{2}}} - 1 \right]. \qquad (8.3)$$

Since the energy resolution of this instrument of Mather's has never been surpassed, it is interesting to speculate on its ultimate possibilities. Mather himself discusses the various sources of error and how they could be reduced. There are six effects which cause spread in the intensity distribution of the Čerenkov rays in the achromatic system just described. These are:

(i) Coulomb scattering of the protons.

(ii) Slowing down of the protons.

(iii) Diffraction effects due to finite path-length.

(iv) Second-order chromatic effects.

(v) Intrinsic angular divergence of proton beam.

(vi) Velocity spread among the protons.

The shapes of the distributions, and the relative magnitudes of each of these contributions calculated for this instrument, are shown in Fig. 8.3, in which the abscissae are in minutes of arc in θ. For the combined intensity pattern, the standard deviation $\Delta\theta_{tot} \approx \pm$ 14 min of arc, which agrees quite closely with that obtained from the microphotometer tracing.

Mather then discusses the methods of choosing parameters, such as the refractive index and thickness of converter, in order to get the maximum resolution. The results of this analysis are summarized in the curves shown in Fig. 8.4 in which he plots ΔE(MeV) versus the thickness l of the conversion plate, or rather, the ratio $(l/\beta n)$ expressed in mm. Note that these curves *include* the effects of beam divergence and energy spread, which are not, as we have seen, due to the instrument

N

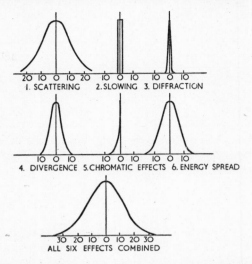

FIG. 8.3. The separate contributions to the overall resolution of Mather's instrument. (Mather, 1951.)

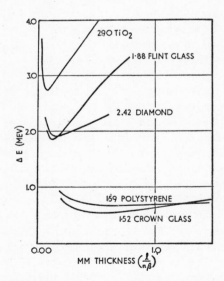

FIG. 8.4. Calculated energy resolution *vs.* thickness of material, for an instrument of the type described by Mather (1951). The refractive indices of the materials are indicated on the curves.

itself. Nevertheless, with a beam free from divergence, using a polystyrene converter ($n = 1.59$), an energy resolution of ~ 0.6 MeV should be attainable, or $\sim 0.2\%$ at 340 MeV.

A severe limitation to the usefulness of this instrument is of course its low sensitivity. An exposure time of several minutes was required to produce a satisfactory image using Ansco Triple S film, when the proton current density was 2×10^{-11} A/cm² and the effective area of the converter was 1 cm².

Of the various focusing systems discussed in Chapter 7, for use with photomultipliers, those described by Marshall (1952, 1954) have proved to be the most suitable. In one model of the large family of this type, Fig. 8.5, the particles are collimated and pass through a large hemi-

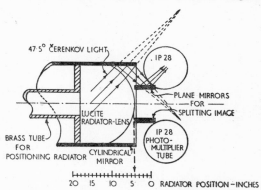

FIG. 8.5. One of Marshall's focusing detectors, using two phototubes connected in coincidence. (Marshall, 1952.)

spherical lens which serves the dual function of radiator and focusing lens. A cylindrical reflector and two small plane mirrors splits the focused image and guides the light to two RCA phototubes Type 1P28. These are run in coincidence, to reduce background effects which would otherwise be serious with the tubes situated so near the beam of particles; in this way it is possible to operate at low levels of bias, thus increasing the overall counting efficiency. Moving the position of the radiator-lens inside the cylindrical mirror varies the range of angles θ at which the emitted light can arrive in focus on the cathodes of the tubes. Marshall used this instrument to count π-mesons from the Chicago synchrocyclotron. The resolution obtained with this arrangement is illustrated in Fig. 8.6 which shows how the coincidence counting rate varied with the position of the radiator. The taller curve refers to 145 MeV π-mesons observed directly, and the lower curve to the same beam after it had passed through 7·6 cm graphite (12 g/cm²), thereby reducing the energy to 121 MeV. The measured angles, 39·9° and 38·0° compared favourably with those calculated, 40·4° and 38·1° respectively. From the spacing of the two peaks it is seen that the resolution in this experiment (full width at half-height) was $\sim$ 19 MeV or $\sim$ 13% at 145 MeV. This resolution was obtained under conditions of relatively high bias on the coincidence circuit. Higher intrinsic efficiencies were obtained at lower bias but at the expense of resolution.

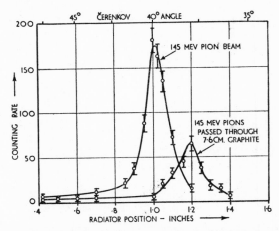

FIG. 8.6. Curves to illustrate the resolution obtained with the instrument shown in Fig. 8.5, in a π-meson beam.

A very similar instrument has since been built by Mather and Martinelli (1953), the only essential difference from Marshall's being the use of three phototubes in coincidence instead of two, to enhance the overall signal to noise ratio. The light beam was reflected off the three sides of a prism placed inside the cylindrical mirror, see section 8.7.

Over limited energy regions, Čerenkov counters of this type are very satisfactory, compact and fairly easy to construct.

A different and very simple type of focused counter has been used by Sutton et al. (1955), in proton–proton scattering experiments at 437 MeV, carried out on the Carnegie synchrocyclotron, Pittsburg. In this instrument, Fig. 8.7, the Čerenkov radiation is produced in a half-inch thick glass plate, and a small portion of the radiation cone, emerging normal to the surface of the plate, is focused by a lens on to the cathode of an RCA 1P21 phototube placed behind a slit. The angle θ is varied by rotating the whole optical system about an axis through the plate. The radiator turns with the rest of the system so that there are no refraction corrections as the light leaves the glass. This instrument, which was only used for measurements of relative energies, had a resolution of ~ 36 MeV (full width at half-height), as deduced from the response curve, Fig. 8.8; this is equivalent to a resolving power of $\sim 8\%$ at 435 MeV. This type of instrument has distinct potentialities

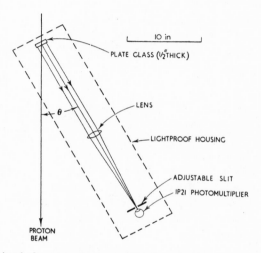

FIG. 8.7. The simple focusing counter used by Sutton et al. (1955) in proton–proton scattering experiments.

in view of its simplicity and the minimum interference with the particle beam. It could be used for absolute measurements, provided it were fitted with a beam collimator or simple "telescope" (e.g. two small scintillators) to define the axis of the particles.

Another type of counter in this category is a development of the very first focusing instrument, proposed by Getting and discussed in Chapter 7.1. A counter of this type, described by Jelley (1956), has been used by Huq (1956) to measure the energy of the scattered proton beam from the synchrotron at Birmingham. In most respects this type of counter is primitive compared with the other focusing instruments. In

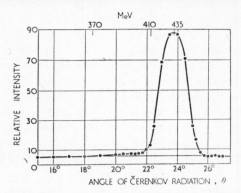

FIG. 8.8. The resolution obtained with the instrument shown in Fig. 8.7.

very limited applications however it has certain merits, among which are its simplicity and large light output, sufficient in the proton beam at Birmingham to operate a vacuum photocell coupled to a simple amplifier.

8.2 Threshold discriminators

Duerden and Hyams (1952) were the first to use a Čerenkov detector, in a cosmic-ray experiment, as a threshold discriminator. It happened, in this first application, that the instrument was used in an anti-coincidence arrangement, see section 6.1, to detect particles of energy *below* the threshold. With a simple water detector of the non-focusing type, they were able to select and study the very low flux of cosmic-ray protons at sea-level against the much higher background of μ-mesons and electrons.

If a particle has a velocity βc and a rest mass M its residual range R can be shown to be:

$$R = \frac{Mc^2}{A} [1 - (1 - \beta^2)^{\frac{1}{2}}]^2 \cdot (1 - \beta^2)^{-\frac{1}{2}} \quad \text{g/cm}^2 \qquad (8.4a)$$

where $A = 1\cdot2$ and Mc^2 is expressed in MeV, and, using the approximate range-energy relation given by Janossy (1948, p. 127):

$$R = \frac{W_k^2}{A(W_k + Mc^2)} \quad \text{g/cm}^2 \qquad (8.4b)$$

Then, if βc is less than or equal to the Čerenkov critical velocity for water, $\beta_0 c$, where $1/\beta_0 = n = 1\cdot33$, it follows that $Mc^2 \geqslant 6\cdot85\ R$ MeV.

Thus, if a charged particle has a range 15 g/cm² and at the same time is observed to give no Čerenkov signal, it must have a rest energy > 100 MeV, and therefore be heavier than a μ-meson.

Curves calculated for the total intensity of the Čerenkov radiation for protons and μ-mesons in water are shown in Fig. 8.9, in which the energies of the particles have been converted to ranges expressed in g/cm². In both cases there are small contributions from knock-on electrons, which are also shown.

The essential features of their detector are shown in Fig. 8.10. The outer metal box H_2 houses the photomultiplier (EMI type VX 5045).

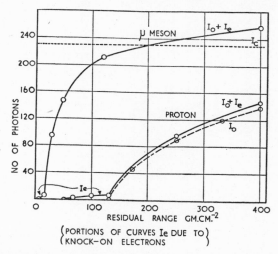

FIG. 8.9. Theoretical curves of photon intensity v. range, for heavy particles in water. (Duerden and Hyams, 1952.)

An inner Perspex box H_1, which has a double wall on all sides, the spacing packed with magnesium carbonate, is filled with distilled water. A very high efficiency was obtained for counting relativistic particles incident on a 400 cm² surface over a cone of half-angle 45° (selected by the Geiger telescope). From the pulse-height distribution for single μ-mesons, used to test the counter, they found that the average output pulse corresponded to a release at the photocathode of ~ 30 electrons, representing an optical efficiency for light collection $\sim 15\%$. If we denote the Geiger trays by A and B, one above and one below the water detector W, then "heavy particles" were selected by registering coincidences of the type $(A + B - W)$; i.e. a Geiger telescope coincidence *not* accompanied by a pulse from the Čerenkov detector. The selection of particles by range was carried out by interposing a 20 cm thick lead plate between B and a further tray C, below the rest of the apparatus. From the observed ratio of counting rates $(A + B - W)/(A + B) = (2 \cdot 15 \pm 0 \cdot 15)/1000$, and, after introducing the range selector C, $(A + B - W + C)/(A + B + C) = (0 \cdot 32 \pm 0 \cdot 1)/1000$, we see that 80% of the "heavy particle" counts are due to unaccompanied protons. The momentum range of the protons selected by this anti-coincidence method was $700 - 1100$ MeV/c; the lower limit is set by the range selector and the upper limit by the Čerenkov threshold in water. This selector counts sea-level protons at a rate of 3·5 protons/

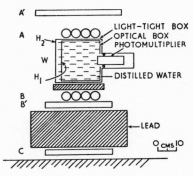

FIG. 8.10. The water detector used by Duerden and Hyams (1952) as a threshold discriminator for cosmic-ray protons at sea-level.

hour, with a discrimination far exceeding that obtained by other methods with relatively simple apparatus.

Counters of this general type have been used by others as threshold detectors, particularly in the cosmic-ray field, where the large counter area and solid angle of acceptance are invaluable in studies of rare events. Barker *et al.* (1955a), for example, have used the same technique in conjunction with a cloud chamber for the efficient detection of K-particles. The same group (Barker *et al.*, 1955b) has used these detectors with fast circuits, for measurements of the life-times of these particles.

Similar threshold counters have also been used by Ogilvie (1955) for further work on cosmic-ray protons, both at sea-level and in aircraft up to 25,000 ft., and by Baccalin *et al.* (1955) at sea level.

8.3 Velocity selectors

Čerenkov counters played an important rôle in the recent discovery of the anti–proton (Chamberlain *et al.*, 1955), where they were used to select particles in a narrow range of velocities. In this experiment the information obtained from one of two Čerenkov units was used to supplement cruder measurements of velocity made by a time-of-flight technique. The essential features of this velocity selector, described elsewhere by Chamberlain and Wiegand (1956), and illustrated in Fig. 8.11(a), were developed from one of the many types discussed by Marshall (1952).

Light generated in a solid cylindrical radiator by particles travelling through it along paths parallel to its axis, emerges from the flat end-

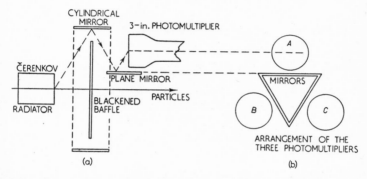

FIG. 8.11. The simple focusing counter used by Chamberlain and Wiegand (1956) for studying anti-protons.

face where of course it suffers refraction. The light then spreads out over the surface of a wide-angled cone, and, after reflexion from a cylindrical mirror, is returned and concentrated in a small area on the axis. If the velocity is either appreciably greater or appreciably less than the velocity for which the counter has been adjusted, the light is intercepted by the blackened baffle. In practice it is unsuitable to place the photomultiplier in the particle beam; in this instrument therefore, the light is split by three plane mirrors and directed on to the cathodes of three separate multipliers, see Fig. 8.11(b). With the instrument adjusted correctly, the image diameter is the same as that of the radiator, whose dimensions are chosen to match the cathode diameter of a 3 in. Du Mont photomultiplier. In the completed instrument (built in a large light-tight cylindrical can), the two ends, on which the radiator and phototube assemblies were mounted, could be moved in and out to select different angles of light emission.

Since the number of initial photoelectrons in each photomultiplier is quite small (estimated between 2 and 4) the bias on the coincidence circuit was adjusted so that a count would be registered when any two of the three phototubes produced pulses in coincidence. With this arrangement, the efficiency of the counter for particles of just the right velocity was measured to be 97%. Under the same conditions the efficiency would drop to 75% if triple coincidences had been demanded.

The resolution is such that the counting rate drops to 3% when the velocity is changed by $0 \cdot 03c$. from that for which the counter is adjusted. This background contribution of 3% remains over a wide range of velocities, and is assumed to be due to nuclear interactions in the radiator. In the conditions existing in the first experiments with anti–protons, the counter operated so that the velocity-gate was set in the range $0 \cdot 75 < \beta < 0 \cdot 78$.

Chamberlain points out that this counter is limited to use with heavy particles. Lighter particles such as π-mesons, if moving appreciably slower than the velocity of light, are near the end of their range so that their velocity is then changing rapidly. They will then emit insufficient light before coming to rest and will have a different velocity in different parts of the radiator.

In a very elaborate counter application, in which no less than six Čerenkov detectors and three scintillators are used, to measure the lifetime of K^+ mesons, Fitch and Motley (1956) refer to a velocity selector of a rather different type. The gate is defined, on the lower energy side, by the threshold and, at higher energies, by the trapping of the light inside the radiator through total internal reflexion. The velocity band selected by this device is however much wider than that in Chamberlain's instrument, Fitch quoting a range $0 \cdot 62 < \beta < 0 \cdot 78$. Moreover, it is unlikely that the velocity range can be adjusted in this counter.

8.4 "Deep" counters (Total absorption spectrometers)

The first satisfactory total absorption Čerenkov counter was constructed by Jester (1955) who used a large cylinder of lead glass 14 in. long and 12·25 in. diameter. This cylinder was built up from two shorter pieces each 7 in. long, optically sealed to one another by Dow Corning 200 silicone compound, and its curved surface was wrapped in aluminium foil. Four Dumont type 6364 photomultipliers (cathode diameter $5\frac{1}{4}$ in.) were pressed against one end of the cylinder, using the same sealing compound, and their outputs coupled together and fed to a pulse-height analyser. The composition and characteristics of the glass are listed in Table 6H. With a radiation length of 2·81 cm, and a value of 13 MeV for the critical energy, this counter can be shown to contain 85% of the energy of an incident 430 MeV electron. The pulse-height distributions were relatively wide, $\sim 60\%$ (full width at half-height) at a mean electron energy of 167 MeV. The linear response of this counter is shown in Fig. 8.12(b).

A full description of an improved version of this counter, its performance with respect to efficiency and resolution, and calibration procedures, has recently been given by Brabant et al. (1957). This instrument, the main features of which are shown in Fig. 8.12 (a), was modified by the addition of a coincidence-anticoincidence telescope in front of the lead glass radiator; in this way it was possible to distinguish clearly between γ-rays and fast charged particles. The addition of the γ-ray telescope also enhanced the resolution of the counter, by ensuring that all cascade showers started at approximately the same place in the radiator, and near the axis of the system. When calibrated with fast electrons of energy ~ 1 GeV, the width of the pulse-height distribution was found to be 50% (full width at half-height), so that energies differing by 25% could be resolved.

This large and very satisfactory instrument, see Plate II, has been used in a number of experiments on the Bevatron at the University of California Radiation Laboratory; it has been applied by Brabant et al. (1956 (a) and (b)) to study decay products from interactions caused by the stopping of anti-protons within the glass radiator, in particular γ-rays from π^0-mesons, and direct γ-radiation from anti-proton annihilation. It is also being used by Brabant et al. (1956c) for measurements of electron-pair production cross-sections at energies of several GeV.

Similar types of instrument have been described by Cassels (1956), Hofstadter (1956) and Filosofo and Yamagata (1956), among others. Cassels used a lead glass counter to measure the relative intensities of the 69 and 129 MeV γ-ray peaks resulting from the absorption of stopped π^--mesons in liquid hydrogen, associated with the reactions

$$\pi^- + p \to \pi^0 + n \to 2\gamma + n$$

and
$$\pi^- + p \to \gamma + n$$

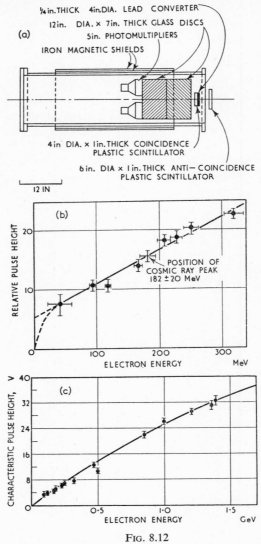

FIG. 8.12

(a) The essential features of the lead-glass total absorption spectrometer first made by Jester (1955) and later developed by Brabant (1957). See also Plate II.

(b) The calibration curve obtained by Jester for monoenergetic electrons with energies 42–300 MeV, and with cosmic-ray μ-mesons.

(c) Brabant's extension of the calibration up to electron energies of 1·5 GeV.

(Reproduced by kind permission of the Information Division of the Radiation Laboratory, the University of California, Berkeley, California.)

PLATE II. The large lead-glass total absorption spectrometer built by Brabant *et al.* (1957). The essential features of this instrument are shown in Fig. 8.12(a) and the applications are described briefly in the text. The instrument is here shown tilted up for calibration with cosmic-ray μ-mesons, which were selected by coincidence counters placed above and below the spectrometer; these counters and the associated electronic units are clearly visible.

(Facing page 194)

PLATE III. The lead-glass radiator used by Cassels (1956) in his total absorption spectrometer described in the text. The γ-rays enter the radiator through the area of small cross-section, while the base of the cone is optically sealed to the photocathode of the multiplier which is also visible. The taper helps to trap light by total internal reflexion, because of the divergence of the particles in the electron-photon cascade.

(*Facing page 195*)

which led to a new determination of the Panofsky ratio. The lead-glass block, multiplier, housing and magnetic screen used by Cassels in these experiments, are shown in Plate III.

The total absorption instrument described by Hofstadter is interesting; he uses a single thallous chloride crystal of $5\frac{1}{2}$ in. length and $5\frac{1}{2}$ in. diameter sealed to a single Schaetti $10\frac{1}{2}$ in. diameter phototube. The performance of this counter, for 200–300 MeV electrons, was such that the total width of the pulse-height distribution (at half max.), was $\sim 26\%$ at any energy in this range.

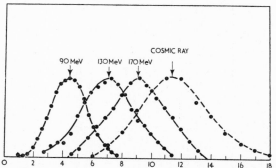

FIG. 8.13. Pulse height distributions obtained with monochromatic electrons in the "deep" counter described by Filosofo and Yamagata (1956).

Moffat and Stringfellow (1958) also describe a thallous chloride counter, which they have used in experiments on small-angle Delbrück scattering of X-rays at energies ~ 100 MeV, with the electron synchrotron at the Clarendon Laboratory, Oxford. (This effect is a form of small-angle elastic potential scattering arising from the creation of virtual electron–positron pairs followed by their annihilation.) Details of their thallous chloride crystal are given on page 153 and in Table 6I in Chapter 6.

The instrument discussed by Filosofo and Yamagata, was used by Auerback et al. (1956) for measurements of the Compton effect on protons. The radiator, a lead-glass cylinder of length 35 cm and diameter 30 cm (a lead screen restricting the effective aperture to 16·5 cm) was viewed by twelve 5819 RCA tubes optically sealed to the end-face. At energies ~ 100 MeV the efficiency was $\sim 100\%$, even for electrons entering parallel to but displaced from the axis by 8 cm. The pulse-height distributions for monochromatic electrons of several energies is shown in Fig. 8.13, while the distributions in Fig. 8.14 are those obtained with photons scattered from protons (Compton scattering), and γ-rays from π^0-meson decays. Resolutions obtained in the photon-scattering experiment were $\pm 25\%$ and $\pm 30\%$ at photon energies of 200 and 100 MeV respectively.

Another total absorption counter has been described by Jones *et al.* (1957), who used CCl_4 for the dielectric medium. Since the average atomic number of this liquid is so much lower than that for the lead

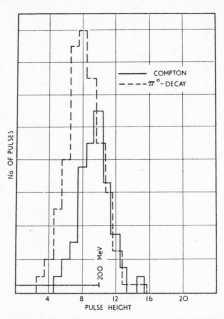

FIG. 8.14. The pulse-height distributions obtained by Auerback *et al.* (1956) with the counter shown in Fig. 8.13, in experiments on the Compton scattering of γ-rays from protons.

glass instruments, the energy range over which the response is linear, for a given volume, is correspondingly smaller. On the other hand, the lower cost of CCl_4 makes it possible to use very much larger volumes.

The CCl_4 is contained in a large glass cylinder of 36 in. length and 12 in. diameter, and is viewed by seven Du Mont photomultipliers, Type 6364, which are optically coupled by oblique Plexiglas light guides to a flat glass plate at one end of the cylinder; this ensures the maximum possible collection of light. Doubly-distilled commercial CCl_4 was used at first (which, relative to distilled water, had 100% light transmission down to a wavelength of 3500 Å) but this was found to corrode the aluminized walls of the cylinder; in the final model Mallinckrodt sulphur-free CCl_4 was used instead. The wavelength shifter POPOP was added to enhance the light output, see section 7.6.

The CCl_4, of specific gravity 1·6, refractive index 1·46, and an average atomic number $\bar{Z} \sim 16$, has a critical energy ~ 50 MeV for photon-electron cascades, corresponding to a value of 12·6 cm for one radiation length X_0. The size of this CCl_4 radiator is such that, on average, $\sim 90\%$ of the energy of a primary 300 MeV x-ray can be contained within the liquid.

This instrument has been used as a high efficiency detector for x-rays from electron accelerators in the energy range 50–300 MeV, and has found a particular application to studies of the scattering of x-rays by protons.

The response is accurately linear over the range 47–200 MeV, and the linearity is preserved when the angle between the optic axis and the incoming beam of radiation are out of alignment by as much as 9·5°.

Using monoenergetic electrons for calibration, the ratio $(\Delta h/h)$ of this counter was found to vary with the kinetic energy E, as shown in Table 8B; h is the mean pulse-height, and Δh the full width at half-height of the pulse-height distributions so obtained. The resolutions are however considerably better than the figures for $(\Delta h/h)$.

TABLE 8B

E(MeV)	$(\Delta h/h)$ %
47	44
97	33
147	26
217	22

The difficulties involved in applying the total absorption technique to cosmic-ray problems are two-fold. In the first place the photons and electrons have very high energies, so that the depth of the counter has to be considerably greater than that of the instruments already described. And secondly, it is necessary that the counter should have a large effective area and that its response should be reasonably uniform over this area. In spite of these difficulties, the total-absorption counter has recently been applied to studies of extensive cosmic-ray air showers (see Appendix III), where it is being used to obtain information on the *energy density* of the photon-electron component of the showers. This is a departure from the more conventional techniques which aim at measuring the *number* of particles in various regions of the shower.

Porter and Sherwood (1956) have described a very large counter consisting of a rectangular tank 150 cm long, 113 cm wide and 90 cm deep. It has a sensitive area of 17,000 cm², is filled with 1400 l. of commercial kerosene, and is lined with a white diffuse reflector. This consists of a close-fitting bag of polyvinyl chloride loaded with TiO_2 and having a reflexion coefficient of 85% (4000–6000 Å). A single EMI phototube of area 100 cm², situated in the roof of the tank, projects down below the surface of the liquid.

The counter was tested and calibrated on single vertical μ-mesons selected by a counter telescope. Approximately 3 photoelectrons are produced at the cathode of the multiplier by a single fast μ-meson, and the response varies by $\sim 30\%$ over the main sensitive area of the tank. Using equations (7.21) and (7.26) for Porter's counter, we find $\rho = 1\cdot2 \times 10^{-3}$, $\mu = 0\cdot15$, $\eta_\infty = 0\cdot008$, and the average light absorption in the kerosene is $\sim 50\%$. Even a counter of this size is barely adequate, for its depth is only about two radiation lengths. In kerosene the critical energy is 115 MeV, while ~ 200 MeV is about the highest energy that will be completely absorbed in the counter.

Two types of deep counter have also been used by Matano *et al.* (1957), at the University of Tokyo, for studying the energy density in cosmic-ray showers. The first instrument is a large liquid cylindrical detector of depth 80 cm (~ 6 or 7 radiation lengths) and cross-sectional area 2500 cm². The medium, which consists of a 30–35% solution of $Pb(NO_3)_2$ in water, is viewed by a single Du Mont 5 in. phototube type 6364 mounted at the top looking downwards into the container which was painted white inside. Their second instrument consists of a block of lead glass (made by the Nippon Kogaku K.K.) of area 2000 cm² and thickness 30 cm (12 radiation lengths) which also uses a similar 5in. phototube.

A more ambitious design has been proposed by Chudakov (unpublished, 1956) who intends to use a tank (in the form of a truncated cone with the wide base at the bottom) 5 m. high, filled with 60,000 l. of demineralized water. To obtain uniformity and increase the signal to noise ratio, it is planned to couple 12 small photomultipliers together, mounting these on the surface of the cone about one-third of the way up.

8.5 "Thin" counters (Instruments for charge selection)

Counters in this category have been described by Linsley and Horwitz (1955), who used them to identify cosmic rays as to charge and, in particular, to measure the flux of α-particles in the primary

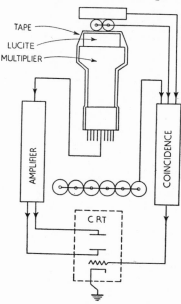

FIG. 8.15. The arrangement of a "thin" Čerenkov counter, and a Geiger counter telescope, used by Linsley and Horwitz (1955) in studies of the flux of cosmic-ray α-particles at the top of the atmosphere.

radiation (Linsley, 1954 and 1955; Horwitz, 1955). Their preliminary experiments were carried out with the apparatus shown in Fig. 8.15. Cosmic-rays at sea-level, selected by a Geiger counter telescope, passed through a Lucite radiator of thickness 2·5 cm (3 g/cm²) which was sealed with Canada balsam to the cathode of a Du Mont 5 in. K-1198 photomultiplier. With this arrangement, pulse-height distributions were obtained, which could be fitted closely to Poisson curves. In a typical case, for which the diameter of the radiator was

o

(a)

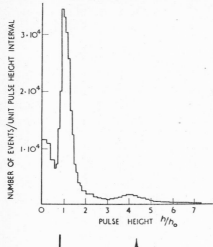

FIG. 8.16. Pulse-height distributions obtained by Horwitz (1955) with a "thin" counter, from cosmic-ray particles at an altitude of 16 g/cm² atmospheric depth.

(a) The main peak is due to protons, and the secondary peak to α-particles.

(b) The α-particle peak of (a) on an enlarged scale.

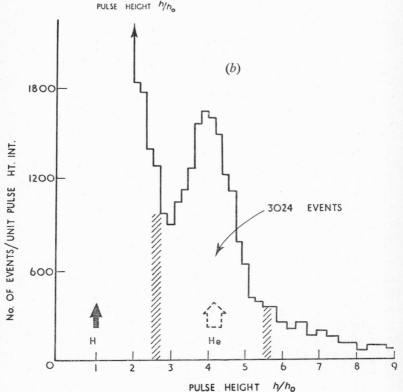

10·2 cm, the cross-sectional area of the particle "beam" 30 cm², and the geometrical factor 9·5 cm² × sterad, the most probable value of the number of photoelectrons (for best fit to a Poisson distribution) was 35. This gave a total width at half-height of 42%.

Some idea of the charge resolution obtained by Horwitz with this type of counter, may be seen from Fig. 8.16 which shows the distribution found in an experiment in which the apparatus was flown at an altitude of 16 g/cm² atmospheric depth, in a balloon flight lasting 6 hr. The isolated peak in Fig. 8.16(b) is due to helium nuclei in the

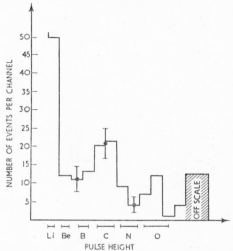

FIG. 8.17. The pulse-height distribution obtained by Horwitz (1955) at higher charge values.

primary cosmic radiation; the proton peak to the left, off-scale, is of comparable resolution.

There is also evidence, Fig. 8.17, for peaks at higher charge values, namely those corresponding to nuclei of carbon and oxygen. Owing to the very limited statistics and the inherent width of the distributions, the much discussed Li, Be and B region is obscured by the background due to protons. Nevertheless, the thin Čerenkov counter has proved itself a most worthwhile instrument in this field.

With the radiator coupled directly to the phototube, it is not possible to avoid the particles from traversing the dynode structure. This however did not cause any difficulties, presumably on account of the large light pulses obtained, even from such a thin radiator.

The technique has been refined by a number of workers whose results will be briefly mentioned. For instance, Linsley (1956) has used a Čerenkov detector in association with a cloud chamber, to assist in the identification of the particles, and McDonald (1956) has combined a Čerenkov detector with a scintillator. The latter experiment is perhaps the most advanced of its kind; taking advantage of the different characteristics of the two detectors, see Fig. 6.2, it is possible to have charge resolution independent of velocity.

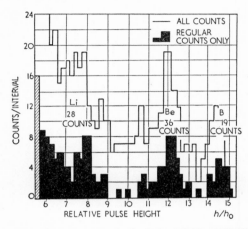

FIG. 8.18. Pulse-height distributions obtained by Webber (1956) with a "thin" counter, in the Li, Be and B regions of the charge spectrum of primary cosmic-ray particles, at an atmospheric depth of 18·5 g/cm². "Regular" counts refer specifically to the case of particles which have travelled through the apparatus without traversing the guard counters; these are mostly due to primary particles coming in near the zenith and which do *not* produce nuclear interactions in the counter.

Webber and McDonald (1955) report further work on the primary α-particles, using a single Čerenkov counter, while Webber (1956), combining a Čerenkov counter with anti-coincidence guard counters, has obtained the remarkable resolution of the Li, Be and B peaks shown in Fig. 8.18. In this work great attention was paid to the problems of nuclear interactions in the radiator, knock-on electrons, and interference from the tail of the strong α-particle peak.

8.6 Anti-directional counters

The first application of a Čerenkov counter for determining the direction of fast particles was made by Winckler (1952) who constructed the counter shown in Fig. 8.19 and used it to measure the cosmic-ray "albedo"* at high altitudes. A Lucite block L, of rectangular section, was used to generate Čerenkov radiation from particles selected by

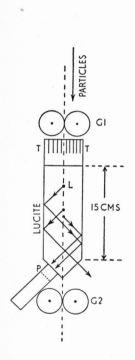

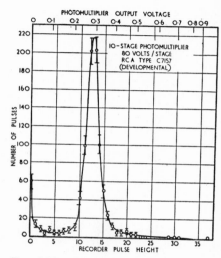

FIG. 8.20. The pulse height distribution obtained with an improved detector constructed by Winckler and Anderson (1952), using cosmic-ray particles observed underground.

FIG. 8.19 The apparatus first designed by Winckler (1952) to measure the cosmic-ray "albedo" in the upper atmosphere.

Geiger counters $G_1 G_2$ operated in coincidence. The light is guided down the block by internal reflexion until it reaches the bottom where it emerges through the slant faces of the block, one of which is optically sealed to the phototube P. Particles on the same track but travelling the other way, produce Čerenkov radiation which is guided upwards and

* The term "albedo" is used in cosmic-ray work to denote the ratio of upward-moving to downward-moving particles in the atmosphere.

then absorbed in a light trap T consisting of a number of slots filled with black paint.

With this apparatus, Winckler obtained some preliminary measurements on the ratio of the number of relativistic particles travelling upwards to the number travelling downwards, at various altitudes and orientations.

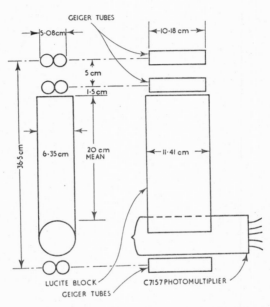

FIG. 8.21. The second detector described by Winckler and Anderson (1952, 1954) for studies of the cosmic-ray albedo. This instrument, which has a total stopping power of 30 g/cm² and a solid angle of acceptance of 1·86 sterad × cm², was flown on a balloon to an atmospheric depth of 23·6 g/cm².

An improved instrument of this type has been described by Winckler and Anderson (1952). Prior to its use for further "albedo" studies, it was tested with cosmic-rays underground, and found to give an extremely good pulse height distribution, Fig. 8.20, of width 23 % at half-height; this performance was attributed to the relatively large amount of light available and the high efficiency for collecting it.

This second counter, Fig. 8.21, was flown on balloons at a geomagnetic latitude of $\lambda = 40°$, to obtain more detailed information on the "albedo", at heights up to 23·6 g/cm² atmospheric depth. A typical pulse-height distribution obtained in this later work (Winckler and Anderson, 1954) for singly-charged particles is shown in Fig. 8.22, the

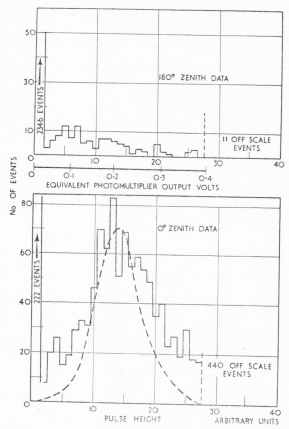

FIG. 8.22. The pulse-height distributions obtained by Winckler and Anderson (1954) with the apparatus shown in Fig. 8.21. The lower histogram applies to downward-travelling particles, and the upper histogram to upward-moving particles. The dotted curve is a calibration on sea-level μ-mesons.

lower histogram for downward travelling particles and the upper histogram for particles coming up from below. The dotted curve is from experimental data obtained with sea-level μ-mesons. The discrepancies between the sea-level and high-altitude distributions arise from two causes. The broadening on the low-energy side of the μ-meson peak is attributed to particles of rather lower energy, giving a light output less than the maximum possible. The broadening on the high-energy side is attributed to nuclear interactions which arise with such a thick radiator, for its stopping power of 30 g/cm^2 is nearly half of a geometrical mean free path for collision of protons in Lucite. It is certainly not due to electron collisions, for these are already included in the μ-meson peak.

The large number of events at the extreme left of the lower histogram are due to particles that have sufficient energy to penetrate the Lucite block but which give no Čerenkov pulse. The velocity interval for these events corresponds to $0.34 < E/mc^2 < 4.0$ which, if they are protons, lie within an energy band $210 < E < 319$ MeV.

A deep radiator of this type is quite unsuited for studies of the charge distribution of the primary cosmic-radiation, owing to the effects of nuclear collisions. Winckler and Anderson were, nevertheless, able to detect peaks at four and nine times the average pulse-height for singly charged particles, which were assumed to be due to He and Li nuclei respectively.

8.7 Direction selectors

It follows from the arguments presented in section 7.2, that all counters of the focusing type may be used as direction selectors. To take an example, consider the instrument built by Mather and Martinelli (1953), referred to in section 8.1 and used for measurements of the production of π^0-mesons by 340 MeV protons on a liquid hydrogen target, see Fig. 8.23 and Plate IV. The γ-rays from the decay of the π^0-mesons in the target, convert into positron–electron pairs in a 1/16 in. lead converter placed just in front of the Lucite radiator inside the cylindrical mirror. The directional features of this instrument made it possible to avoid π^0 contamination from the walls of the hydrogen container, and also helped to discriminate against radiations from other parts of the apparatus. The directional performance of this detector was determined using 320 MeV x-rays which were collimated in a beam of $\frac{1}{8}$ in. diameter and allowed to impinge on the Pb-converter.

Figure 8.24 shows how its sensitivity varied when it was rotated about the point C (Fig. 8.23), giving an angular acceptance at half-maximum of $2.7°$; for this test the optic axis of the instrument had previously been carefully aligned with the x-ray beam.

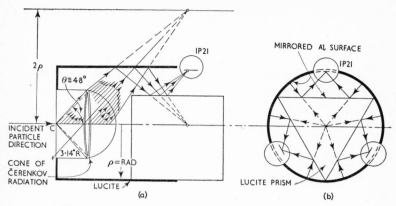

(a) SIDE VIEW OF TRIPLES DETECTION SCHEME SHOWING ONLY 1 TUBE
(b) END VIEW SHOWING PLACEMENT OF 3-IP21 PHOTOMULTIPLIERS

FIG. 8.23. The essential features of the directional selector described by Mather and Martinelli (1953), and used in experiments on π^0-meson production, see also Plate IV.

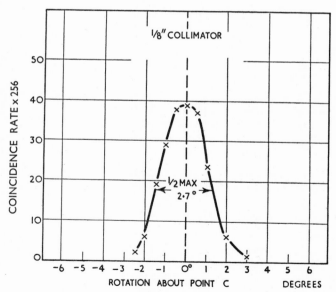

FIG. 8.24. The variation of response of the counter shown in Fig. 8.23, under rotation about the point C.

In a second test, the variation of response of the counter was measured while the distance between the axis of the x-ray beam and the optic axis was varied, the two axes being maintained parallel; the width at half-height of this distribution was measured to be 0·63 in. (see Fig. 8.25).

A similar directional performance has been obtained by Huq (to be published) using the modified Getting-type conical detector described by Jelley (1956) (see Fig. 8.26). The performance with 910 MeV protons

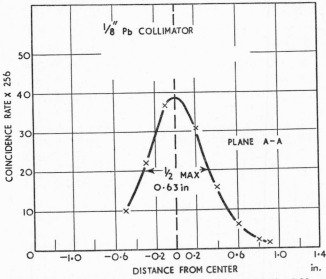

FIG. 8.25. The variation of response of the counter shown in Fig. 8.23, across the diameter of the Lucite radiator.

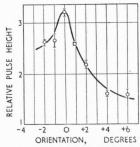

FIG. 8.26. The variation of the response of a detector of the Getting type, as its optic axis was rotated out of alignment with a 910 MeV proton beam. This instrument has been described by Jelley (1956) and by Huq (1956).

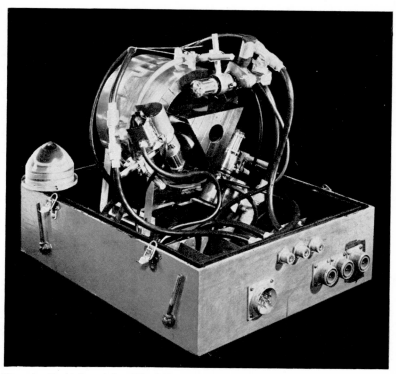

(*Reproduced by kind permission of Dr. J. W. Mather, and Dr. R. K. Wakerling of the Information Division, the Radiation Laboratory, the University of California, Berkeley, California.*)

PLATE IV. The focusing Čerenkov counter developed by Mather and Martinelli (1953) and used as a direction selector; see Fig. 8.23 and the text. The shaped Lucite radiator is shown on the left-hand corner of the mounting tray. Also may be seen the three 1P21 phototubes in their adjustable supports, the cylindrical mirror, the three-faced reflecting prism and the escape hole for the electron pairs.

(*Facing page* 208)

was such that the pulse-height dropped to a half for a change of orientation of $\sim 2.5°$.

8.8 A detector for high-energy neutrons

A simple non-focusing counter has recently been described by Booth and Ledley (1957) for the detection of neutrons in the energy region 400–900 MeV. In this instrument, the essential features of which are shown in Fig. 8.27(a), the neutrons are detected by observing the Čerenkov radiation emitted by charged secondary particles produced in the Perspex radiator. Since the average pulse-height increases with the incident neutron energy, the effective energy threshold may be raised by pulse-height selection. This neutron detector has a higher efficiency than other detectors in the above energy range, the absolute value being $\sim 1.3\%$ at 800 MeV.

The dominant process in this detector is the production of elastically scattered protons from the hydrogen in the Perspex, the Čerenkov threshold for which is 325 MeV. The overall efficiency η increases with energy, partly because the light production increases with energy, and also because, as the velocity of the centre of mass increases, the charged secondaries are emitted at smaller angles to the axis and the efficiency of collecting the light therefore increases. A third effect, that the light collection might be expected to *decrease*, since the angle of light emission increases with particle energy, appears to be offset by the other two factors.

The calculation of the overall efficiency and how it varies with the neutron energy T_n is straightforward, provided the various functions are known or can be measured. It entails knowing the scattering cross-section as a function of neutron energy, the energy and angular distributions of the protons, and the light collection efficiency as a function of the various velocities and trajectories of the particles.

Still confining ourselves to the elastic scattering process, the problem is amenable to attack by a direct experiment with high-energy protons. Booth and Ledley therefore performed tests using monoenergetic protons of various energies; these protons were selected to traverse the Perspex radiator at various angles to the axis, and at various positions along the axis. From pulse-height distributions obtained in this way, it was possible to construct the curves shown in Fig. 8.27(b) which give the pulse heights for recoil protons produced by neutrons of a given energy T_n, as a function of θ_p, the angle between the axis and the direction of the recoil protons.

At these energies, the analysis is however complicated by contributions from processes other than elastic scattering. These arise mainly from inelastic events in the hydrogen, carbon and oxygen nuclei of the Perspex. In all three nuclei there is production of $\pi^{\pm}$-and π^0-mesons, and in the case of C and O there are direct interactions leading to energetic protons. The cross-sections for these various processes are at least comparable with the np elastic-scattering cross-section.

The π^0-mesons present little difficulty, for the chance of the decay γ-rays interacting in the Perspex is small and can be allowed for. However, while there is adequate data for the production of $\pi^{\pm}$-mesons in np events, the information on inelastic processes in C and O is less complete, and a number of assumptions had to be made.

Taking all these effects into account, Booth and Ledley derive the following expression for the overall efficiency as a function of T_n and V_b, the discriminator bias:

$$\eta(T_n, V_b) = \bar{\sigma}(T_n, V_b) \, [1 - \exp\{-\Sigma_t NL(T_n, V_b)\}]/\Sigma_t \qquad (8.5)$$

where N is Avogadro's number and $L(T_n, V_b)$ is the effective length of the detector. $\bar{\sigma}$ is defined by:

$$\bar{\sigma} = \frac{N_H \sigma_H + N_C \sigma_C + N_O \sigma_O}{N_H + N_C + N_O}$$

where σ_H, σ_C and σ_O are the apparent cross-sections (at a given T_n and V_b) for the various processes added up for each of the elements, and N_H, N_C and N_O are the relative numbers of H, C and O nuclei. Likewise,

$$\Sigma_t = \frac{\sigma_t(H) \, N_H +, \text{etc.}}{N_H +, \text{etc.}}$$

where $\sigma_t(H)$, etc., are the neutron total cross-sections for the three elements.

Figure 8.27(c) shows $\bar{\sigma}(T_n)$ plotted in absolute units, for three values of the bias V_b. As an example of the application of (8.5) to a specific case, Booth and Ledley find, for neutrons of energy $T_n = 760$ MeV at $V_b = 15$ V, $\bar{\sigma} = 5\cdot4$ mbn, $L \approx 30$ cm, $\Sigma_t = 194$ mbn (published figure) and hence $\eta = 1\cdot3\%$.

Using a finely collimated beam, it was found that at $T_n = 760$ MeV and $V_b = 15$ V, the effective diameter of the detector was 88% of the geometrical diameter. Under the same conditions, the directional characteristics of the instrument were also determined; these are shown in Fig. 8.27(d), with the rather surprising result that the total width to half efficiency is only 18°.

Although the analysis of the behaviour of this novel detector presents some difficulty, it nevertheless shows promise as a threshold neutron detector of high efficiency and with reasonable directional features. It has, in addition, the merits of simplicity, ease of construction and low cost, and has been used successfully by Booth *et al.* (1958) in measurements of nuclear cross-sections with neutrons of energy 765 MeV.

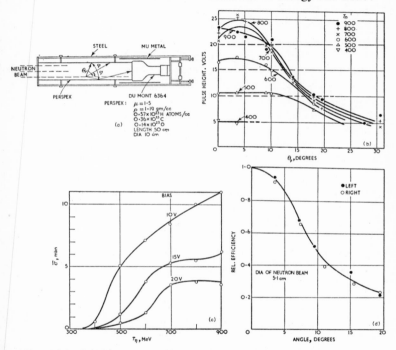

FIG. 8.27. The high energy neutron detector of Booth and Ledley (1957).
(a) The essential features of the instrument.
(b) Pulse heights of recoil protons as a function of the proton recoil angle. T_n is the neutron energy.
(c) Effective cross-sections in Perspex for the detection of neutrons of kinetic energy T_n at three bias levels.
(d) The angular variation of the efficiency of the counter for neutrons of average energy 760 MeV.

CHAPTER 9

ČERENKOV RADIATION IN THE ATMOSPHERE

9.1 The discovery of light pulses from the night sky

Blackett suggested in 1948 that there should be a small contribution to the light of the night sky from Čerenkov radiation produced by cosmic-ray particles traversing the atmosphere. From a knowledge of the total flux of particles, the fraction of these that would produce Čerenkov light, the known rate of production of this light, and some early estimates by Déjardin (1936) of the average intensity of the light of the night sky (airglow, starlight and other sources), Blackett showed that the contribution due to Čerenkov radiation would be $\sim 10^{-4}$ of the total light.

It was at once obvious that such a low light intensity could not be detected by normal methods, nor could it be correlated with the general intensity of the cosmic radiation, which is remarkably constant with time.

If however *individual* cosmic-ray events of the highest energy were isolated, namely the extensive air showers,* in which there are bursts of great numbers of particles, there would be momentary pulses of light of an intensity considerably greater than the mean intensity produced by the general cosmic radiation, and indeed perhaps strong enough to be detected against the much more intense background light of the night sky itself. The adoption of such a pulse technique would at the same time enable the light pulses to be correlated with the cosmic-ray events, using normal coincidence techniques. If a light detector, such as a photomultiplier, is exposed to the background light of the night sky, the intensity of which we will denote by B, then its cathode will be emitting electrons at a mean rate $\propto B$. The output of the photomultiplier will then show fluctuations or "noise", the average amplitude of which will depend on the time-constants of the associated circuits. If

---

* An elementary account of cosmic-ray extensive air showers will be found in Appendix III.

212

the resolving time of these circuits is $\Delta\tau$, then the average number of photoelectrons emitted in this, the sampling time of the system, will be $\propto B.\Delta\tau$. The "noise" will then correspond to the fluctuations of this quantity and thus will be $\propto \sqrt{(B.\Delta\tau)}$. The larger the bandwidth of the recording system, i.e. the faster the amplifier and circuits associated with the light detector, the lower will be the noise level and the better the discrimination between the Čerenkov light pulses and the general background.

As will be seen in due course, this "noise" from the night sky is very intense compared with the dark-current noise of the photomultiplier. For example, a good phototube in the dark has a dark-

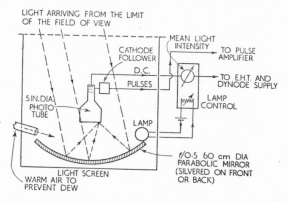

FIG. 9.1. The essential features of a light receiver used by Galbraith and Jelley (1955) to study pulses of light from the night sky, due to Čerenkov radiation in the atmosphere associated with cosmic-ray air showers.

current corresponding to the emission of 10^3–10^4 electrons/sec, while the background light from the night sky in a typical light receiver corresponds to an emission rate $\sim 10^8$ photoelectrons/sec.

It was with these ideas in mind that Galbraith and Jelley (1953), working at Harwell, first discovered light pulses from the night sky correlated with large cosmic-ray showers. They used an apparatus similar to that shown in Fig. 9.1, in which a photomultiplier was situated with its cathode in the focal plane of a parabolic mirror of diameter 25 cm and focal ratio f/0·46. This device, which was mounted inside a light screen, had a field of view of 0·13 sterad, determined by the area of the photocathode of the multiplier and the focal length of the mirror. The output of the photomultiplier was connected through an amplifier (with a cut-off frequency ~ 5 Mc/s), to a recording oscilloscope via a discriminator. This simple light receiver, when directed to the zenith on a dark clear moonless night, detected light pulses at a rate of ~ 1/min, when operating at a bias level set at twice "noise". "Noise" was defined, quite arbitrarily, as that level at which the tail-end of the noise pulse-height distribution fired the discriminator at a

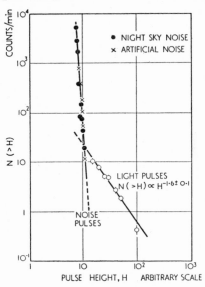

Fig. 9.2. A typical integral pulse-height distribution for light pulses from the night sky superimposed on noise due to background light. A bias curve is also shown for "artificial" noise, produced by a small lamp, for comparison. (Jelley and Galbraith, 1955.)

rate of 1/sec. Typical bias curves for the night-sky noise, superimposed on which are the light pulses, are shown in Fig. 9.2. Also shown is the bias curve for noise from a small lamp, which was heated to give the same mean current in the collector circuit of the phototube when a lid was placed over the light-screen. The first experiments were carried out with the light receiver at the centre of an array of sixteen Geiger counters used by Cranshaw and Galbraith (1954) for other experiments on cosmic-ray air showers. Coincidences between the light pulses and one or more of the counters provided means of correlating the light flashes with the showers, and confirming that the pulses were not due to pile-up of noise, spurious effects in the recording equipment or other phenomena in the atmosphere, such as meteors or distant lightning. The light receiver, having a field of view small compared with that of the counter array (which is sensitive to showers over the whole upper hemisphere), detected only a small fraction of all the showers that fired counters in the array. Thus a higher coincidence rate was obtained when the light pulses fired the oscilloscope on which the counter pulses were displayed, than with the alternate system in which counters were caused to trigger the oscilloscope while the light pulses were displayed.

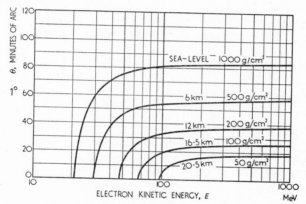

FIG. 9.3. Curves relating θ and E for electrons at different heights in the atmosphere; also shown are values for $E_{\text{threshold}}$ and $\theta_{\max}$.

At this stage in the work there was no evidence that the pulses were necessarily due to Čerenkov radiation, though there were various theoretical reasons for supposing this to be the most likely source of the light. In anticipation of matters discussed in section 9.3, it is convenient here to say a few words about the Čerenkov effect for electrons in air. Since electrons form the dominant component in air showers, the contribution to the Čerenkov light from mesons and protons may be neglected. In air at sea-level, the refractive index is 1·00029, from which we calculate that the threshold energy E_T is 21 MeV, the maximum angle of the light emission is 1·3°, and the rate of production of light is $\sim 0\cdot 3$ photons/cm of path per electron (for an energy well above the threshold, and a wavelength interval of about

P

4000–5000 Å). It is at once seen how different are these figures from those with which we are more familiar in the case of solid and liquid media. For example, in water, the corresponding figures (again for electrons) are $n = 1·33$, $E_T = 260$ keV, $\theta_{max} = 41°$ and $(dN/dl) = 250$ photons/cm.

Since a typical energy for electrons in an air shower is ~ 100 MeV, it was expected that most of the electrons would indeed have sufficient energy to produce Čerenkov light, though it was not obvious that it would successfully compete in intensity with light that might be associated with ionization and ionic recombinations. Compensations arise however, since the light is highly "beamed" (with such a small Čerenkov angle), and, more important, the light from all the individual electrons will arrive at the light receiver within a time interval short compared with the response time of the recording system.

9.2 Early experimental work

Experiments of an exploratory nature were continued at the Pic du Midi Observatory in France (altitude 2860 m) where ideal conditions for this type of work are to be found; extreme clarity of the atmosphere there is combined with another essential requirement, that of the constancy of this clarity during several hours throughout a single night. Only a summary of the main results of these experiments will be presented here; for further details the reader is referred to the papers by Galbraith and Jelley (1955) and Jelley and Galbraith (1955). In these experiments light receivers of the same general type were used, though larger mirrors and photomultipliers had by then become available; with an f/0·5 mirror of diameter 60 cm, and a photomultiplier of cathode diameter 12·5 cm (EMI type 6099), about 7 light pulses were observed per minute. Plate V shows one of the light receivers used in this work, and recordings of the light pulses on a 15 μsec time-base, using an amplifier with cut-off frequency of 5 Mc/s. In these experiments, one or more light receivers were used, either alone, or in coincidence with Geiger counters which were portable and could be set up as required. Provision was made for maintaining a constant noise level throughout a given experiment by controlling the brightness of a small lamp placed near the photomultiplier; in this way it was possible to allow for variations in the brightness of the sky as groups of stars crossed the field of view of the receiver.

The most conclusive evidence in favour of the hypothesis that the

PLATE V (a).

(a) One of the light receivers used by Galbraith and the author (1955) for experiments on the Čerenkov light pulses from the night sky associated with cosmic-ray showers. In this instrument an EMI 12·5 cm dia. photomultiplier is mounted with its cathode in the focal plane of an f/0·5 61 cm dia. parabolic mirror, silvered on the under side. Also will be seen the cathode follower unit, the supporting "spider", and (close to the rim of the mirror by the nearest pillar), the small lamp used for maintaining a constant level of background light. The entire instrument is surrounded by a light screen, and warm air is arranged to blow across the mirror to prevent the formation of dew.

(*Facing page* 216)

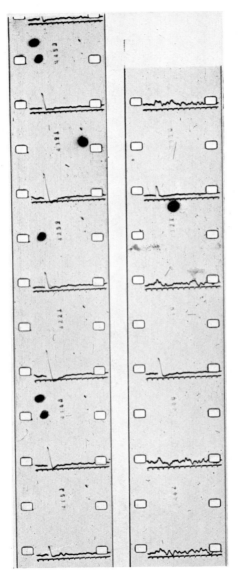

PLATE V (b).

(b) Typical recordings of light pulses from the night sky obtained with the light receiver shown in Plate V(a), pointing to the zenith on a clear night. The resolution of the night-sky "noise" is seen in relation to the 1μ sec calibration pips, when operating with an amplifier whose cut-off frequency was ~ 5 Mc/s. The first, second, fourth and last traces in the lower group were caused by distant lightning. The black blobs indicate hodoscope data obtained with Geiger-counter trays operating in coincidence with the light receiver.

(*Facing page* 217)

light was due to Čerenkov radiation, came from an experiment in which coincidences were observed between two light receivers placed side by side, each having a field of view of "radius" a, and finding how the coincidence rate varied with the angle of separation Ψ between their optic axes. It was found that the light was highly directional, arriving in a pencil beam, the coincidences vanishing almost to zero when $\Psi \geqslant 2a$, i.e. when the fields of view of the light receivers, projected on the celestial sphere, ceased to overlap. It was concluded that the light in the two receivers was parallel to within about 1° and therefore comes from the core of the shower where the scattering of the particles is small. Additional evidence for Čerenkov radiation was obtained from polarization experiments, and from a crude analysis of the colour of the light using simple gelatine colour filters.

From among the other experiments carried out at the Pic du Midi, the following results were obtained: (i) The pulse-height distribution was found to obey a power law, of the form $N(> h) = h^{-1\cdot6 \pm 0\cdot1}$. (ii) The rate of light pulses as a function of the zenith angle Z was of the form $N(Z) = \cos^{(2\cdot5 \pm 0\cdot5)}Z$. This was a much flatter distribution than that for the shower particles themselves, revealing that the light was behaving as a "penetrating component" of the air showers. (iii) An absolute calibration of the light flux for those showers that were just detectable above noise was obtained. A figure of ~ 3 photons/ cm^2 per flash was found, for the case of an f/0·5 mirror of diameter 25 cm, with a field of view 0·13 sterad, and an amplifier with a cut-off at 5 Mc/s. (iv) Using the directional features of a light receiver, a search was made for possible "point" sources of cosmic-ray showers. It had been suggested by Ryle (1949), among others, that possibly the radio "stars" might be sources of cosmic-rays, in view of the presence in these objects of regions of strong magnetic field. The experiments showed however no evidence for any increase in counting rate from these regions, in agreement with the findings of other cosmic-ray workers using conventional techniques.

The two main features of a light receiver are, first, that though relatively small in physical dimensions, it will detect air showers over a large effective area, and secondly, that it is highly directional, the field of view being determined by simple optical considerations. The properties of this instrument are therefore very different from those of the conventional detectors used in work on air showers. The potentialities of the device are severely restricted however, owing to the stringent requirements of clarity of atmosphere and its constancy, and, as a result, the very small fraction of the total time available for continuous runs. Furthermore, the air showers of highest energy, which are at the same time those of most significance from the cosmological point of view, are very infrequent, so that the number of such events recorded in a single night will be very low. It would not seem feasible to run light receivers on an automatic basis, as is usually the case for more conventional types of detector used in cosmic-ray air-shower experiments, which operate day and night under all weather conditions.

9.3 Theoretical considerations

Some of the more elementary theoretical problems will now be presented, problems which are peculiar to the phenomenon of the light pulses in the atmosphere. It must be stated at the outset that these results, many of which have not been tested, are based on numerous and various assumptions, and that very coarse approximations have to be made. Rigorous calculations, for example of the light distribution on the ground, besides their intrinsic difficulty, cannot be attempted at this stage until a more detailed knowledge of air showers is available. For example, the energy spectrum of the electrons in the showers is required, together with information on the lateral and angular distributions of the particles; furthermore, the abundances and energies of the mesons and other components in the showers may also have to be considered. The whole phenomenon of cosmic-ray air showers is exceedingly complicated and for further study the reader is referred to the review articles by Cocconi (1949) and Greisen (1956).

Threshold Energies and Čerenkov Angles

The refractive index n_0 for air at sea-level may be written in the form

$$n_0 = 1 + \eta_0 \text{ where } \eta_0 = 2 \cdot 9 \times 10^{-4} \qquad (9.1)$$

The refractive index at height h may then be obtained from

$$\eta_h = \eta_0 e^{-h/\lambda} \qquad (9.2)$$

where λ, the relaxation length for the pressure variation in an exponential atmosphere, is 7·1 km.

At the *threshold*, the Čerenkov angle $\theta = 0$, and the Čerenkov relation gives $\beta(1 + \eta) = 1$. For $\eta \ll 1$, the threshold kinetic energy

$$E_T = m_0 c^2 \left[1/\sqrt{(2\eta)} - 1 \right] \qquad (9.3)$$

which, at sea-level for electrons, is $E_T = 21$ MeV. To obtain the *maximum* value for the Čerenkov angle θ_{max}, one writes, for $\beta = 1$,

$$\cos \theta = 1 - \frac{\theta^2}{2} \cdots = \frac{1}{n} = \frac{1}{1 + \eta} = 1 - \eta \ldots, \text{ from which}$$

$$\theta \approx \sqrt{(2\eta)} \tag{9.4}$$

which, at sea-level, is $1 \cdot 3°$.

Curves relating θ and E at different heights are shown in Fig. 9.3 on which are also indicated the corresponding values of E_T and θ_{max}.

Estimates of the Intensity of the Flashes

The absolute sensitivity of a light receiver may be estimated from the noise level, which in turn may be calculated directly from measured values of ϕ_B, the mean flux for the background light of the night sky. If A is the collecting area of the light receiver and Ω its field of view, the mean current flowing from the photocathode of the multiplier is given by:

$$i = \phi_B A \Omega \epsilon \text{ photoelectrons/sec,}$$

where ϵ is here the cathode conversion efficiency,* expressed as the number of photoelectrons liberated per photon absorbed. The average number of photoelectrons emitted per unit resolving time $\Delta\tau$ of the system (where $\Delta\tau = 1/f_c$, if f_c is the cut-off frequency of the amplifier) is thus $\overline{\delta q} = \phi_B A \Omega \epsilon . \Delta\tau$, so that the noise-level, due to the fluctuations on this number, is given by:

$$N = \sqrt{(\phi_B A \Omega \epsilon / f_c)}$$

An average figure for the brightness of the night sky is first obtained, using the data of Chuveyev (1952) and Babcock and Johnson (1941) which is summarized in Table 9A.

The mean value from these two groups of results is $2 \cdot 55 \times 10^{-4}$ erg.sec^{-1}.cm^{-2}.sterad^{-1}. i.e. 16×10^7 eV or $\sim 6 \cdot 4 \times 10^7$ photons cm^{-2}.sec^{-1}.sterad^{-1}† (4300–5500 Å).

Consider now a typical light receiver, with $A = 510$ cm^2 and $\Omega = 0 \cdot 11$ sterad. The background light of the night sky then corresponds to a rate of light reception at the photocathode of $3 \cdot 7 \times 10^9$

---

* The quantum efficiency, denoted here by ϵ, is the same as that denoted by η in Chapter 5.

† These figures are also in substantial agreement with those published recently by Rodionov (1957), who obtains differential fluxes of $(0 \cdot 8–4 \cdot 0) \times 10^{-7}$ and $(1–4) \times 10^{-7}$ erg.cm^{-2}.sec^{-1}.sterad^{-1} Å^{-1} in the two wavelength bands of (3200–3600) and (5400–5750) Å respectively.

TABLE 9A

Chuveyev (4720–5580 Å)	Max.	Min.	Mean	Units
Continuous spectrum from the atmosphere	6·77	1·20	4·0	$\times 10^{-8}$ erg.sec^{-1}.cm^{-2}.deg^{-2}
Oxygen line O_1 5577 Å	1·38	0·29	0·8	$\times 10^{-8}$ erg.sec^{-1}.cm^{-2}.deg^{-2}
Starlight and zodiacal light			3·6	$\times 10^{-8}$ erg.sec^{-1}.cm^{-2}.deg^{-2}
Total			8·4	$\times 10^{-8}$ erg.sec^{-1}.cm^{-2}.deg^{-2}
(1 sterad $= 3\cdot3 \times 10^3$ deg^2)		$=$	2·8	$\times 10^{-4}$ erg.sec^{-1}.cm^{-2}.sterad^{-1}

Babcock and Johnson (4000–5500 Å)
4000–4250 Å at $1\cdot3 \times 10^{-7}$ erg.cm^{-2}.sec^{-1}.sterad^{-1} Å^{-1}
and   4250–5500 Å at $2\cdot0 \times 10^{-7}$ erg.cm^{-2}.sec^{-1}.sterad^{-1} Å^{-1}
i.e. a total of $2\cdot3 \times 10^{-4}$ erg.sec^{-1}.cm^{-2}.sterad^{-1}

photons/sec, or $3\cdot7 \times 10^8$ photoelectrons/sec, for a cathode efficiency of 10% (i.e. 40 μA/lm quoted by the makers). With an amplifier of cut-off frequency 5 Mc/s, we then find $\overline{\delta q} = 74$ and $N = \pm 8\cdot6$ photoelectrons.

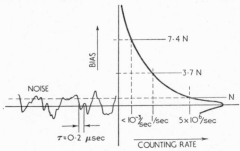

FIG. 9.4. To illustrate how the absolute intensity of light pulses from the night sky may be obtained from the noise level.

We have already defined a level for purposes of setting the threshold of the recording system as that at which the noise, in the absence of light pulses, triggers the equipment at a rate of 1/sec, see Fig. 9.4. We then need to know this level in terms of N. From the quoted resolving time, the noise is sampled $5\cdot10^6$ times/sec, and the probability that the triggering rate of the recorder is 1/sec is therefore

$2 \cdot 10^{-7}$. Assuming the noise to obey a normal error function, we find that our definition of "noise level" corresponds to a bias of $3 \cdot 7$ N. "Twice noise", the bias used in the experiments, is then $7 \cdot 4$ N or 64 photoelectrons. The smallest detectable light pulse has thus an intensity of 640 photons and the corresponding light flux is 640/510 or $1 \cdot 2$ photons/cm². This figure agrees well with the experimental figure of 3 photons/cm², considering the large number of assumptions in making his estimate and the uncertainties in the experiment.

Estimates of the Mean Intensity of the Čerenkov Light from the General Cosmic Radiation

There have been three independent estimates of the *average* flux of Čerenkov radiation from the atmosphere. This mean flux arises not from the high energy events that give rise to the air showers but from an integration of the contributions from all the single particles observed at sea-level.

Taking, first, Blackett's figure of $\sim 10^{-4}$ for the fraction of the total light of the night sky, and the above value of $6 \cdot 4 \times 10^7$ photons.cm⁻². sec⁻¹.sterad⁻¹ (4300–5500 Å) for the total light, we arrive at a Čerenkov flux of $\sim 6 \times 10^3$ photons.cm⁻².sec⁻¹.sterad⁻¹. In the same units, and taking into account the additional contributions from the μ-mesons and protons, Goldanskii and Zhdanov (1954) arrive at a figure of $\sim 6 \times 10^4$ for the flux. From quite simple considerations Polikarov (1954) shows that a single cosmic-ray particle should produce $\sim 2 \times 10^5$ photons in traversing the atmosphere. On this basis, assuming a flux at sea-level $j \sim 10^{-1}$ particles. cm⁻².sec⁻¹ over the upper hemisphere, he estimates that the mean flux of Čerenkov light should be $\sim 1 \cdot 6 \times 10^3$ photons.cm⁻².sec⁻¹.sterad⁻¹.

Maximum Radius of the Pool of Light

Consider a single fast electron traversing the atmosphere vertically, and neglect scattering and slowing down of this electron, and scattering and refraction of the light. Suppose light generated at a height h, and at a certain Čerenkov angle θ, arrives at the ground at a point distant r from where the electron strikes the ground, so that $r = h\theta$. From this, and equations (9.2), (9.1) and (9.4), the radius of the light-cone at sea-level is

$$r = (5 \cdot 8 \times 10^{-4})^{\frac{1}{2}} h \, e^{-h/2\lambda} \tag{9.5}$$

which is found to have a maximum value when $h_{max} = 2\lambda$, i.e. when $h = 14$ km; r_{max} is then 126 m, the atmospheric pressure at this height is 140 g.cm^{-2}, $\eta = 4 \times 10^{-5}$, $\theta = 9 \times 10^{-3}$ rad, and $E_T = 56$ MeV.

Distribution of Light Intensity as a Function of r (see Fig. 9.5(a))

With the same assumptions as in the last section, and again considering the case of a single electron only, the lateral distribution of the light $I(r)$ on the ground may be obtained as follows. The light

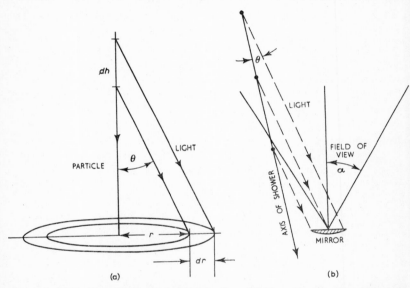

FIG. 9.5. (a) To illustrate the lateral distribution of light on the ground, produced by a single electron in the absence of Coulomb scattering. (b) The angles involved, in the case of an oblique shower and a restricted field of view for the light receiver.

intensity generated in a height interval dh and falling in an annulus of radius r can be calculated from the equation of Frank and Tamm (equation (2.17) in Chapter 2) which may here be written in the form

$$\frac{dW}{dh} \propto \left(1 - \frac{1}{\beta^2 n^2}\right) \propto \sin^2\theta.$$ With $\beta = 1$, θ small, and using (9.4), one obtains

$$\frac{dW}{dh} \propto 2\eta \qquad (9.6)$$

if dispersion is neglected. Writing $I = dW/2\pi r dr$ and $dh = dr/\theta$, it is seen from equations (9.2), (9.4) and (9.6), that:

$$I(r) \propto \frac{1}{r} e^{-h/h_{max}} \qquad (9.7)$$

showing that the intensity falls off slightly more rapidly than $1/r$.

Extension to Air Showers

If we neglect the lateral and angular spread among the electrons in a shower, (9.7) may be extended from the case of a single particle to that of a shower, by introducing a function $N(h)$ in (9.6), representing

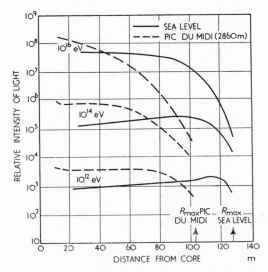

FIG. 9.6. Lateral distribution functions for light from showers of different energy at two altitudes of observation. Calculated on the assumptions of no Coulomb scattering, $\beta = 1$ and that the showers have narrow cores.

the number of shower electrons as a function of height. Numerical integrations of functions of this type have been carried out by Galbraith for three typical shower energies, for the case of light receivers at sea-level and at an altitude of 2860 m. The main feature of these distributions, Fig. 9.6, is that a plateau region exists whenever the $(1/r)$ factor in (9.7) is compensated by an increase in the electron density with height. Again it is necessary to emphasize the crudeness of the approximations. Even apart from these assumptions, it would be necessary to integrate over the primary energy spectrum to obtain distributions which could be related to actual experiments with a light receiver.

There is one essential point to emphasize, namely that in the absence of scattering, a light receiver will only detect the Čerenkov radiation from a small portion of a given shower track quite irrespective of the field of view of the instrument, see Fig. 9.5(b).

A rigorous solution of the theoretical problems presented by the light flashes from cosmic-ray showers, is at present virtually impossible. Although some of the difficulties are purely mathematical, the main problem stems from insufficient data on the structure and density of particles in showers. Most of the information on showers is of a statistical type, and very few experiments at present are able to give detailed information on individual showers. In spite of these difficulties however, Goldanskii and Zhdanov (1954) have attempted to obtain curves for the variation of light intensity as a function of the distance between the core of the shower and optic axis of a light receiving system. Although theirs is indeed a bold attempt at the problem, it is seen that they make, of necessity, a very large number of assumptions, some of which are rather crude. They at once appreciated the problem that in air the Čerenkov angle θ_c is often comparable or even small compared with the multiple Coulomb scattering angle θ_s. Goldanskii and Zhdanov tackle the problem of scattering by considering the total light flux as composed of two components, one of which arises from those particles for which $\theta_c < \theta_s$, and the other from particles for which $\theta_c > \theta_s$. The first is termed "diffuse radiation" and will be distributed fairly evenly over a large area on the ground; this light will be detected by a light receiver from a large range of altitudes in the shower. The second component, when $\theta_c > \theta_s$, is called "directed radiation" and is detected, as we have already seen, from only a small portion of the core of the shower, depending on the distance between this core and the axis of the light receiver. The total light flux at sea-level is obtained by calculating the contributions from these two components and integrating both over the altitude above ground, and the particle energy.

Counting Rates and Thresholds of Different Receivers

It was soon discovered that the rate of reception of light pulses did not vary markedly with the aperture or field of view of the optical systems used. The relative counting rates and threshold sensitivities of receivers of different apertures and fields of view will now be derived. The following assumptions are made: (i) the number of showers of a given energy arriving per unit time and unit area of ground, is proportional to the solid angle subtended by the light receiver on the celestial sphere (i.e. the zenith-angle distribution of shower frequency is assumed to be flat over the fields of view considered); (ii) the intensity of the background light of the night sky is likewise assumed to be uniform; (iii) the background light of the night sky, in terms of the emission rate of photoelectrons from the cathode of the photomultiplier, is assumed to be so high that the recording system and amplifier cannot resolve the separate electron pulses, i.e. complete "pile-up" of photoelectrons is assumed; (iv) the "noise" observed from the light receivers arises solely from statistical fluctuations in the mean emission-rate of the primary photoelectrons, these fluctuations having a Gaussian distribution; (v) the intensity of the light pulse is, to a first approximation, proportional to the primary energy of the shower.

The following symbols will be used:

D Aperture of the light receiver; receiving area $A \propto D^2$.

a "Radius" of the field of view projected on the celestial sphere; the solid angle of acceptance of the light receiver $\Omega \propto a^2$.

f_c Cut-off frequency of the amplifier, $\propto (1/\Delta \tau)$.

S Amplitude of a light-pulse signal.

N Average noise level from the light of the night sky.

B Average level of the brightness of the light of the night sky, as measured by the number of photoelectrons emitted per second at the cathode of the photomultiplier.

R Counting rate for light pulses above the bias level set at "twice noise", with the noise criterion already defined. The observed integral pulse-height distribution is used; this is of the form $n(> h) \propto h^{-1.5}$ where n is the counting rate of pulses of height greater than h. It is assumed that the integral spectrum of showers of primary energy E_0 is also of this form, namely $n(> E_0) \propto E_0^{-1.5}$.

In designing a light receiver there are three essential parameters at one's disposal, the aperture of the instrument (which determines the light gathering power), its field of view, and the bandwidth of the amplifier.

With these assumptions, simple relationships can be derived between the rate of detection of light pulses and the limiting energy of the showers* detected, as functions of these parameters. We first obtain

* By shower energy is here meant the energy E_0 of the primary cosmic-ray particle at the top of the atmosphere, as deduced from standard cascade theory, see Appendix III.

expressions for the relative counting rates of different light receivers, irrespective of their threshold sensitivities.

$R(D)$, *with* a *and* f_c *constant*

For a light pulse, $S \propto A \propto D^2$

For the background, $B \propto A \propto D^2$

From assumption (iv) above, $N \propto \sqrt{B} \propto D$

$\therefore (S/N) \propto D$, and hence

$$R \propto D^{1 \cdot 5} \tag{9.8}$$

$R(a)$, *with* D *and* f_c *constant*

The rate of reception of light pulses from showers of given E_0 is $\propto \Omega \propto a^2$, but their signal size $S = $ constant

The background light $B \propto \Omega \propto a^2$

Again, $N \propto \sqrt{B} \propto a$, when $\Delta\tau$ (or f_c) is constant

The threshold sensitivity $(S/N) \propto 1/a$

The overall rate is thus

$$R \propto (1/a)^{1 \cdot 5} \times a^2 \propto a^{0 \cdot 5} \tag{9.9}$$

$R(f_c)$, *with* D *and* a *constant*

We have seen, early in section 9.1, that $N \propto \sqrt{(B.\Delta\tau)}$, i.e. $\propto \sqrt{(B/f_c)}$. Provided the duration of the light flash is $\ll \Delta\tau$, S is independent of f_c. Thus $(S/N) \propto \sqrt{f_c}$, and

$$R \propto (\sqrt{f_c})^{1 \cdot 5} \propto f_c^{0 \cdot 75} \tag{9.10}$$

Let us now see how the threshold sensitivity of a light receiver varies with these same parameters. With assumption (v) above, the smallest detectable light pulse S_{min} (having a given signal/noise ratio) will correspond to a shower having some minimum primary energy E_{min}. The lowest detectable light intensity will clearly depend directly on the noise level, and the corresponding threshold light *flux* will depend on the collecting area of the receiver, so that $E_{min} \propto (N/A)$ (9.11)

E_{min} (D), *with* a *and* f_c *constant*

$N \propto \sqrt{B} \propto \sqrt{A} \propto D$, therefore from (9.11)

$$E_{min} \propto (D/A) \propto (1/D) \tag{9.12}$$

E_{min} (a), *with* D *and* f_c *constant*

$N \propto \sqrt{B} \propto \sqrt{\Omega} \propto a$, therefore again from (9.11)

$$E_{min} \propto a \tag{9.13}$$

E_{min} (f_c) *with* D *and* a *constant*

$N \propto \sqrt{(B/f_c)}$, and again from (9.11)

$$E_{min} \propto 1/\sqrt{f_c} \tag{9.14}$$

Thus, for a high counting rate, irrespective of primary shower energy, an optical system of large aperture and field of view is required, with a photomultiplier operating into a wideband amplifier. Already on the optical side, practical limits have been approached, at least with a parabolic mirror. A receiver consisting of an f/0·5 mirror of diameter 150 cm, and having a field of view of 4°, with a 12·5 cm diameter photomultiplier has been in use. This unit counts showers at a rate of $\sim 11/$min with a 5 Mc/s amplifier. Further improvements in light gathering power and field of view might be attained with larger photomultipliers, and an optical system having spherical symmetry such as, for example, a form of Schmidt camera.

The improvements that may be made by increasing the bandwidth, equation (9.10), are ultimately limited by the two following factors: first, when the resolving time has been reduced to such a point that the photoelectron pulses arising from the background light of the night sky become completely separated, no further reduction of "noise" is then possible. Secondly, when the resolving time becomes comparable with or short compared to the duration of the light pulse, there will be loss of amplitude of the signal. If we neglect scattering of the light in the atmosphere (which might lead to measurable delays), the spread in the time of arrival of the light is expected to be comparable with that for the arrival of the electrons in the showers; this, according to Bassi *et al.* (1953) is $\sim 10^{-8}$ sec. A value of ~ 100 Mc/s is thus probably an upper limit to the useful bandwidth. It so happens that this same bandwidth is also about that required to resolve the photo-electron pulses, if we take the figures obtained by Chuvayev (*see* section 9.3), for the brightness of the night sky.

Although the above relationships have not been individually tested, there is substantial evidence that they are at least qualitatively correct; this stems from figures for the observed counting rates with various types of light receiver in use. Table 9B shows the observed counting rate of light pulses for five different light receivers, all the figures referring to observations at sea-level and an amplifier cut-off frequency of 5 Mc/s. The calculated rate for the first receiver has been normalized so as to agree with the observed rate, while the other rates have been calculated using the relations derived above. The light flux ϕ_{min} and threshold shower energy E_{min} for this same receiver are taken from the published results, while the other values for these two quantities are worked out using relations (9.12 and 9.13).

TABLE 9B

LIGHT RECEIVER		D (cm)	A (cm^2)	α (deg.)	Ω (sterad)	CALC R (min^{-1})	EXPT R (min^{-1})	ϕ_{min} (photons cm^{-2})	E_{min} (eV)
Light collector	Photomultiplier								
10 in. diam. mirror	2 in. diam. EMI 6260	25	490	12	0·15	1·5	1·5	3	10^{14}
2 ft diam. mirror	2 in. diam. EMI 6260	61	2,900	5·8	0·032	3·9	5	0·57	$2 \cdot 10^{13}$
2 ft diam. mirror	5 in. diam. EMI 6099	61	2,900	14	0·20	6·0	7	1·4	$5 \cdot 10^{13}$
5 ft diam. searchlight	5 in. diam. EMI 6099	150	17,700	4·9	0·022	14	11	0·2	$7 \cdot 10^{12}$
No optical system	5 in. diam. EMI 6099	12·7	126	30	0·85	0·84	1·0	14	$5 \cdot 10^{14}$

9.4 Further experiments and future possibilities

If the effects of particle scattering do not seriously blur the directional feature of the Čerenkov radiation, it should be possible to obtain the vertical density distribution of electrons in a shower from measurements of the lateral distribution of the light on the ground. An experiment described by Barclay and Jelley (1956) revealed that quite a considerable proportion of the light detected by their receivers fell well outside the radial distance of 126 m, calculated on the simple theory in the absence of scattering. In this work they used two types of light receiver, operated in turn, and placed at the centre of a large air shower array used by Cranshaw and Galbraith (1957) in other studies

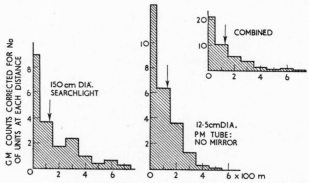

FIG. 9.7. Evidence obtained by Barclay and Jelley (1956) for light produced by airshower particles, Coulomb scattered from the axes of showers at angles greater than the Čerenkov angle. The distance of 126 m, indicated by the arrows, is the maximum possible, in the absence of Coulomb scattering, and assuming the showers have no lateral spread.

of showers. Our results are shown in Fig. 9.7, in which the frequency of Geiger counters in coincidence with light pulses at various distances from the light receiver, is plotted as a function of this distance. Within the limits of the statistics, it is evident that light is detectable out to distances of at least 600 m, revealing that a significant proportion of the shower particles are scattered through angles large compared with the original angle of emission of the light. These results confirmed our earlier views and also the predictions of Goldanskii and Zhdanov (1954).

The air shower array used in these experiments was barely adequate, for it was not possible to obtain the particle density or the location of the core of an individual shower with any great precision. The first serious attempt to obtain information on the vertical structure of showers from the lateral distribution of the light, was made by Chudakov and Nesterova (1957). In this experiment, which was conducted at an altitude of 3860 m in the Pamir mountains, the locations of the cores of the showers, and their particle densities, were determined with considerable precision using a Geiger counter array of high resolution; this array had five stations each containing ninety-six counters.

The Čerenkov light flashes were detected by an arrangement of eight light receivers set up at the centre of the array. Each light receiver consisted of a 45 cm diameter f/0·4 parabolic mirror aluminized on its upper surface and at the focus of which was mounted a photomultiplier (type FEU-19) with a photocathode diameter of 3·5 cm, giving a half-angle for the acceptance cone of the field of view of 5·3°.

Two light receivers were set up with their axes vertical and the other six were disposed around the centre two, with their axes tilted outwards at an angle of 5° to the vertical. By selecting only those events for which the light signals from the central receivers were at least not less than the signals from any of the outer units, it was possible to concentrate predominantly on vertical showers. The apparatus was triggered by the array, and data obtained from a hodoscope operated from the Geiger counters was used to determine the total number of particles N in the shower, and the distance R away from the light receivers at which the shower core struck the ground. The light flux Φ was obtained by adding the pulse amplitudes from the six inclined telescopes.

Assuming that the form of the lateral distribution of the light does not depend on the size of the shower, and that the light intensity is directly proportional to the number of particles in the shower, then $\Phi(R, N) = N\phi(R)$, where the function $\phi(R)$ is a measure of the lateral distribution of the light flux for a wide range of shower sizes.

The distribution function obtained in this experiment, see Fig. 9.8, was measured over distances from 5 to 200 m from the shower core, and corresponds to a range of shower size from $N \approx 10^5$ to $N \approx 3 \cdot 10^6$. The experimental distribution is fitted to a theoretical one based on a development of the methods due to Goldanskii and Zhdanov (1954). The best fit was obtained with the assumption that the birth of the showers occurs at the top of the atmosphere, and that the number of particles N at an atmospheric depth p is given by $N \propto p \exp(-p/p_0)$ where $p_0 = 150$ g/cm². The interesting conclusion of this experiment is that the deviations

$\Delta(\Phi/N)$ between the observed and calculated curves for (Φ/N) shown in Fig. 9.8, which lie outside the statistical errors, have been interpreted by Chudakov as being real, and due to fluctuations in the height of origin of the shower. With $\Delta \sim 1.5$ to 2, it is deduced that the point of origin of the showers occurs at a depth < 200 g/cm². Thus, at least in principle, it would seem possible to use the light pulse technique to study the mean free path for the interactions caused by the primary particles.

Millar (1957) and Brennan (1958), have recently presented some preliminary results of an experiment carried out at Sydney, with a light

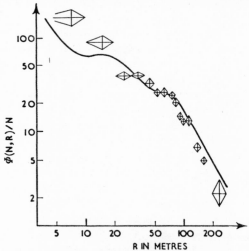

FIG. 9.8. The lateral distribution of light observed by Chudakov and Nesterova (1957), using eight light receivers in conjunction with a large Geiger counter air-shower array.

receiver used in conjunction with a large array containing Geiger counters, scintillators and a cloud chamber. The receiver consists of a single f/0·5 searchlight mirror of diameter 110 cm, at the focus of which are mounted seven photomultipliers, one on the vertical optic axis and the other six clustered round the central one. Each phototube accepts light from a cone of half-angle 3°, and the axes of the acceptance cones of the off-centre phototubes are inclined at an angle of 7° to the vertical. This optical arrangement is therefore essentially the same as that used by Chudakov, except that only one mirror is required and the parabola is used under off-axis conditions. Under the operating con-

Q

ditions imposed by stray light from the city, the threshold sensitivity of this receiver is set at light flashes having an intensity of $\sim 10^4$ photons.

The recording equipment in the Sydney experiment was also triggered by the shower particles rather than by the light flashes. The main conclusion from this work is that the Coulomb scattering of the shower particles plays a most important rôle, so that the effective field of view of a light receiver is considerably larger than the geometrical field.

Although a shower whose core traverses the acceptance cone of a light receiver is more likely to produce a light pulse than one that does not, light pulses have been detected from cores falling well outside this cone. A further indication of the magnitude of the Coulomb scattering is that when three colinear photomultipliers at the focus of the mirror were in use, several events were recorded with detectable pulses from all three; this showed that the angular spread of the light from these showers was at least $9°$.

A further analysis of Millar's results showed that for 28 events in which light pulses were detected, from a total of 226 showers, no correlation between the shower size and light intensity was established. Moreover, no correlation was evident between the light intensity and the distance r between the light receiver and the shower core.

When however one plots the *ratio* of the Čerenkov pulse-height to shower size, $(\check{C}/N)$, as a function of r, there appears to be a marked correlation, as shown in Fig. 9.9. Nevertheless, with the available statistics, it is not possible at present to carry through an analysis of the type undertaken by Chudakov.

Returning to the directional property of the light receiver as a shower detector, mention should be made of some work by George (1955, unpublished) in Sydney, who used a small receiver to investigate whether there was any evidence for sources of cosmic-radiation from the Magellanic Clouds, the nearest extra-galactic nebulae to our own system. With the receiver alternately pointing at and away from each cloud in turn, no significant results were obtained; this is not surprising in view of the relatively low energy of the showers detected, namely $\sim 10^{14}$ eV.

Future Possibilities

In view of the stringent observing conditions required, and the very indirect information obtained by light receivers in their present form, it is unlikely that their use will constitute a major development in cosmic-ray technique. Nevertheless, if a large number of light receivers were set up simultaneously, and used in conjunction with the more conventional types of detector, in a really large array, there is hope that much supplementary information could be obtained about the large showers, e.g. the vertical density distribution of the particles therein, the Coulomb scattering, the time-spread among the various constituents of the showers, and possibly the solution of the problem of multiple cores, if these exist. If only the largest showers are selected, i.e. those having

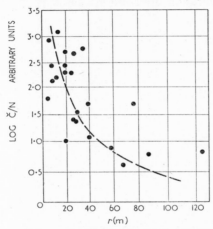

FIG. 9.9. The ratio of the intensity Č of light flashes from the night sky, to the number of particles N in the showers causing the flashes, as a function of the range r from the light receiver at which the shower cores struck the ground. (D. Millar, 1957.)

energies $> 10^{16}$ eV say, the light receivers can be quite simple, consisting merely of a single photomultiplier and a light screen, with no optical system.

On the technical side a very attractive possibility is that of measuring the light distribution across the image in the focal plane of a light receiver of large field of view and low distortion, e.g. one visualizes some form of Schmidt telescope used with a pulsed image converter.

Returning to the vexed question of climate, it seems reasonable to suppose that the best conditions might be found in a desert area, preferably at low latitudes where the duration of twilight is short; second to this the polar regions come to mind where much longer periods of darkness are to be found. Mountain stations are not ideal, for the air density is lower, the Čerenkov light therefore weaker and there is seldom sufficient space available for the associated shower-particle detectors.

A mountain plateau of medium altitude (say 2000 m) would however have certain advantages; it would provide ample space for a counter array and at the same time enable the receivers to be situated above the haze so often present near the ground.

The possibility of detecting Čerenkov pulses in the microwave region of the spectrum is discussed in section 11.5.

CHAPTER 10

GAS COUNTERS

10.1 General considerations

It would seem that the potentialities of the gas Čerenkov counter have not yet been adequately explored, and it is to be hoped that the completion of the large accelerating machines at present under construction may stimulate interest in these detectors.

Since the refractive indices of gases are so much lower than those of solids and liquids, the threshold energies are correspondingly higher. This feature alone offers distinct possibilities in the high energy field, both in machine physics and in cosmic-ray studies. The unique characteristic however of the gas counter is that the refractive index can be varied over a wide range, by the simple expedient of varying the pressure. In this way, with a suitable choice of gas, it is possible to vary the refractive index over a range from unity to values that almost overlap the lower limits of refractive index covered by liquids. Owing however to practical difficulties at the extremely high pressures, it is not yet possible to attain complete overlap.

The small values of the emission angle in gas counters enhances the directional characteristics common to many types of Čerenkov counter, and this enables such counters to possess an exceptionally high discrimination between particles travelling along the optic axis of the system and particles passing through the counter at angles of only a few degrees to this axis.

The main limitation to the gas counter is the extremely low yield of light, usually so low that the photoelectron pulses in the photomultiplier cannot be directly distinguished from the dark-current pulses. To obviate this difficulty, it is therefore essential to operate the counter in coincidence with one or more other detectors, which may be scintillators or other (solid or liquid) Čerenkov counters. In view of the smallness of the pulses, it is usual to arrange for the photomultiplier to be removed from the direct line of the particles, in order to avoid spurious effects. For instance, if a minimum ionizing particle passes right through a phototube, it has a high probability of producing a count, either by

Čerenkov or scintillation radiation in the glass envelope, the production of δ-rays in the photocathode, or knock-on electrons in one or more of the dynodes.

Even when the main stream of particles is prevented from traversing the phototube, there will be some knock-on electrons produced by the particles in the gas. These knock-ons may have energies above the threshold for electrons, and this may still occur when the counter is being operated under conditions below the threshold for the particles themselves. In practice, however, the Čerenkov radiation from the knock-on electrons produces a negligible effect.

Although most of the work with gas counters up to the present time suggests that ionization and recombination radiations are insignificant compared with the Čerenkov radiation, it is as well to carry out suitable tests to check this. These effects may not however be negligible in all cases, particularly in the inert gases, and in any gas at the lower pressures.

10.2 Thresholds, light yields and emission angles

In view of the low refractive indices of gases, it is easy to derive simple formulae relating the threshold energy E_T, the light yield (dN/dl), and the emission angle θ, with the refractive index n and the gas pressure p.

Refractive Index v. Pressure

On the assumption that the polarization P in a gaseous medium is produced solely by the presence of the electric field vector E in the light wave, the refractive index of a medium at a frequency ω is given by

$$n^2 = 1 + \frac{N(e^2/m)\epsilon_0}{\omega_0^2 - \omega^2} \tag{10.1}$$

where N is the number of electrons per unit volume taking part in the dispersion, ϵ_0 is the static dielectric constant, ω_0 is some (perhaps distant) resonant frequency of the system, and e and m are the charge and mass of the electron. Equation (10.1) is not, as it stands, accurate enough to obtain the variation of n with N, because an exact calculation of P must include effects due to the electric moments of neighbouring molecules. When these effects are taken into account, the (single resonance) formula for the refractive index takes the modified form:

$$\frac{n^2 - 1}{n^2 + 2} = \frac{1}{3} \frac{N(e^2/m)\epsilon_0}{\omega_0^2 - \omega^2} \tag{10.2}$$

(see, for example, Sommerfeld, 1954, page 93). The units adopted in this section are the same as in Chapter 2, e.g. equation (2.3a). Since N is proportional to the density ρ of the medium, (10.2) reduces to the expression:

$$(n^2 - 1)/(n^2 + 2) = \rho K \tag{10.3}$$

which is known as the Lorenz–Lorentz formula, K being a constant for the medium in question.

In a gas $n \approx 1$ at moderate pressures, so to this degree of approximation we may write (10.3):

$$(n - 1) = \tfrac{3}{2}K\rho$$

Writing, as we did in section 9.3,

$n = (1 + \eta)$, and taking $\rho \propto p$, we have:

$$\eta = kp \tag{10.4}$$

where k is another constant, again characteristic of the medium, and p is the gas pressure.

The Maximum Čerenkov Angle

As already shown in section 9.3, when θ is small, and $\eta \ll 1$, the maximum angle is given by:

$$\theta_{max} \approx \sqrt{(2\eta)} \text{ rad, or } 81 \sqrt{\eta} \text{ deg} \tag{10.5a}$$

If θ_{p1} is θ_{max} at atmospheric pressure p_1, θ_{max} at a pressure p_2 is given by:

$$\theta_{p2} \approx \theta_{p1} \sqrt{(p_2/p_1)} \tag{10.5b}$$

The Threshold Kinetic Energy E_T, measured in terms of the rest energy of the particle, (see equation 9.3), is given by:

$$E_T = \left[\frac{1}{\sqrt{(2\eta)}} - 1 \right] \tag{10.6a}$$

and the corresponding pressure dependence is therefore:

$$E_{T(p2)} \approx E_{T(p1)} \cdot \sqrt{(p_1/p_2)} \tag{10.6b}$$

with the further approximation that $E_T \gg$ the rest energy.

The Light Yield, in photons per unit path length, for an ultra-relativistic particle, $\beta \approx 1$, is obtained from equation (2.21) in Chapter 2, and takes the form:

$$\frac{dN}{dl} = 2\pi a \left(\frac{1}{\lambda_2} - \frac{1}{\lambda_1} \right) \sin^2\theta \tag{10.7a}$$

where $a = 1/137$. With the approximation $\sin^2\theta \approx \theta^2$, we find that between wavelengths of 3500 Å and 5000 Å (covering the effective range of the Cs–Sb response curve; see Chapter 5), equation (10.7a) may be re-written:

$$\frac{dN}{dl} \approx 390 \sin^2\theta \approx 780 \, \eta \text{ photons/cm.} \tag{10.7b}$$

10.3 Design data

The choice of gas depends on the threshold energy required, and this in turn upon the refractive index. There are certain limitations imposed by the critical pressure and the critical temperature, though quite a large range may be covered, from helium with $n = 1.000035$ to ethyl ether with $n = 1.0015$ at atmospheric pressure. Higher indices are then obtained by increasing the pressure; high index vapours are not suitable since they liquefy at about room temperature and pressure. Lower index gases will however provide a large range of n, if a chamber capable of withstanding the corresponding pressure is used. The most useful gases are air, nitrogen, helium, argon, methane, freon and carbon dioxide. For all these except the last, the refractive index is limited by the strength of the pressure vessel.

The characteristics of most of the gases likely to be used are drawn up in Table 10A, arranged in the order of ascending n. The quantities θ_{max}, E_T and (dN/dl), tabulated in the last columns, are calculated from equations (10.5a), (10.6a) and (10.7b) respectively, and are therefore subject to the approximations already discussed. In most cases, however, except at the highest pressures, these expressions are quite adequate for practical purposes.

Table 10A

Gas	Formula	$\eta = (n-1)$ for Na D-line at $\lambda = 5893$ Å, 0°C, 760 mm Hg	Critical temp. (°C)	Critical pressure (atm.)	$\theta_{max}.$ ($\beta = 1$) degrees at N.T.P.	E_T in terms of rest energy at N.T.P.	(dN/dl) Photons/cm, between 3500 Å and 5000 Å at $\beta = 1$ at N.T.P.
Helium	He	$3\cdot5 \times 10^{-5}$	-268		$0\cdot48$	119	$0\cdot027$
Neon	Ne	$6\cdot7 \times 10^{-5}$	-229	26	$0\cdot66$	85	$0\cdot052$
Hydrogen	H_2	$1\cdot38 \times 10^{-4}$	-240	13	$0\cdot95$	59	$0\cdot11$
Oxygen	O_2	$2\cdot72 \times 10^{-4}$	-119	50	$1\cdot33$	42	$0\cdot21$
Argon	A	$2\cdot84 \times 10^{-4}$	-122	48	$1\cdot36$	41	$0\cdot22$
Air	—	$2\cdot926 \times 10^{-4}$	-141	37	$1\cdot38$	$40\cdot4$	$0\cdot23$
Nitrogen	N_2	$2\cdot97 \times 10^{-4}$	-147	34	$1\cdot40$	40	$0\cdot23$
Nitric oxide	NO	$3\cdot03 \times 10^{-4}$	-94	65	$1\cdot41$	40	$0\cdot24$
Carbon monoxide	CO	$3\cdot34 \times 10^{-4}$	-139	35	$1\cdot48$	38	$0\cdot26$
Krypton	Kr	$4\cdot27 \times 10^{-4}$	-63	54	$1\cdot67$	33	$0\cdot33$
Methane	CH_4	$4\cdot41 \times 10^{-4}$	-83	46	$1\cdot70$	33	$0\cdot34$
Carbon dioxide	CO_2	$4\cdot50 \times 10^{-4}$	31	73	$1\cdot72$	32	$0\cdot35$
Nitrous oxide	N_2O	$5\cdot15 \times 10^{-4}$	37	72	$1\cdot84$	30	$0\cdot40$
Methyl alcohol	CH_3OH	$5\cdot86 \times 10^{-4}$	240	79	$1\cdot96$	28	$0\cdot46$
Hydrogen sulphide	H_2S	$6\cdot19 \times 10^{-4}$			$2\cdot01$	27	$0\cdot48$
Sulphur dioxide	SO_2	$6\cdot60 \times 10^{-4}$	157	78	$2\cdot08$	27	$0\cdot51$
Ethylene	CH_2CH_2	$6\cdot96 \times 10^{-4}$			$2\cdot14$	26	$0\cdot54$
Xenon	Xe	$7\cdot02 \times 10^{-4}$	17	58	$2\cdot15$	26	$0\cdot55$
Ethane	C_2H_6	$7\cdot06 \times 10^{-4}$	32	49	$2\cdot24$	26	$0\cdot55$
Chlorine	Cl	$7\cdot68 \times 10^{-4}$	144	76	$2\cdot38$	24	$0\cdot60$
Freon 13 B1	CCl_2F_2	$8\cdot64 \times 10^{-4}$	42	14	$2\cdot39$	23	$0\cdot67$
Ethyl alcohol	C_2H_5OH	$8\cdot71 \times 10^{-4}$	243	63	$2\cdot57$	23	$0\cdot68$
Propane	$CH_3CH_2CH_3$	$1\cdot005 \times 10^{-3}$	22	9	$2\cdot72$	21	$0\cdot78$
Bromine	Br	$1\cdot13 \times 10^{-3}$	302	—		20	$0\cdot88$
Chloroform	$CHCl_3$	$1\cdot455 \times 10^{-3}$	263	—	$3\cdot1$	18	$1\cdot1$
Carbon disulphide	CS_2	$1\cdot48 \times 10^{-3}$	273	76	$3\cdot1$	17	$1\cdot2$
Ethyl ether	$C_2H_5OC_2H_5$	$1\cdot52 \times 10^{-3}$	35	1	$3\cdot2$	17	$1\cdot2$
Pentane	C_5H_{10}	$1\cdot71 \times 10^{-3}$	197	33	$3\cdot3$	16	$1\cdot3$
Phosphorous trichloride	PCl_3	$1\cdot73 \times 10^{-3}$			$3\cdot4$	16	$1\cdot35$
Carbon tetrachloride	CCl_4	$1\cdot77 \times 10^{-3}$	283	45	$3\cdot4$	16	$1\cdot4$

TABLE 10B

Threshold Kinetic Energies in the Common Gases at N.T.P.

Gas	n	Electrons and positrons (MeV)	μ-mesons (GeV)	π-mesons (GeV)	K and τ-mesons (GeV)	Protons (GeV)	α-particles (GeV)
Helium	1·000035	61	13	17	59	112	446
Argon	1·000284	21	4·3	5·7	20	38·5	154
Air	1·000293	21	4·3	5·6	20	38	151·5
Nitrogen	1·000297	20	4·2	5·6	20	38	150
Methane	1·000441	17	3·5	4·6	16	31	124
Carbon dioxide	1·000450	16	3·4	4·5	16	30	120
Freon	1·000864	12	2·4	3·2	11	22	88

The threshold kinetic energies for the fundamental particles in the more common gases are listed in Table 10B. These energies are derived from column 7 in Table 10A and are expressed in MeV or GeV, using the masses of the particles quoted in Appendix I. The figures refer to N.T.P.

The curves given in Fig. 10.1 show how the characteristics of counters filled with these seven common gases vary with the pressure.

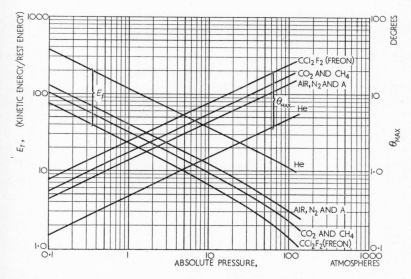

FIG. 10.1. The variation of θ_{max} and E_T as a function of pressure, for the common gases listed in Table 10B. The threshold energies E_T are *kinetic* energies, expressed in terms of the rest energy of the particle, and are therefore universal to all particles.

Having decided on the gas, the dimensions of a counter are determined by the path-length required to obtain a given amount of light, and the diameter of the optical system by the emission angle of the light. When the threshold energy of a gas counter is varied by changing the pressure, it must be remembered that the overall sensitivity will also vary. The light production will increase with pressure but the light collection may decrease, if the base of the Čerenkov cone becomes larger than the dimensions of the optical system; the focus conditions will also vary with change in the Čerenkov angle

It should be mentioned that for single-particle counting, the light yield from a gas counter is usually much too small to tolerate the geometrical loss factors inherent in counters of the non-focusing type, see section 7.4. Counters of this type may have possibilities when very intense beams of particles are available, in which case the d.c. current in the phototube might be used to measure the light intensity; coincidence counting of single particles would then be prohibited by the high chance rate.

Gas counters will thus usually be of the focusing type, and suitable optical systems are described in section 7.3.

10.4 Some practical counters

Although a number of gas counters have been built and used from time to time, the information in the literature is very scanty. The exploratory work of Balzanelli and Ascoli (1953, 1954) and of Barclay and Jelley (1955) has been discussed in section 4.4. Most of the gas counters that have been used with accelerating machines were mentioned in the discussion following a paper by J. Marshall (1956), read at the CERN symposium, Geneva 1956.

Tollestrup and Wentzel (1954) used a helium-filled gas counter for measuring the intensity of the γ-ray beam from a 500 MeV electron synchroton. The tube in this counter was 10 cm in diameter and 100 cm long and was filled at low pressure, ensuring a high threshold and therefore a good discrimination against low-energy radiation. A thin radiator was placed at one end of the tube in which electron pairs were produced, and the light arriving at the far end was reflected off a 45° front-silvered mirror to a photomultiplier mounted out at the side. This instrument was essentially a d.c. device, there being no counting of individual pulses.

A few years ago Lindenbaum and Yuan (1956) constructed a pressurized CO_2 counter for use at Brookhaven. The pressure was variable and could be raised as high as 200 atm. In this way they were able to cover a range of refractive indices from 1 to 1·1. This counter had "good" geometry, and the design was based on the cylindrical mirror arrangement described by Marshall.

Kinsey and Wentzel (1956) describe a particularly simple counter, the essential features of which are shown in Fig. 10.2. This counter, filled with nitrogen to a pressure of a few atmospheres, was used to select π-mesons from the synchrocyclotron at Berkeley, having an energy threshold around 3 GeV. Taking triple coincidences between the two plastic scintillators S_1 and S_2, and the 1P21 phototube at the focus of a small deep paraboloidal mirror, they were able to attain a counting efficiency close to 100% when the meson energy was only 0·5 GeV above the threshold. Their optical arrangement was not ideal,

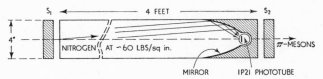

FIG. 10.2. The pressurized nitrogen counter used by Kinsey and Wentzel (1956) as a threshold detector for π-mesons having an energy $\sim$ 3 GeV.

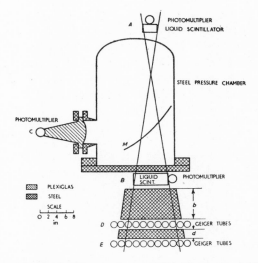

FIG. 10.3. The pressurized CO_2 counter used by Hanson and Moore (1956) to detect sea-level cosmic-ray μ-mesons with an energy > 1 GeV.

for the internal cathode of an 1P21 is very small, and no provision was made to eliminate pulses caused by the passage of the mesons through the phototube. Nevertheless, the discrimination was satisfactory, and the counting rate dropped by a factor of 30 when the instrument was rotated 180° about a vertical axis.

Owing to the small solid angle and cross-sectional area inherent in a focused gas counter, the applications of this type of detector in cosmic-ray work are very restricted. In spite of this limitation, however, Hanson and Moore (1956) were able to count μ-mesons of energy $> 1{\cdot}06$ GeV with an efficiency of $(86 \pm 2)\%$ in the short pressurized CO_2 counter shown in Fig. 10.3. The average path length in the gas was ~ 60 cm and the area $\times$ solid-angle product was $\sim 2{\cdot}2$ cm$^2 \times$ sterad. Selection of events of the type (ABC-D), with suitable thickness of steel absorber b, enabled the performance to be measured and spurious effects isolated. They were able to show that the efficiency for counting μ-mesons with velocities below the threshold was $< 3\%$. Very fast electrons, knock-on electrons, and the few high-energy protons at sea-level, accounted for some but not all of this residual counting rate. Although Hanson and Moore were unable to assess the contribution of fluorescence to the total light produced, it was certainly insignificant in comparison with the Čerenkov radiation, a reassuring feature of CO_2 as a counter gas. Their optical arrangement of using a spherical mirror at $45°$ to the direction of the light has little to commend it, but to have used a plane mirror in this case, with such a large area $\times$ solid-angle factor, would have required a very large side port to their container and a correspondingly larger light-gathering arrangement outside.

CHAPTER 11

MISCELLANEOUS IDEAS AND APPLICATIONS*

11.1 Standard light sources

There is a great demand for a source of light of known intensity and spectral composition, but there are considerable problems involved in attaining the necessary constancy and reliability. Most of the standard light sources, in particular those using tungsten filaments, require strict control of the running conditions, possess a spectral distribution often unsuited to the work, and are liable to changes in intensity and colour as they age.

After the earlier work of Belcher (1953) reported elsewhere (section 4.3), Anderson and Belcher (1954) developed a series of standard light sources of very low intensity, based on the Čerenkov radiation produced in dilute aqueous solutions of radioactive isotopes. Light sources of this type have great possibilities and the features of particular merit are the following:

(i) Extreme simplicity; the sources are self-contained, being sealed in thin-walled cylindrical glass phials.

(ii) The absolute intensity and spectral distribution can be calculated to considerable accuracy.

(iii) The intensity will remain constant indefinitely, or at least will wane at a precisely known rate, determined by the half-life of the isotope used for excitation.

(iv) The intensity is unaffected by temperature or the presence of moderate quantities of impurities.

(v) The intensity may be varied over a range of at least 500 to 1 by the simple expedient of changing the concentration of the active isotope.

With these points in mind, the requirements of a radioactive isotope for such a light source are the following:

---

* Although some of the topics in this chapter are of a controversial nature, they have been deliberately introduced in the hope of stimulating further interest.

(a) The maximum energy of the β-ray spectrum should be well above the Čerenkov threshold for electrons in water, i.e. $E_\beta > 0.26$ MeV.

(b) It should preferably be free from associated γ-radiation.

(c) It should be long-lived.

(d) It should be available at a high specific activity, so that the source may be small and compact, and:

(e) It should be stable in aqueous solution and be free from self-absorption effects in the spectral region of interest.

Among the very wide range of isotopes now available, Anderson and Belcher selected three which were found to be particularly suitable, namely ^{204}Tl, ^{90}Sr in equilibrium with its daughter product ^{90}Y, and ^{32}P. The latter has an inconveniently short life but was included since it is available in solutions of accurately known specific activity.

In order to ascertain the energy-conversion efficiency for these or any other isotopes, it is necessary to calculate the yield of Čerenkov light from a complete β-ray spectrum, bearing in mind the cut-off imposed by the threshold limit.

If $p(E)$ is the probability that an emitted β-particle shall have an energy between E and $(E + dE)$, the average total intensity I_β of Čerenkov radiation per disintegration, will be given by:

$$I_\beta = \int_{E \text{ thresh}}^{E \text{ max}} p(E) \cdot \check{C}(E)\, dE \qquad (11.1)$$

where E_{max} is the end-point of the β-ray spectrum, and $\check{C}(E)$ is the yield of Čerenkov radiation per unit path (over a fixed wavelength interval) at an electron energy E. If $\check{C}(E)$ is of the fourth form given in equation (2.23) in Chapter 2, then I_β will be in units of photons per distintegration.

The properties of the three sources just mentioned are shown in the following table:

TABLE 11A

Radioactive isotope	Half-life	Maximum β-energy (MeV)	I_β; Quanta per β-particle $\lambda 3000$–7000 Å	Chemical form
^{204}Tl	2.7 years	0.775	5.0	Tl_2SO_4 in dilute H_2SO_4
^{90}Sr $+ ^{90}$Y	25 years	$2.2 + 0.53$	47	$SrCl_2 + YCL_3$ in 0.1 N HCL
^{32}P	14.3 days	1.69	51	Na_2HPO_4 in normal saline

The sources were prepared in 5 ml samples and the sealed glass phials were of diameter 1·5 cm, length about 3 cm and wall thickness 0·5 mm; the specific activities ranged from $\sim 0·1$ $\mu c/ml$ to ~ 50 $\mu c/ml$.*

As an indication of the absolute light yield from such a source, a 5 ml sample of the $^{90}Sr-^{90}Y$ solution having a specific activity of ~ 1 $\mu c/ml$, will emit light at the rate of $\sim 9 \times 10^6$ photons/sec between the wavelength limits of 3000–7000 Å.

Light sources of this type will find many applications. They have been used for daily checks on the overall sensitivity of photomultiplier equipments and in studies of luminescence, and they would be useful in biological research and possibly also in astrophysical measurements.

It must be remembered that these sources emit bursts of quanta randomly distributed in time, and not single quanta as in most luminescent processes.

While therefore a d.c. measuring equipment will give readings proportional to the genuine integrated light intensity, a counting apparatus will in general only indicate the number of light bursts, i.e. the disintegration rate in the sample. However, if it is arranged that, on average, each flash of Čerenkov light causes only one or less electrons to be emitted from the photocathode, the counting arrangement may equally well be used to measure the mean light intensity.

To ensure therefore a pulse amplitude distribution corresponding to the emission of only single photoelectrons, for comparison with luminescence sources (the random emission of single quanta), it is necessary that either the β-ray energy, the optical efficiency of the system, or the quantum efficiency of the photocathode shall be sufficiently small.

Corrections for the emission of two, three, etc., photoelectrons simultaneously may be made by use of the Poisson distribution function, see Appendix II, Fig. II.10.

11.2 The Čerenkov interferometer

Accurate measurements of the velocity of a charged particle are limited to quite a small range of the velocity. Chuvilo (1956) proposed an interferometric method which in principle would extend considerably the velocity sensitivity of a counter of the focusing type, particularly at the highest energies when β is very close to unity. The idea, though ingenious, is wholly impractical since the interference pattern would

* For the definition of a curie, see Appendix I.

R

be blurred by the effects of Coulomb scattering and the slowing-down of the particle in the radiator. The arrangement, furthermore, would require a high degree of collimation of the particles resulting in a negligible counting rate, and the necessary bandwidth restrictions would reduce the light-yield to an intolerably low level. Although Chuvilo proposed to use a single radiator, in conjunction with an interference filter, the basic idea may be best understood in terms of two separate detectors, see Fig. 11.1.

Suppose a fast particle of velocity βc traverses two small Čerenkov detectors $\check{C}_1$ and $\check{C}_2$ separated by a distance D. Let us assume for simplicity that there is no scattering or slowing down of the particle,

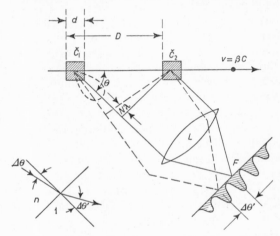

FIG. 11.1. To illustrate the principles of a Čerenkov interferometer.

either inside the detectors or in the space between, and let us further assume that the radiation is restricted to a single wavelength λ.

Under these conditions, it follows that the radiations from the two detectors will be mutually coherent and may be combined (for simplicity by a lens L) to form an interference pattern at the focus F. The arrangement is analogous to a double-slit interferometer illuminated by an oblique plane wave-front. The intensity distribution in the fringes at F will be modified by the diffraction pattern (shown dotted) of each of the two detectors taken singly. If D is $\gg d$, the thickness of either detector, there will be a large number of fringes within the main lobe of the diffraction pattern.

We wish to know the spacing of these fringes in order to find the theoretical resolution of such a device, i.e. by how much β may be changed so that the fringe pattern moves on a single fringe period. For simplicity let us further suppose each detector has one face cut normal to the direction of the light emerging at the Čerenkov angle θ. Any deviation $\Delta\theta$ from this direction, measured *inside* the medium, will appear as a deviation $\Delta\theta'$ outside, so that when $\Delta\theta$ is small, $\Delta\theta' = n\Delta\theta$, see inset in Fig. 11.1.

Fringe Spacing and Energy Resolution, neglecting Dispersion

From Fig. 11.1, we see that a fringe shift of N wavelengths will be related to a change $\Delta\theta'$ in the observed direction of the light, by:

$$N\lambda = D \sin\theta . \Delta\theta' = nD \sin\theta . \Delta\theta \qquad (11.2)$$

while differentiation of the Čerenkov relation gives:

$$\Delta\beta = n\beta^2 \sin\theta . \Delta\theta \qquad (11.3)$$

Combining (11.2) and (11.3), putting $\beta \approx 1$ and $N = 1$, we have

$$\Delta\beta = (\lambda/D) \qquad (11.4)$$

If now the *total* energy of the particle W is expressed in terms of its rest energy, so that $W = (1 - \beta^2)^{-\frac{1}{2}}$, then

$$\Delta W = W^3 . \beta\Delta\beta \qquad (11.5)$$

Consider a specific case, for instance $\lambda = 4000$ Å, $D = 10$ cm, and a proton of kinetic energy 5 GeV. From (11.4) we find $\Delta\beta = 4 \times 10^{-6}$. For a proton, $Mc^2 \approx 1$ GeV, so that $W \approx 6$, and (11.5) gives $\Delta W = 864$ keV.

The sensitivity is therefore such that the fringe pattern would shift one complete period for an energy change of ≈ 0.9 MeV, or $\approx 0.0002\%$ of the initial kinetic energy. From equations (11.2) and (11.3) we find, for Perspex ($n = 1.50$) that $\Delta\theta \approx 4.5 \times 10^{-6}$ rad, which is clearly much smaller than the unavoidable Coulomb scattering. Furthermore, the energy sensitivity of ~ 0.9 MeV is less than the slowing-down within the radiators, which is ~ 2 MeV for a relativistic particle in a thickness of only 1 cm of Perspex.

Bandwidth Limitation

Another serious difficulty is the dispersion. Again differentiating the Čerenkov relation, this time with respect to n, we obtain:

$$\Delta n = n\sqrt{(\beta^2 n^2 - 1)} \times \Delta\theta \approx n\sqrt{(n^2 - 1)} \times \Delta\theta \qquad (11.6)$$

For Perspex, $\bar{n} = 1\cdot50$ and $(n_D - 1)/(n_F - n_C) = 58$. With this value of the dispersion, with $\lambda_C = 6563$ Å and $\lambda_F = 4861$ Å, we have $\Delta n = 9 \times 10^{-3}$ for $\Delta\lambda = 1700$ Å. But, from (11.6), the fringes will be completely blurred if $\Delta n \geqslant 1\cdot7\,\Delta\theta \geqslant 7\cdot6 \times 10^{-6}$. The maximum permissible bandwidth for the resolution not to be limited by dispersion is thus only $1\cdot4$ Å. The light yield in such a narrow bandwidth would of course be intolerably low.

Although the above analysis was carried out for a specific type of interferometer, the general conclusions will apply for other arrangements.

11.3 Čerenkov radiation in linear accelerators

The Čerenkov radiation produced by a single particle travelling down the axis of an assembly of loosely coupled cylindrical resonators has already been discussed in section 3.4. Since a linear accelerator consists of just such an arrangement, it follows that radiation may be expected under certain conditions. The radiation will occur whenever the particle velocity is equal to, or greater than, the phase velocity of radiation in the system, and for continuous acceleration to exist in a machine of this type, the two velocities are indeed the same. It follows that the radiated wavelength is therefore the same as the wavelength of the external radio-frequency accelerating field.

We have seen, equation (3.45), that the radiation from a single particle is quite negligible. In an accelerator, however, the number of particles involved is very considerable, and the resultant radiation may become appreciable. Moreover, the intensity will be greatly enhanced by the feature that the particles are "bunched". Since the size of an individual bunch is usually small compared with the wavelength of radiation in the system, the radiation from all the particles in a single bunch will be coherent, with the intensity proportional to N^2, where N is the number of particles in a bunch. Furthermore, there will be a second degree of coherence arising from interference among the radiations of separate bunches, because these are spaced apart by precisely one wavelength. If I_s is the radiation from a single particle, equation (3.45), it follows that the total intensity of the radiation in the system will be proportional to $I_s\, n^2 N^2$ where n is the number of bunches in the system at any one instant.

With these considerations, Akhiezer and his colleagues (1956) show that when the currents are of the order of several amperes, the fields associated with the Čerenkov radiation may become comparable to the Coulomb fields between the particles; the effect is however of negligible importance in existing machines.

A second consideration discussed by Akhiezer, is that under certain conditions it is possible for the emission of Čerenkov radiation in a linear accelerator to lead to instabilities in the beam, such that small fluctuations in beam densities and velocities will be propagated down the system with increasing amplitude. Again however these effects are in practice small compared with other sources of instability.

11.4 The emission of radio waves from sunspots

The possible astrophysical significance of the rôle of Čerenkov radiation in an ion plasma has already been mentioned in section 3.6. An interesting application of these ideas to a specific problem has been discussed by L. Marshall (1956) who speculates on the origin of the non-thermal radio emissions from the sun. The particular emissions which might be attributed to Čerenkov radiation are those correlated with sunspots; these last only for a short time, of the order of some minutes, and are characterized by a relatively narrow bandwidth in which the mid-band frequency drifts, during the emission, from a high to a lower value, see for example Pawsey and Smerd (1953).

As will be seen later, it is probable that Čerenkov radiation is in this case not the main contribution to the observed radio noise, as it does not explain a particularly noticeable characteristic of the phenomenon, namely that *two* bands are emitted, the mid-band frequency of one of which is precisely half the frequency of the other (see Wild *et al.* 1953). The analysis is nevertheless interesting, as it serves to indicate the general approach to problems of this type.

Marshall suggests that jets of electrons are created in sunspots, directed at an arbitrary angle with respect to the magnetic field associated with the spot. Some of the electrons will have directions such that they may spiral up out of the sunspot, thereby producing Čerenkov radiation. From equation (3.55) we see that the refractive index of the medium is particularly high at frequencies ω approaching either the plasma or the cyclotron frequencies, ω_0 and ω_H respectively. We would thus expect the emission of two bands of Čerenkov radiation separated by an interval of comparatively weak emission. As the electrons stream up out of the spot, they will pass through regions of decreasing field and electron density, so that ω_0 and ω_H will both decrease with height above the spot. Therefore, as the electron jet rises, the radiation frequencies would be found to decrease with time, during the outburst.

The known electron densities and field strengths above sunspots provide frequencies of the right order of magnitude, and the observed radio intensities on the earth are also consistent with this hypothesis.

The cyclotron frequency $\nu_H = eH/2\pi mc = (2\cdot8H)$ Mc/s where H is the magnetic field in gauss. A large sunspot has a field of 5000 G, and a small spot a field ~ 50 G, so that the corresponding frequencies are 14,000 Mc/s and 140 Mc/s respectively. The plasma frequency $\nu_0 = (Ne^2/\pi m)^{\frac{1}{2}} = 9000 \sqrt{N}$ c/s, where N is the electron density in the plasma, in electrons/cm³, Values of N range (van de Hulst, 1953) from 10^{10} cm^{-3} at $1\cdot006$ sun's radii to 10^6 at 2 sun's radii from the centre of the sun, corresponding to a range in ν_0 from 900 to 9 Mc/s. Although Marshall shows that with plausible values of H and N, it is certainly possible to find emission bands separated in frequency by a factor of two, over quite a wide range in altitude above the spot ($1\cdot1$ to $1\cdot3$ sun's radii, from the centre of the sun), the Čerenkov hypothesis cannot explain why the two bands should always differ in frequency by a factor so close to two.

The radio intensity received on the earth is obtained as follows: If the Čerenkov radiation intensity in photons per centimetre of path per unit frequency interval per particle, is given by $\Delta I/\Delta \nu = \dfrac{4\pi e^2}{hc^2} (1 - 1/\beta^2 n^2)$ $= 1\cdot7 \times 10^{-12} \times (1 - 1/\beta^2 n^2)$, the radio energy per square metre per unit frequency interval received on the earth is given by:

$$\frac{1}{4\pi R^2} \times v \times \left\{ \begin{matrix} \text{volume of} \\ \text{gas above} \\ \text{sunspot} \end{matrix} \right\} \times \left\{ \begin{matrix} \text{density} \\ \text{of} \\ \text{electrons} \end{matrix} \right\} \times \left(\frac{\Delta I}{\Delta \nu} \right) \times \left\{ \begin{matrix} \text{energy} \\ \text{per} \\ \text{photon} \end{matrix} \right\}$$

$$(11.7)$$

where v is the velocity of the particle, and R is the earth–sun distance.

The diameter of a large sunspot is ~ 7000 km. If we assume the electron jet has a diameter of 3000 km and a height of 10,000 km, the volume of gas involved is 10^{26} cm³. With a reasonable electron density of $10^8/cm^3$, the average frequency $\bar{\nu}_0$ is 100 Mc/s. With $R = 1.5 \times 10^{11}$ m, the intensity, from (11.7), is found to be

$$\frac{v}{25 \times 10^{22}} \times 10^{26} \times 10^8 \times 1.7 \times 10^{-12} \times (1 - 1/\beta^2 n^2) \times 6 \times 10^{-27} \times 10^8,$$

which $= 0.5 \times 10^{-19} v (1 - 1/\beta^2 n^2)$ erg/m² sec per c/s.

Taking $v = 10^8$ cm/sec, $(1 - 1/\beta^2 n^2) \approx 1$, and 1 W $= 10^7$ erg/sec, the flux is found to be 5×10^{-19} W/m² per c/s which agrees well with typical values observed for the sunspot emissions.

In general, Čerenkov radiation produced above a sunspot in the above manner will have difficulty in escaping, for it has to pass through regions in which the refractive index has a large imaginary component. However, as pointed out in a postscript to a later paper, by Kruse, Marshall and Platt (1956), radiation which is travelling at small angles to the magnetic field vector, will encounter only stop bands of very narrow width. In this way it can be shown that o-type waves (see section 3.6) will in fact escape, while the e-waves will still be trapped.

Kruse *et al.* point out that this particular type of sunspot radiation may alternatively be interpreted as a form of Schwinger or synchrotron radiation. Moreover, it is then possible to explain the double-frequency emissions by the generation of harmonics. This alternative mechanism nevertheless also encounters difficulties.

11.5 Radio pulses associated with cosmic-ray air showers?

Following the first experiments on light pulses from the night sky, see Chapter 9, the writer enquired whether radio pulses might likewise be produced in the atmosphere, by Čerenkov radiation associated with the particles in an extensive cosmic-ray shower (see also Appendix III). The possibility of detecting showers by a direct radio method is obviously attractive, since a directional detector of large effective area would then be available which would be uninfluenced either by daylight or atmospheric conditions. Moreover, such a receiver, operating at a sufficiently short wavelength, would not be subject to undesirable background radiations, unless high temperature sources lay within the field of view.

Since the output of Čerenkov radiation is proportional to $\omega . d\omega$, where ω is the mid-band frequency and $d\omega$ the bandwidth, we require a sensitive wide-band receiver operating at the highest possible frequency.* A second requirement is that the wavelength should be small compared with the average spacing of the electrons in the core

---

* In this section ω and $d\omega$ are used to denote natural rather than cyclic frequencies; the units are c/s.

of the shower, to avoid decoherence between the electrons and positrons, which are present in approximately equal numbers. The upper limit to frequency is set by the O_2 and H_2O atmospheric absorption bands at wavelengths $\lambda = 0.5$ and $\lambda = 1.3$ cm respectively, and by the noise factor of the receiver, which gets progressively worse below $\lambda \sim 3$ cm. The bandwidth is limited to ~ 100 Mc/s by the duration of the radio pulses, for the reasons already discussed in connexion with the light flashes.

We shall estimate the signal to noise ratio for the radio pulses associated with a 10^{16} eV shower, on the basis of the *measured* light flux of ~ 3 photons/cm² for showers of energy $\sim 10^{14}$ eV. We will assume a wavelength $\lambda = 0.8$ cm (falling within the trough between the O_2 and H_2O absorption bands), and consider the receiver to have a bandwidth of 100 Mc/s and a linear detector. To gather the radiation, we will further assume that a parabolic mirror is used, having a diameter of 300 cm, i.e. 10 ft.

At 10^{16} eV the light flux ϕ_L will be assumed to be 300 photons/cm² or 1.2×10^{-9} erg/cm², on the basis of 1 photon ≈ 2.5 eV.

For light pulses, at $\lambda = 4500$ Å, $\omega_L = 6.7 \times 10^{14}$ c/s
and, between 4000 and 5000 Å, $d\omega_L = 1.5 \times 10^{14}$ c/s
so that $\omega_L \cdot d\omega_L = 10^{29}$ (c/s)² $\qquad$ (11.8)

For radio pulses, at $\lambda = 0.8$ cm, $\omega_R = 3.8 \times 10^{10}$ c/s
and, for a bandwidth of 100 Mc/s, $d\omega_R = 10^8$ c/s
so that $\omega_R \cdot d\omega_R = 3.8 \times 10^{18}$ (c/s)² $\qquad$ (11.9)

Therefore the relative sensitivity of the light receiver to that of the radio receiver will be

$$S = (\omega_L \cdot d\omega_L)/(\omega_R \cdot d\omega_R) = 2.6 \times 10^{10} \qquad (11.10)$$

The radio flux ϕ_R will be:

$$\phi_R = \frac{\omega_R d\omega_R}{\omega_L d\omega_L}\phi_L = \frac{1.2 \times 10^{-9}}{2.6 \times 10^{10}} = 4.6 \times 10^{-20} \text{ erg/cm}^2$$

If the receiving aerial (i.e. the parabola) has an area A, the energy collected will be $W = A\phi_R$. The duration of the pulse at the output of the receiver will be $\Delta\tau = 1/(2\pi \cdot d\omega_R)$ sec, if $d\omega_R$ is in c/s. The observed power, during the pulse, will thus be:

$$P_R = 2\pi A\phi_R \cdot d\omega_R \qquad (11.11)$$

With $A = 7 \cdot 2 \times 10^4$ cm^2 (for the 300 cm diameter mirror), $d\omega_R = 100$ Mc/s, and the above value of $\phi_R = 4 \cdot 6 \times 10^{-20}$ erg/cm^2, we find $P_R = 2 \cdot 1 \times 10^{-6}$ erg/sec $= 2 \cdot 1 \times 10^{-13}$ W.

In this region of the spectrum the effective temperature of the aerial will be much less than the temperature of the input circuits of the receiver (unless the aerial is directed at a star or other "hot" region), so that the noise power in a perfect receiver will be:

$$P_N = kT_{273} \cdot d\omega_R = 4 \times 10^{-13} \text{ W} \tag{11.12}$$

for a bandwidth of 100 Mc/s.

The signal to noise ratio from (11.11) and (11.12) will thus be given by $\dfrac{2 \cdot 1 \times 10^{-13}}{4 \times 10^{-13}} \sim 0 \cdot 5$, so that the signal will not be visible above noise under these conditions. If however we were to consider a shower energy of 10^{17} eV, the signal to noise ratio would then be 5/1.

It must of course be realized that, unlike the light receiver, the field of view will be severely restricted by the diffraction width of the aerial beam, which is $\sim (\lambda/D)$. For a 10 ft mirror and $\lambda = 0 \cdot 8$ cm, the beam-width will thus be $\sim 0 \cdot 2°$ and the counting rate therefore extremely small. It must also be borne in mind that the elementary diffraction theory of such an aerial will be modified since the wave-front will not be plane; this will lead to an increase in beam-width and a reduction in gain.

11.6 The magnetic moment of the neutrino

The possibility of detecting the neutrino through Čerenkov radiation induced by its magnetic moment, if indeed it possesses a magnetic moment, has been considered by a number of investigators.

We have seen, section 3.1, that the ratio R of the radiation yield from a pure magnetic dipole of moment μ, to that from a point charge e having no associated magnetic moment, is given by:

$$R = W_\mu/W_e = \left(\frac{\mu\omega n}{ec}\right)^2 \text{ or } \left(\frac{2\pi\mu n}{e\lambda}\right)^2 \tag{11.13}$$

where n is the refractive index of the medium and λ the wavelength corresponding to the circular frequency ω. The expression (11.13) represents the maximum possible yield, i.e. when the dipole axis is perpendicular to the line of motion.

Ridley (1956) has pointed out that the Čerenkov effect provides a less sensitive test for the magnetic moment than does the search for direct ionization effects. It is nevertheless worth considering what sensitivity might be attained in a practical counter, taking limiting values for the neutrino magnetic moment deduced from other experiments. In a typical arrangement discussed by Whitehouse and the writer (unpublished), it was proposed to look for the solar neutrinos in a long cylindrical water detector set up in a horizontal position deep underground, the axis of the detector pointing east-west. If L is the length of the instrument, A its cross-sectional area, ϕ_v the neutrino flux, and η the quantum efficiency of the photocathode of the multiplier situated at one end of the tube, the expected counting rate from the detector would be:

$$\frac{dN}{dt} = \eta A \phi_v L R (dN/dl)_e \text{ photoelectrons/sec.} \tag{11.14}$$

For the upper limit to the magnetic moment, we will take the figure $\mu_v < 10^{-7}$ Bohr magnetons or $< 9 \times 10^{-28}$ erg/G. This limit, determined experimentally by Cowan et $al.$ (1954) with neutrinos from a reactor, agrees closely with that deduced by Crane (1948) from geophysical arguments. With $n = 1{\cdot}3$, $e = 5 \times 10^{-10}$ e.s.u. and $\lambda = 4000$ Å, we then deduce from (11.13) that $R < 1{\cdot}3 \times 10^{-25}$.

An upper limit to the solar neutrino flux has been obtained from experiments by Davis (1956) who arrives at the conclusion that $\phi_v < 2 \times 10^{13}$ neutrinos/cm² sec.

If we consider a tube of length $L = 10$ m, $A = 120$ cm² (5 in. photomultiplier) and take $(dN/dl)_e = 250$ photons/cm, we find from (11.14), that $(dN/dt) < 8 \times 10^{-6}$ photoelectrons/sec, if we assume $\eta = 10\%$.

A counting rate of this magnitude is clearly quite undetectable against the background effects of dark-current pulses, residual cosmic-ray counts not removed by an anti-coincidence shield, and residual radioactivity in the water and its container.

Furthermore, if the solar neutrinos are polarized with their spin axes parallel to the line of motion, a further large factor $(1 - \beta^2)$ is lost, owing to the Lorentz contraction of the dipoles, see equation (3.3) in section 3.1.

Assuming that the solar neutrinos arise from the positron decays of ^{13}N and ^{15}O in the C–N cycle in the core of the sun, for which the maximum energies are 1·2 and 1·7 MeV respectively, the average kinetic energies of these neutrinos is $\sim 0 \cdot 7$ MeV. Combining this with an upper limit to the rest mass of the neutrino, of $m_\nu < 1$ keV/c^2, deduced by Langer and Moffat (1952), we see then $(1 - \beta^2) \sim 2 \times 10^{-6}$.

Recent evidence, from experiments which demonstrate non-conservation of parity in weak interactions, leads to the suggestion that neutrinos are in fact polarized with their spin axes parallel to the direction of motion. The factor $(1 - \beta^2)$ would therefore appear in the radiation yield. The "two-component" neutrino theory, which has been successful in interpreting many of the parity experiments, implies that both the rest mass and magnetic moment of the neutrino are zero. If either the mass or magnetic moment is zero, there is no Čerenkov radiation.

11.7 Reflection of microwave radiation from a Čerenkov electron gas

The search for ways of generating millimetre waves has produced an abundance of ideas, of which some have already been mentioned in section 3.4, namely the direct Čerenkov radiation from electrons moving near a dielectric, and the complex Doppler effect produced by an oscillator moving through a dielectric medium; the latter is very similar to the "undulator" scheme proposed by Motz (1951).

Landecker (1952) proposed to reflect electromagnetic waves from an electron beam moving in a vacuum in the opposite direction to the waves. With this scheme, in which a Doppler effect is produced analogous to a moving mirror in optics, a substantial increase in frequency requires the use of relativistic electrons; for instance, a hundredfold frequency increase calls for an electron energy of 2 MeV.

Lampert (1956) realized however that the Doppler effect is relative to the velocity of the waves in the medium in which they are travelling, and if therefore the phase velocity is suitably reduced, large frequency shifts are possible using a beam of non-relativistic electrons.

Temporarily postponing the technical problems involved, consider a plane electromagnetic wave of frequency ω_i moving with a phase velocity V_p head on to an electron beam moving at a velocity V in the opposite direction to the waves. It is assumed the electron beam has a sharp leading edge, see Fig. 11.2(a). A proportion of the energy of the incident wave will be reflected by the moving beam, and the frequency of this reflected component is given by $\omega_r = \omega_i (1 + \zeta)/(1 - \zeta)$ where $\zeta = (V/V_p)$. This is analogous to the vacuum Doppler effect, with ζ replacing $\beta = (V/c)$.

In the sub-Čerenkov region, i.e. when $\zeta < 1$, unless the electron density N exceeds some critical value N_c, there is only partial reflection of the wave, and a transmitted wave t enters the "gas". If $N > N_c$, the beam acts as a perfect mirror and the component t is reactively attenuated behind the leading edge, analogous to the skin effect in the reflexion of radio frequency waves at the surface of a conductor.

When $\zeta > 1$, the electron beam behaves as a "Čerenkov electron gas", that is, a medium which is moving faster than the velocity of the waves impinging upon it, these waves having been slowed down by a dielectric medium or some other "slow-wave" structure. In this, the

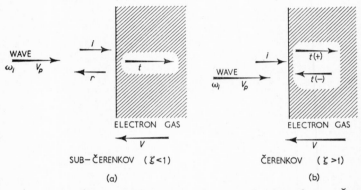

FIG. 11.2. To illustrate the reflection of electromagnetic waves from a Čerenkov electron gas. (After Lampert, 1956.)

Čerenkov case, when $\zeta > 1$, it is evident there can be no reflection in the normal sense of the word, since the electron gas will overtake waves travelling in the same direction as the gas. Nevertheless, under certain conditions of electron density, such a gas will exhibit a "mirror-like" quality, in that it will reverse the direction of propagation of a wave incident upon it, even though this wave becomes immersed in the electron beam. As in the sub-Čerenkov case, the energy of the incident wave i of frequency ω_i becomes divided between two components; these will be denoted by t_+ and t_-, of frequencies ω_+ and ω_- respectively, the first representing in general a "forward" moving wave and the second a "backward" moving wave, see Fig. 11.2(b). The frequencies and relative amplitudes of the two components are summarized in Table 11B.

TABLE 11B

	ω_+/ω_i	Amplitude t_+	ω_-/ω_i	Amplitude t_-
$P \ll 1$ + forward wave − backward wave	$1 + P\left\{\dfrac{\zeta}{2(\zeta+1)}\right\}$	$(1 + \tfrac{1}{4}P)$	$-\left(\dfrac{\zeta+1}{\zeta-1}\right) - P\left\{\dfrac{\zeta}{2(\zeta+1)}\right\}$	$-\tfrac{1}{4}P$
$P = P_o = (\zeta+1)^2$	$(\zeta + 1)$	$\dfrac{(\zeta+1)^2}{2\zeta}$	$-\left(\dfrac{\zeta^2+1}{\zeta-1}\right)$	$-\dfrac{\zeta^2+1}{2\zeta}$
$P \gg 1$ + backward wave − backward wave	$\dfrac{\zeta}{(\zeta^2-1)^{\frac{1}{2}}}\sqrt{P}$	$\dfrac{\zeta}{2(\zeta^2-1)^{\frac{1}{2}}}\sqrt{P}$	$-\dfrac{\zeta}{(\zeta^2-1)^{\frac{1}{2}}}\sqrt{P}$	$-\dfrac{\zeta}{2(\zeta^2-1)^{\frac{1}{2}}}\sqrt{P}$

The quantity P is given by:

$$P = (\omega_p^2 \epsilon_0 / \gamma \omega_i^2 \epsilon)$$

where ϵ_0, the dielectric constant of the electron gas, is related to ω_p, the plasma frequency, by:

$$\omega_p^2 = (e^2 N / m \epsilon_0)$$

where e and m are the charge and mass of the electron, and N the electron density in the "gas". $\gamma = (1 - \beta^2)^{-1/2}$ and ϵ is the dielectric constant of the slow-wave medium *outside* the gas, i.e. in front of the beam.

In general, we see that there are two frequencies, but in the special case when $P \gg 1$, both waves are "backward" moving, and both have the same frequency.

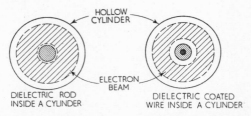

FIG. 11.3. Two schemes suggested by Lampert for obtaining Doppler-shifted microwaves.

The practical possibility of using these properties of a Čerenkov electron gas to increase substantially the frequency of an incident wave, depends on incorporating some slow-wave structure (i.e. a metal helix or loaded waveguide) inside a vacuum tube around a dense electron beam; there are considerable technical difficulties with the effects of space charge, and there is also the problem of producing the required sharpness at the leading edge of the beam.

Two possible arrangements mentioned by Lampert are shown in Fig. 11.3. As he points out, both these configurations differ considerably from the idealized case considered above, in which the wavefronts are plane, and the waves and medium are unbounded. Nevertheless, the general properties are still expected to be valid in these cases.

11.8 Čerenkov radiation in water-moderated reactors

A water-moderated reactor running at a power of say 100 kW offers a unique opportunity for seeing Čerenkov radiation; indeed, the intensity is such that it is easy to obtain a direct photograph of the glow in the water surrounding the core of the reactor, as is evident from the very beautiful picture reproduced as a frontispiece in this book (Plate I). These unique circumstances are presented by the combination of an exceptionally high local intensity of nuclear radiations, the good transparency of the great depth of water and, above all, the ample screening of the nuclear radiations provided by the water.

The radiation one observes arises mainly from the secondary electrons (mostly Compton-scattered electrons) produced by the absorption of γ-rays emitted from the core. These γ-rays have four origins; γ-rays generated in the fission process itself, neutron capture γ-rays (in water, in the core structure and in ^{238}U), fission product γ-rays and γ-rays from the decay of activated core material. The first group and the capture γ-rays are called "prompt" γ-rays and cease when the fission chain-reaction is stopped, while the second group are "delayed" γ-rays. The latter are associated with the β-decay processes of the fission products and have half-lives ranging from a fraction of a second to several years.

The characteristic angular distribution of the Čerenkov radiation is obliterated under these circumstances, for a variety of reasons. For instance, the reactor core is not a point source, the angular distribution of the secondary electrons in the scattering process is broad, and the energy distribution of these electrons is wide, so that the Čerenkov angle itself has a wide range, extending from 0° to a value just below the maximum (θ_{max} in water = 41°).

In view of the complexity of the problem, it would be very difficult to calculate the intensity and angular distributions of the light inside such a reactor, though a very approximate estimate may be made if a number of simplifying assumptions are introduced.

Estimate of Light Intensity

We will consider the case of a reactor running at a power of 100 kW; the Atomic Energy Authority's reactor LIDO at Harwell is a typical example.

We start from the following two fundamental figures:

(i) Of the total energy release of $\sim$ 200 MeV per fission, approximately 12 MeV appears in the form of γ-radiation, and

(ii) A power output of 1 W corresponds to about 3×10^{10} fissions/sec.

It is then easy to show that at a power level of 100 kW there are of the order of 10^{16} γ-rays emitted per second. Hyder (unpublished) has calculated the spectral distribution of the γ-rays in LIDO to be of the general form shown in Fig. 11.4. It is difficult to estimate the average energy of the γ-rays, but for our purposes here we will assume an energy of 1 MeV and a γ-ray yield of $\sim 3 \times 10^{16}$ quanta/sec. We will now

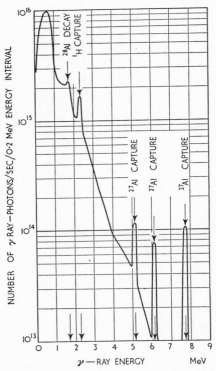

FIG. 11.4. The spectral distribution of γ-rays from the A.E.R.E. reactor LIDO at Harwell. (Hyder, unpublished.)

assume that the average energy of the secondary electrons is ~ 0.7 MeV. These electrons will only produce Čerenkov radiation while they are being slowed down (by ionization) to the threshold energy in water, which is 0·26 MeV; i.e. over a range of ~ 0.23 cm. The *total* path-length travelled per second, for *all* the secondary electrons together is thus $0.23 \times 3 \times 10^{16} \approx 7 \times 10^{15}$ cm/sec. On the basis of a Čerenkov yield of 250 photons/cm (in the optical region) for an ultra-relativistic electron ($\beta = 1$), the rate of production of light for electrons of average energy 0·5 MeV (between 0·7 and 0·26 MeV) will be $\sim$ 140 photons/cm, with $\bar{\beta} = 0.86$. The total yield of light from the whole reactor is then seen to be $7 \times 10^{15} \times 140 \approx 10^{18}$ photons/sec.

We assume that the reactor core has an open structure so that there is no screening of the light. If now we were to use a 2 in. diameter photomultiplier at the top of the water tank, distant 5 m from the core, the geometrical factor for the light collection would be 6×10^{-6}; at a power level of 100 kW the received light would then have an intensity of $\sim 6 \times 10^{12}$ photons/sec and the photoelectron yield, with a 10% photocathode efficiency, would be $\sim 6 \times 10^{11}$ electrons/sec. In the absence of background light, it would appear quite feasible to detect the light from this reactor core when the power level was as low as 1 mW.

The Monitoring and Control of Reactors

The power level in a reactor is normally measured with neutron detectors which give a direct indication of the neutron population density. Both the reactor power and the radiation leaking from a typical reactor shield are directly dependent on the neutron density in the reactor; this quantity therefore provides the most useful signal for operating reactor control systems.

In principle it would be possible to use the signal from a simple Čerenkov detector to control a reactor, but because the γ-ray intensity is not simply related to power or reactivity, such a system would have severe disadvantages. For example, a short time after shutting a reactor down from full power, the residual γ-ray activity from fission products might completely mask a dangerously rapid increase in neutron population. Furthermore, measurements of low power levels, deduced from γ-ray activities due partly to previous operation at full power, might well be in error by many orders of magnitude, even several hours after shutdown.

In spite of these limitations, however, it has definite possibilities in certain specific applications. It might, for instance, be useful in studies of the variations of the γ-ray fluxes themselves during pile operation, and several light receivers looking at different parts of the core and connected up differentially could be used to look for non-uniformities in the γ-ray flux.

s

From a practical point of view the idea is distinctly attractive, for the detector itself, the photomultiplier, can be mounted right outside the reactor away from the nuclear radiation fields, the light being transmitted down a light guide. Furthermore, by the insertion of suitable optical filters, a single photomultiplier could be set up to cover a very wide range of power levels, a range very difficult to achieve with a single neutron monitor.

A possible use of a Čerenkov detector is as a monitor of the power variation during an accidental surge. The wide range would be an advantage and a remote instrument of this type might escape the effects of an accident which could destroy normal neutron detectors. For instance, such a light receiver could be adjusted to operate over a range from full normal power to say one thousand times this value.

As an example of the overall sensitivity of a simple light receiver operating on the Čerenkov radiation in a water reactor, consider the measurements reported by Skarsvåg and Lundby (1953). An EMI photomultiplier type 6260 was used; this, mounted 30 cm above the water surface in the heavy-water reactor JEEP, gave an output of ~ 10 V across a load resistor of 10^7 Ω when the voltage across the multiplier was 475 V, and the reactor was running at a power of 2 kW. The current in the phototube (~ 1 μA in this case) was amplified by a d.c. amplifier and fed to a pen recorder. The experiments, which included tests with and without a light pipe dipping into the water, and with the photomultiplier withdrawn various distances up a tube through the concrete shielding, showed that there was a linear relationship between the light output and reactor power, over a range from ~ 80 W up to 5 kW.

11.9 Optical radiation from a charge moving across a grating

When an electron moves over the surface of a metal diffraction grating, in a direction at right angles to its rulings, a directed radiation is produced which has certain similarities with Čerenkov radiation, both as regards the condition of coherence and the intensity. The effect is closely related to the interpretation of Čerenkov radiation presented by Pierce (1955), discussed elsewhere, section 3.4.

That radiation should be produced in this way was first proposed by Purcell, and some experiments are described by Smith and Purcell (1953) in which coherent light was observed from an optical grating placed in an intense electron beam from a Van de Graaff generator.

The radiation is produced by the periodic motion of the charge induced on the surface of the grating, see Fig. 11.5(a). Very simply, we may regard the electron, in a position say e_1 as it passes over a crest of the grating, as setting up a dipole between itself and its image charge e_1. When the electron then moves on to a point e_2, above a trough, the image charge will be in a position e_2' and the dipole moment will therefore have changed. Clearly, the periodic fluctuations in this dipole moment will only be appreciable if the electron is moving very close to the grating, or to be more specific, if its distance from the surface is much less than the spacing of the rulings d.

The coherence condition may be derived directly from the Huygens construction, Fig. 11.5(b). Suppose the electron takes a time $\Delta\tau_1$ to

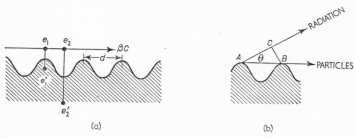

(a) (b)

FIG. 11.5. To illustrate the production of radiation from a charge moving across the surface of a grating.
(a) Modulation of the dipole moment.
(b) Construction to obtain the coherence condition.

move the distance d between two adjacent rulings A and B, while radiation emitted at A takes a time $\Delta\tau_2$ to move to the point C for which the angle $\widehat{BAC} = \theta$. If the electron velocity is βc, we have

$$\Delta\tau_1 = d/\beta c \text{ and } \Delta\tau_2 = d\cos\theta/c.$$

For coherence to exist, so that BC is a wavefront common to all wavelets emitted along the track, the time difference must be a multiple N of the fundamental period of an oscillation whose corresponding wavelength is λ.

Thus, $\Delta\tau_1 - \Delta\tau_2 = \dfrac{d}{\beta c} - \dfrac{d\cos\theta}{c} = \dfrac{N\lambda}{c}$, or

$$\lambda = \left(\frac{d}{N}\right)\left[\frac{1}{\beta} - \cos\theta\right] \tag{11.15}$$

It follows from (11.15) that for an electron moving at a given velocity βc, a certain wavelength will be observed at only one angle. Conversely, if λ is fixed (say by an interference filter), β may be determined from the angle θ at which this specific wavelength is found.

For example, consider an 81 keV electron beam moving across a grating having 15,000 lines/inch. In this case $d = 16\cdot9 \times 10^3$ Å, $\beta = 0\cdot5$ and we may take a wavelength of $\lambda = 4000$ Å. For the fifth order spectrum, $N = 5$, we find from (11.15) that $\theta = 41°: 24'$.

The intensity of the light is estimated as follows:

The rate of loss of energy by radiation at a wavelength λ for a dipole of moment p (see Joos, 1946, p. 328), is

$$\frac{dW}{dt} = \frac{16\pi^4 c}{3\lambda^4} \cdot p^2 \tag{11.16}$$

Writing $p = el$, and considering only grazing paths of the electron for which $l = (d/10)$, the total radiation in the first order, $N = 1$, from a grating of length L, is

$$W = \frac{16\pi^4 c}{3\lambda^4} \times \frac{e^2 d^2}{100} \times \frac{L}{\beta c} = \frac{16\pi^4 e^2 L}{300\beta\lambda^2} \tag{11.17}$$

since $d = N\lambda$.

With typical values of $L = 1$ mm, $\beta = 0\cdot5$, $N = 4$ and $\lambda = 4000$ Å, it is easy to show that the light yield is of the order of 10 photons/ sterad per millimetre of path per electron, in the forward direction.

The width of the image is of course influenced by diffraction and it is essential that the particles be very accurately collimated; in the experiments of Smith and Purcell, the divergence of their electron beam was less than 0·004 rad.

The radiation is polarized with the electric vector perpendicular to the surface of the grating.

This phenomenon, in which the light output is similar to that of Čerenkov radiation, might find application in the measurement of particle energies when intense and well-collimated beams are available.

11.10 The inverse Čerenkov effect; a new type of accelerator?

Among a number of new ideas for accelerating charged particles, Veksler (1956) proposed a scheme based on an inverse Čerenkov effect. The essential idea is that a medium, in this case the electrons of an ion plasma, should move at high velocity past the heavy ions to be accelerated. It is in this way possible to convey energy to the ions, the process being an application of the Čerenkov effect in a moving medium, see section 2.3. For this to occur, it is of course necessary that the refractive index should exceed unity; in an ion plasma such a condition may be achieved in the presence of a magnetic field, as described in section 3.6.

The process is extremely inefficient for the acceleration of *single* particles. It is however possible to invoke the idea of "bunching" the particles to be accelerated; the effect will then be enhanced due to coherence between the fields from the separate particles. If N is the number of charges in the bunch, the associated electric field E is proportional to N and the accelerating force proportional to N^2. Veksler has shown that the resulting field E is given by:

$$E = e \, \frac{N\omega_0^2}{v^2} \cdot F \cdot \ln\left(\frac{v}{\lambda_0 \omega_0}\right) \qquad (11.18)$$

where e is the charge of a single particle being accelerated, ω_0 the plasma frequency, given by $\omega_0^2 = 4\pi e^2 \rho/m$ (m is the electron mass and ρ the number of electrons/cm^3), v the velocity of the electron plasma, λ_0 the Compton wavelength, and F is a form factor which depends on the size of the bunch. ($F \to 1$ when the dimensions of the bunch are $\ll \lambda_p$, the plasma wavelength, $= v/\omega_0$).

It is in principle possible to obtain values of E of the order of many millions of volts per centimetre, if sufficiently high values of N and ω_0^2 are chosen. In practice however there are several practical difficulties; the scheme would only work for very high pulse-currents of accelerated particles, which in turn imply exceptionally large input powers.

11.11 A simple radiation monitor

For monitoring γ-radiation at very high flux levels, of the order of a kilo-curie, the light output from Čerenkov radiation in a small radiator is sufficient to operate a photovoltaic cell. Thomas *et al.* (1957) have recently shown that it is then quite feasible to dispense with the conventional photomultiplier and its associated electronics. They claim that the advantage of Čerenkov radiators over phosphors is that the majority of the latter are subject to temperature changes and are affected by high dosages, in the region of 10^3–10^{10} rep/sec.*

Their own detector consisted of a small plastic container filled with

* For definition of the rep, see E on p. 274.

water, which was viewed by a Bradley laboratory selenium barrier-layer photovoltaic cell of dimensions 1·75 in. × 0·75 in. Fused silica is however recommended for the water container, as it has been shown that this can withstand $\sim 10^9$ rep/sec without discoloration. Alternative light detectors which were suggested are CdS, CdTe and photo-electric semi-conducting silicon or germanium junctions.

Some of their experiments were conducted with a milliammeter of internal resistance $\sim 2000 \, \Omega$. However, with a high impedance load, a photovoltaic cell gives an output proportional to the logarithm of the light intensity; this is useful when it is required to cover a wide range of fluxes. To measure the overall sensitivity of their instrument, they irradiated the cell directly with a beam of 2 MeV electrons. It was found that a beam current of 4 μA yielded an output from the cell of 20 μA, while a beam of 50 μA gave an output of 100 μA. Data on a number of commercially available photovoltaic cells will be found in Tables 5G and 5H in section 5.9.

Instruments of this type may prove useful for monitoring intense γ-ray sources and fuel elements from reactors, etc.; they are simple, cheap, robust and are naturally relatively insensitive to neutrons.

11.12 Detecting fission products in reactors

The presence of fission products in water-cooled reactors may be revealed by the Čerenkov radiation produced by certain of the β-ray emitting isotopes in these products. Gordon and Hoover (1957) have described a method for the detection of burst slugs, in which the contaminated water is monitored in a small glass cell in front of a photomultiplier. Their detector, which was calibrated with a uranium nitrate solution, was biased so that it would record only those β-ray activities for which the end-point energies were in excess of 5 MeV. The following table contains details of five fission-product isotopes

TABLE 11C

Fission product isotope	Half-life	β-particles per disintegration, %	β-ray end-point energy (MeV)
87 Br	55 sec	30	8·0
136 I	86 sec	100	6·4
90 Rb	2·7 min	100	5·7
94 Y	16·5 min	100	5·4
88 Kr–88 Rb	2·77 hr	78	5·3

which are particularly suitable indicators with regard to β-ray energy and half-life. It is the analysis of the decay curve of the water sample which is used to identify the contamination with fission.

11.13 The Čerenkov effect and the polarity of the charged particle

It has been suggested by Critchfield (see Winckler *et al.*, 1955) that there might be a detectable difference between the Čerenkov radiation emitted from a positive and a negative particle. These workers looked for this effect with positive and negative π-mesons at an energy of 109 MeV, and deduced that the polarity effects, if any, were very small.

That such an effect should exist or be detectable would however seem to be impossible, for the following fundamental reason. Returning to Fig. 3.13, we see that the axial component of the electromagnetic pulse at a given point in the medium consists of two δ-functions side by side and of opposite sign. From this, the classical picture of the process, it follows that if the diagram refers to the state of affairs for, say, a π^+-meson, the wave-form for a π^--meson will be reversed, in the sense that the two separate pulses will be reversed, the negative one preceding the positive. Since the "widths" of these δ-functions are $\sim 10^{-15}$ sec (if the cut-off frequency of the spectrum is imposed by a resonance in the ultra-violet, at say $\lambda = 3000$ Å), it follows that a determination of the polarity of the charge demands that the position of the particle shall be known to at least $3 \cdot 10^{-5}$ cm (for $\beta = 1$), which is clearly impossible.

There are in addition several practical difficulties. First, in a real medium, the multiple Coulomb scattering of the particle is sufficient to produce path differences much greater than $3 \cdot 10^{-5}$ cm (or time fluctuations $\gg 10^{-15}$ sec). Secondly, the dispersion is such that over any reasonable path length, the two components of the pulse will overlap, over a bandwidth adequate to produce sufficient light intensity. And last, although the photoelectric yield of a surface depends on the angle of incidence of the electric vector as Winckler points out, it is not clear how the photoeffect will be sensitive to the *phase* of this vector.

11.14 Mesonic Čerenkov effect

In the course of the protracted controversy of the multiple and plural production of mesons in nuclear interactions, Wada (1949) proposed that mesons might be produced in cascade within a nucleus (plural production, in the accepted nomenclature) be a process closely analogous to the normal Čerenkov effect. Thus, the mesonic Čerenkov effect, might be expected to occur when a nucleon traverses nuclear matter at a velocity exceeding the phase velocity for the propagation of the mesonic field. In this analogy the fast nucleon is the source of the meson field, as the fast charged particle in normal Čerenkov radiation is the source of the polarization field in a dielectric. The emitted mesons correspond to materialization of the meson field, as the photons in the normal effect correspond to quantized fragments of the electromagnetic field associated with the polarization.

The relativistic energy–momentum relationship gives

$$\omega/\kappa = c(1 + \kappa_0^2/\kappa^2)^{\frac{1}{2}}$$

as the phase velocity of the meson field *in vacuo*, where ω and κ are the frequency and reciprocal wavelength of the phase wave respectively, κ_0 is the reciprocal Compton wavelength of the meson, and c is the velocity of light. (ω/κ) is always $>c$ *in vacuo*, and therefore spontaneous creation of mesons along the track of a nucleon *in vacuo* cannot take place. (ω/κ) may however become $<c$, and a Čerenkov process take place, provided the nucleon is moving through nuclear matter which is endowed with characteristics analogous to the refractive index in electromagnetic theory.

When the Klein–Gordon equation is set up, there appear, at most, two "indices of refraction", one corresponding to the electromagnetic case, n_1, and the other, n_2, associated with the Compton wavelength. A plane-wave solution of this equation gives, for the phase-velocity of the meson-wave,

$$v_\rho = (\omega/\kappa) = (c/n_1)\,[1 + \kappa_0^2/(n_2^2\kappa^2)]^{\frac{1}{2}} \qquad (11.19)$$

It is clear from (11.19) that for $n_1 > 1$, it is possible to find values of $v_\rho < c$, and hence less than the nucleon velocity, provided κ is large. Following the lines of Cox (1944), see also section 2.4, it is found that the opening angle θ for the jet of emitted mesons will be:

$$\cos\theta = c/(n_1\beta)\,.\,\{1 + \kappa_0^2/(n_2^2\kappa^2)\}^{\frac{1}{2}} + \tfrac{1}{2}\,\varLambda\,\{\kappa(1 - 1/n_1^2) - \\ - \kappa_0^2/(n_1^2 n_2^2\kappa)\} \quad (11.20)$$

where βc is the velocity, and $\varLambda$ the de Broglie wavelength, of the nucleon before the interaction. The second term in (11.20) is the quantum-mechanical correction term, see section 2.4, similar to that in equation (2.34). Considering only the first term, note that θ depends on κ, the momentum of the meson.

In practice the effect is likely to be sensitive to a number of factors not considered in this simplified treatment, and diffraction would no doubt blur the sharpness of the emission cone.

The effect has also been considered in more detail by Indenbom (1951).

APPENDIX I

CONSTANTS AND NUMERICAL DATA

A. Units and Constants

Velocity of light	$c = 2 \cdot 99793 \times 10^{10}$ cm sec^{-1}
Charge of the electron	$e = 4 \cdot 803 \times 10^{-10}$ e.s.u.
Mass of the electron	$m_e = 9 \cdot 108 \times 10^{-28}$ g
Classical electron radius	$r_e = e^2/m_e c^2 = 2 \cdot 8178 \times 10^{-13}$ cm
Compton wavelength of the electron	$\lambda_e = h/m_e c = 2 \cdot 4262 \times 10^{-10}$ cm
Planck's constant	$h = 6 \cdot 625 \times 10^{-27}$ erg sec
Fine structure constant	$\alpha = e^2/\hbar c = 1/137 \cdot 038$
Avogadro's number	$N = 6 \cdot 025 \times 10^{23}$ atoms/g-atom
Bohr magneton	$e\hbar/2m_e c = 9 \cdot 2732 \times 10^{-21}$ erg gauss^{-1}
Nuclear magneton	$e\hbar/2M_p c = 5 \cdot 0504 \times 10^{-24}$ erg gauss^{-1}
Bohr radius of H atom	$a_0 = 0 \cdot 529 \times 10^{-8}$ cm
Thomson cross-section	$\sigma_s = (8/3)\pi r_e^2 = 0 \cdot 665 \times 10^{-24}$ cm^2
Loschmidt's constant (molecules per ml of ideal gas at n.t.p.)	$2 \cdot 687 \times 10^{19}$ cm^{-3} atm^{-1}
Boltzmann's constant	$k = 1 \cdot 380 \times 10^{-16}$ erg deg^{-1}
Energy kT, for 1°K	$8 \cdot 6165 \times 10^{-5}$ eV deg^{-1}

These constants, and the conversion factors in section D have been taken from the compilation of Du Mond and Cohen, *Rev. Mod. Phys.* **25**(3), 691, (1953). A more recent survey of atomic constants may be found in the review article by Bearden and Thomsen: Supplement to Vol. **5**, series X of *Nuovo Cimento*. No. 2, p. 267 (1957).

Notes to Table B on facing page

A comprehensive account of the properties of most of the elementary particles will be found in *High Energy Particles* by B. Rossi, Prentice Hall, New York, 1952.

1. For an account of our present knowledge of the neutrino, see the review article by B. W. Ridley in *Progress in Nuclear Physics*, Vol. **5**, p. 188. Pergamon Press, 1956.

2. The interactions and decay of the positron are discussed in detail by Deutsch (1953).

3. For discussion of the μ–e decay scheme, see B. W. Ridley in *Progress in Nuclear Physics*, 1956 (see above).

4. See for example B. Rossi in *High Energy Particles*, p. 197, 1952 (see above); also Harris *et al.*, *Phys. Rev.* **106**, (2), 327 (1957).

5. A general account of the properties of the π-meson has been given by C. F. Powell, *Rep. Progr. Phys.* **13**, 350, (1950).

B. The Elementary Particles

Name	Symbol	Charge	Rest mass, electron masses	Rest energy	(Free) Mean life (sec)	Modes of decay	Notes
Neutrino	ν	0	$<10^{-3}$	<500 eV	assumed to be stable		1
Electron	e^-	$-e$	1	0·511 MeV	stable		
Positron	e^+	$+e$	1	0·511 MeV	stable	$e^+ + e^- \rightarrow 2\gamma$ (sometimes 1 and 3γ)	2
μ-Meson	$\mu\pm$	$\pm e$	207	106 MeV	$2\cdot2 \times 10^{-6}$	$\mu^+ \rightarrow e^+ + 2\nu$ $\mu^- \rightarrow e^- + 2\nu$, or orbital capture	3
Neutral π-Meson	π^0	0	264	135 MeV	$<5 \times 10^{-16}$	$\pi^0 \rightarrow 2\gamma$	4
Charged π-Meson	$\pi\pm$	$\pm e$	273	140 MeV	$2\cdot6 \times 10^{-8}$	$\pi^+ \rightarrow \mu^+ + \nu$ $\pi^- \rightarrow \mu^- + \nu$, or orbital capture	5
τ-Meson K-meson	$\tau\pm$ $K\pm$	$\pm e$	966	494 MeV	$\sim10^{-8}$	$\tau\pm \rightarrow \pi\pm + \pi^+ + \pi^-$ Various modes of decay	6
Proton	P	$+e$	1836	938 MeV	stable		
Anti-proton	P^-	$-e$	protonic mass to within 5%		$>10^{-8}$ sec assumed stable in free flight	Annihilation, with emission of π-and K-mesons. Alternative, charge exchange, with emission of anti-neutrons	7
Neutron	N	0	1839	939 MeV	20 min	$N \rightarrow P + e^- + \nu$	

6. The present status of our knowledge of the heavy mesons, with an extensive bibliography, will be found in the paper by Crowe. *Nuovo Cimento*, Series X, Vol. **5**, (3), p. 541, 1 March (1957).

7. Experimental work on the properties of the anti-proton is still in progress; see E. Segrè (1956) *CERN symposium, Geneva*, Vol. **2**, p. 107.

Besides the particles listed above, there are others, known as Hyperons, which are heavier than protons. These are not generally considered as "elementary" particles. Research is incomplete but the reader is referred to the reference in Note 6 above.

A more recent discussion of the mass values and modes of decay of the various forms of meson and Hyperons, will be found in the work of Franzinetti and Morpurgo "An introduction to the physics of the new particles", Supplement to Vol. **6**, Series X, No. 2 of *Nuovo Cimento*, p. 472 (1957).

C. Black-body Radiation

Energy density $\div T^4$ $7\cdot5635 \times 10^{-15}$ erg cm^{-3}deg^{-4}
$= \pi^2 k^4/15\, c^3 \hbar^3$

Stefan's constant $\sigma = 5\cdot6687 \times 10^{-5}$ erg cm^{-2} sec^{-1} deg^{-4}

Constants in Planck's formula $c_1 = 8\pi hc = 4\cdot9919 \times 10^{-15}$ erg cm

                         $c_2 = hc/k = 1\cdot43884$ cm deg

Wien's constant $\lambda_{max}.\ T = c_2/4\cdot965 = 0\cdot2898$ cm deg

D. Conversion Factors for Mass, Energy and Wave-number

1 electron volt (eV) $= 1\cdot602 \times 10^{-12}$ erg

1 erg $= 6\cdot24 \times 10^{11}$ eV

1 kilowatt-hour (kWh) $= 2\cdot247 \times 10^{25}$ eV

1 watt $= 10^7$ erg sec^{-1}

1 atomic mass unit (a.m.u.) $= 931$ MeV

1 electron mass $= 0\cdot511$ MeV

Quantum energy and wave-number E/n $= 1\cdot986 \times 10^{-16}$ erg cm

Wavelength and quantum energy $E\lambda$ $= 12398 \times 10^{-8}$ eV cm

Wave-number and quantum energy n/E $= 8066$ cm^{-1}eV^{-1}

Frequency and quantum energy ν/E $= 2\cdot418 \times 10^{14}$ eV^{-1}sec^{-1}

Quantum energy and frequency E/ν $= 4\cdot135 \times 10^{-15}$ eV sec

E. Units of Radiation-dose and Radioactivity

A dose of 1 *Röntgen* at any point corresponds to:

83·8 erg absorbed per gramme of air,

~ 94 erg absorbed per gramme of living tissue (sometimes called the rep, the Röntgen equivalent physical),

$2\cdot08 \times 10^9$ ion pairs per cm^3 of air at n.t.p.,

1 610 $\times 10^{12}$ ion pairs per gramme of air, or

$6 \cdot 77 \times 10^4$ MeV absorbed per cm^3 of air at n.t.p.

1 röntgen hr$^{-1} \equiv 9 \cdot 3 \times 10^{-14}$ A cm^{-3} in air at n.t.p.

Mean energy to produce an ion pair in air 32·5 eV.

The Curie

Original definition: 1 curie is that quantity of radon ($\sim 0 \cdot 66$ mm^3 at n.t.p.) which is in equilibrium with 1 g of radium.

Present usage extended to any radioactive substance. 1 curie is equivalent to $3 \cdot 7 \times 10^{10}$ disintegrations per sec.

The Rutherford: 1 rutherford $\equiv 10^6$ disintegrations per sec.

F. Fission

The energy release in the fission of ^{235}U is divided up in the following way:

Kinetic energy of the fragments	168 MeV
Kinetic energy of neutrons	2 MeV
Prompt γ-rays	5 MeV
Delayed radiations: β-particles	6 MeV
neutrinos	9 MeV
γ-Rays following β-decay	6 MeV
Total	196 MeV

In a reactor running at a power of 1 W, fissions are occurring at a rate of $3 \cdot 1 \times 10^{10}$ per sec.

G. Sources of Fast Particles

(i) *Accelerating machines*

A beam current of 1 A corresponds to a flow of $6 \cdot 24 \times 10^{18}$ singly-charged particles/sec, or 1 μA $\equiv 6 \cdot 24 \times 10^{12}$ charges/sec.

(ii) *Cosmic-rays (sea-level)*

The fluxes of particles of different types depend on the latitude, their energy and on the conditions of measurement. As a general guide, the following data is taken from B. Rossi, *Rev. Mod. Phys.* **20,** (3), 537 (1948).

I_v vertical flux

J_1 total flux crossing a unit horizontal area.

J_2 total flux crossing a sphere of unit radius.

	Total intensity	Hard component	Soft component
I_v	$1 \cdot 14 \times 10^{-2}$	$0 \cdot 83 \times 10^{-2}$	$0 \cdot 31 \times 10^{-2}$ cm^{-2}sec^{-1}sterad^{-1}
J_1	$1 \cdot 79 \times 10^{-2}$	$1 \cdot 27 \times 10^{-2}$	$0 \cdot 52 \times 10^{-2}$ cm^{-2}sec^{-1}
J_2	$2 \cdot 41 \times 10^{-2}$	$1 \cdot 68 \times 10^{-2}$	$0 \cdot 73 \times 10^{-2}$ cm^{-2}sec^{-1}

Very approximately, about 75% of all particles at sea-level are penetrating, and are μ-mesons. The absolute flux of protons at sea-level, in a momentum range 700–1100 MeV/c, is $1 \cdot 5 \times 10^{-5}$ cm^{-2}sec^{-1}sterad^{-1}, or $\sim 0 \cdot 1$% of all particles.

H. Radiation Lengths and Critical Energies

For definitions and notation, see section 6.5 and
(i) B. Rossi and K. Greisen (1941) *Rev. Mod. Phys.* **13**(4), 240.
(ii) A. Kantz and R. Hofstadter (1954) *Nucleonics* **12**(3), 36.
(iii) B. Rossi (1952) *High Energy Particles*, pp. 48–55, Prentice Hall, New York.
(iv) B. T. Price, C. C. Horton and K. T. Spinney (1957) *Radiation Shielding*, p. 83, Pergamon Press, London.

Element or substance	Radiation length X_0 (g/cm^2)	Critical energy ϵ (MeV)	Reference
H	58	400	(iv) above
He	85	260	(iv) above
C	44·6	102	(iii) above
N	39·4	88·7	(iii) above
O	35·3	77·7	(iii) above
Al	24·5	48·8	(iii) above
A	19·8	35·2	(iii) above
Fe	14·1	24·3	(iii) above
Cu	13·1	21·8	(iii) above
Pb	6·5	7·8	(iii) above
Air	37·7	84·2	(iii) above
Water	37·1	83·8	(iii) above
Chance Pb-glass	10·0	16·2	See Table 6H, section 6.7
Corning Pb-glass	11·0	13	See Table 6H, section 6.7
Thallous chloride	6·6	8·3	See Table 6I, section 6.7
Perspex	~ 43	—	

The radiation length for a mixture is calculated from $(1/X_0)_{mixture} = \sum_i (p_i/X_i)$, where p_i is the fraction by weight of the ith component. Very approximately, the critical energy may be obtained from:

$$\epsilon \approx 800/Z$$

where Z is the atomic number.

APPENDIX II

GRAPHICAL DATA

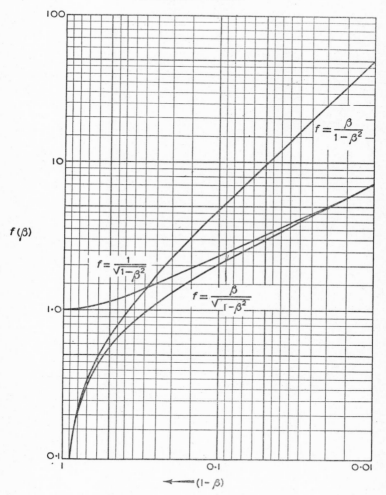

FIG. II.1. The quantities $\beta/(1-\beta^2)$, $1/(1-\beta^2)^{\frac{1}{2}}$ and $\beta/(1-\beta^2)^{\frac{1}{2}}$ as a function of $(1-\beta)$ (after Rossi, *High Energy Particles*, Prentice Hall, New York, 1952, p. 535).

277

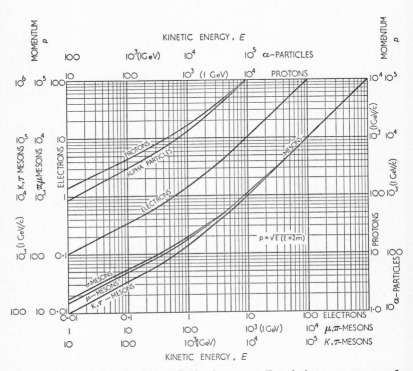

FIG. II.2. The relation between the kinetic energy E and the momentum p for particles of different mass. The units for E are MeV or GeV, and for p, MeV/c or GeV/c.

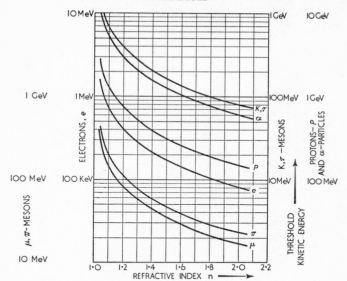

FIG. II.3. The threshold kinetic energies for Čerenkov radiation from the elementary particles, as a function of the refractive index of the medium.

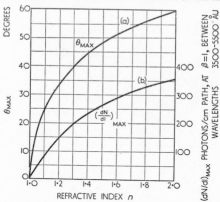

FIG. II.4. (a) The maximum Čerenkov angle θ_{max}, and (b) the radiation yield $(dN/dl)_{max}$, as a function of the refractive index n. (universal to all particles with unit electronic charge; for α-particles multiply $(dN/dl)_{max}$ by 4).

The scale for $(dN/dl)_{max}$ is calculated for a bandwidth of 3500–5500 Å, the region covered by the response of a Cs–Sb cathode surface. To calculate values of $(dN/dl)_{max}$ between other wavelength limits λ_1 and λ_2, multiply the figures read off the graph by the factor:

$$9620 \left\{ \frac{\lambda_2 - \lambda_1}{\lambda_1 \lambda_2} \right\} \text{ when } \lambda_1 \text{ and } \lambda_2 \text{ are expressed in Å.}$$

T

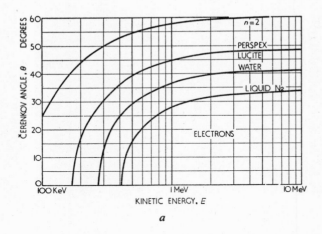

a

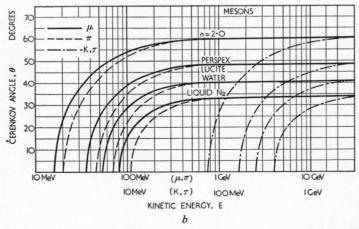

b

FIG. II.5. The variation of the Čerenkov angle θ as a function of the kinetic energy E, for the elementary particles in four media (i) liquid N_2 ($n = 1\cdot205$), (ii) H_2O ($n = 1\cdot33$), (iii) Perspex, Lucite and Plexiglas ($n = 1\cdot50$), and (iv) for $n = 2$.
(a) for electrons;
(b) μ, π, K and τ-mesons.

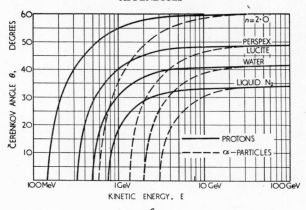

FIG. II.5.   (c) protons and α-particles.

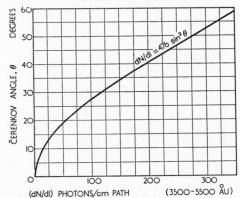

FIG. II.6. The variation of the radiation yield (dN/dl) as a function of the Čerenkov angle θ (universal to all singly charged particles and any refractive index). For α-particles multiply the light output by 4. Values of (dN/dl) are calculated for a band 3500–5500 Å, the region covered by the Cs–Sb response curve. To calculate values of (dN/dl) between other wavelength limits λ_1 and λ_2, multiply the figures read off this curve by the factor:

$$9620 \left\{ \frac{\lambda_2 - \lambda_1}{\lambda_1 \, \lambda_2} \right\} \text{ when } \lambda_1 \text{ and } \lambda_2 \text{ are expressed in Å.}$$

An example to illustrate the use of these curves

What is the light output from an 80 MeV π-meson in a slab of Perspex 1 cm thick, between 4000 and 5000 Å wavelength? From Fig. II.5(b), for a π-meson at 80 MeV $\theta = 30°$. From Fig. II.6, $\theta = 30°$ gives $(dN/dl) = 120$ photons/cm between 3500 and 5500 Å. This, using the factor 9620 $(\lambda_2 - \lambda_1)/\lambda_1 \, . \, \lambda_2$, represents an emission of 58 photons/cm between 4000 and 5000 Å.

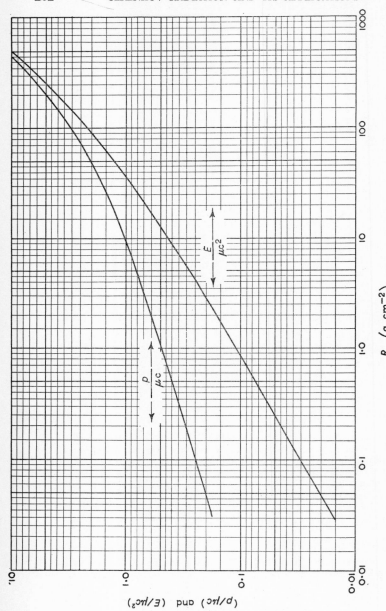

FIG. II.7. $p/\mu c$ and $E/\mu c^2$ as functions of $R/\mu c^2$ in air, where p is the momentum, E the kinetic energy, R the range and μ the mass of the particle. The curves are valid for particles of any mass provided that radiation losses and nuclear interactions are negligible compared with collision losses. (From Rossi, *Rev. Mod. Phys.* **20**(3), 537, (1948).)

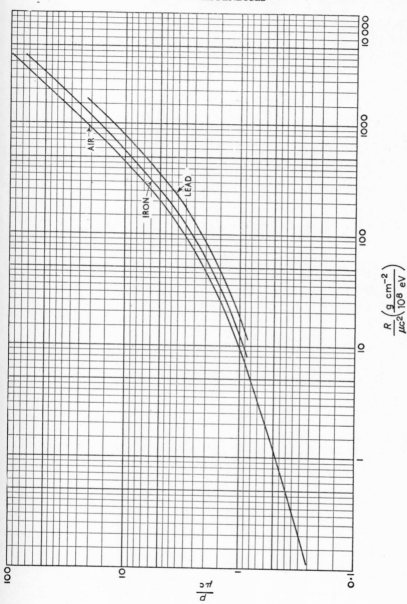

FIG. II.8. $p/\mu c$ as a function of $R/\mu c^2$ in air, iron and lead, where p is the momentum. R the range and μ the mass of the particle. These curves are valid for particles of any mass, provided that radiation losses and nuclear interactions are negligible compared with collision losses. (From Rossi, *Rev. Mod. Phys.* **20**(3), 537, (1948).)

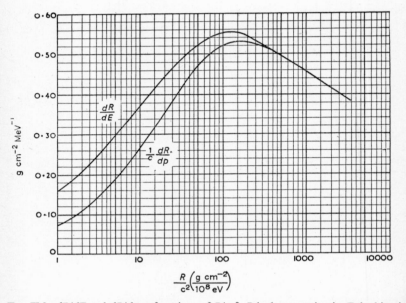

FIG. II.9. dR/dE and dR/dp as functions of $R/\mu c^2$. R is the range in air, E the kinetic energy and p the momentum. (From Rossi, *Rev. Mod. Phys.* **20**(3), 537, (1948).)

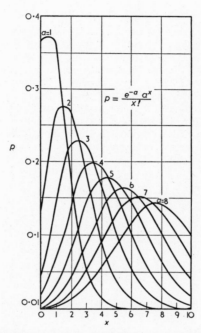

$$p = \frac{e^{-a}\, a^x}{x!}$$

FIG. II.10. Poisson distributions. If, for example, a is the average number of photo-electrons emitted from the cathode of a photomultiplier in a certain type of event, $p(x)$ is the probability that x photoelectrons will be observed. When a becomes large, the distribution is indistinguishable from a Gaussian, the standard deviation of which is $\pm \sqrt{a}$, and the *relative* value of this error becomes $1/\sqrt{a}$.

APPENDIX III

Cosmic-ray Air Showers

The following notes on cosmic-ray air showers are included to assist the reader who may require them for understanding the problems brought forward in Chapter 9.

The primary particles of the cosmic-radiation which enter the earth's atmosphere from outer space, have extremely high energy and give rise to a number of complicated processes throughout the atmosphere. These particles, most of which are protons, cause nuclear disintegrations at the top of the atmosphere, with the emission of further particles which in turn themselves produce disintegrations. Among the products of these nuclear disintegrations are neutral π-mesons, which decay into high-energy γ-rays.

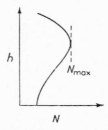

FIG. III.1. To show the general trend in the distribution of the number of particles N in the electron-photon cascade, as a function of the height h above the ground.

These in turn produce a cascade of electrons and further γ-rays by the processes of electron pair-production and Bremsstrahlung; such a cascade is known as an electron-photon shower. When the energy E_0 of the primary particle is sufficiently high, the shower reaches down to sea-level and is then known as an Extensive Air Shower, since the particles are found at considerable distances from the main axis of the shower.

The multiplication of the number of particles in the shower increases with atmospheric depth until their individual energies are reduced to < 100 MeV; below this energy the pair production and Bremsstrahlung processes lose in competition with Compton scattering and ionization energy-loss, and the shower then dwindles. There is thus some level at which there is a maximum number of particles N_{max} for a given E_0; this is shown in the sketch, Fig. III. 1, where the number of particles N is plotted against height above ground.

286

Air showers are observed by conventional counter techniques over a range of values of E_0 from $\sim 10^{13}$ eV to $\sim 10^{18}$ eV, there being a frequency distribution of the form $n(> E_0) \sim E_0^{-1.5}$. To give some numerical data for specific cases, showers of energy $E_0 > 10^{14}$ eV arrive at the earth's surface at a rate ~ 300 km^{-2} sec^{-1} sterad^{-1}, and those with $E_0 > 10^{16}$ eV at a rate ~ 0.2 km^{-2} sec^{-1} sterad^{-1}.* Showers of energies 10^{14} and 10^{16} eV have approximately 10^4 and 10^6 particles at sea-level respectively. The altitudes at which their maxima occur are uncertain but they are believed

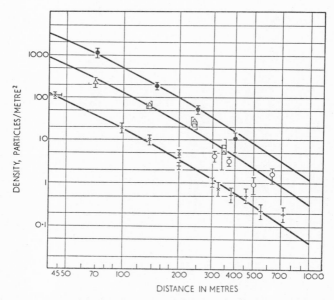

FIG. III.2. The lateral distribution of particles in air showers at sea-level as a function of the distance from the core. (After Cranshaw, Galbraith and Porter, *Phil. Mag.* **2**(19), 891, 1957.)

$\times$, $+$. Showers for which the average number of particles at sea-level is 3×10^6
$\triangle$, $\bigcirc$ and $\square$. Showers for which the average number of particles at sea-level is 2×10^7. $\bullet$. for which the average number of particles at sea-level is 9×10^7

to be of the order of 10 km. The density distribution of the particles as a function of the distance from the core of the shower is of the general form shown in Fig. III.2.

Besides the electrons and photons, there are many other components in air showers including nucleons and various types of meson; the electron-photon component however is dominant as regards *numbers* of particles if

* These figures apply to directions close to the zenith.

not their energy, the electrons being the most significant contributor to Čerenkov radiation.

The angular distribution of the axes of showers is a steep function of the zenith angle Z, and is of the form $n(Z)dZ \sim \cos^6 Z$.

Air showers arrive at the earth's surface at random and at a mean rate which is markedly constant in solar and sidereal time, though there appear to be some correlations with solar time.

REFERENCES

ABELE, M. (1952) *Nuovo Cim.*, Series 9, **9**, Suppl. (3), 207.

AKHIEZER, A. I. (1956) *Nuovo Cim.*, Series 10, **3**, Suppl. (4), 591.

AKHIEZER, A. I., FAINBERG, YA. B. and LYUBARSKY, G. L. (1956) *CERN Symposium, Geneva*, Vol. 1, p. 220.

AKHIEZER, A. I., LYUBARSKY, G. L. and FAINBERG, YA. B. (1950) *Dokl. Akad. Nauk, SSSR*, **73**, 55.

AKHIEZER, A. I. and SITENKO, A. G. (1952) *Zh. eksp. teor. fiz.*, **23**, 161.

ANDERSON, W. and BELCHER, E. H. (1954) *Brit. J. Appl. Phys.*, **5** (2), 53.

ASCOLI BALZANELLI, A. and ASCOLI, R. (1953) *Nuovo Cim.*, Series 9, **10** (9), 1345.

ASCOLI BALZANELLI, A. and ASCOLI, R. (1954) *Nuovo Cim.*, Series 9, **11** (5), 562.

ASCOLI BALZANELLI, A. and ASCOLI, R. (1957) *Nuovo Cim.*, Series 10, **6** (6), 1392.

ASKARIAN, G. A. (1956) *Zh. eksp. teor. fiz.*, **30**, 584, and *Soviet Phys.* (1956); (*J. Exp. Theor. Phys.*), **3** (4), 613.

AUERBACH, L. B., BERNARDINI, G., FILOSOFO, I., HANSON, A. O., ODIAN, A. C. and YAMAGATA, T. (1956) *CERN Symposium, Geneva*, Vol. 2, p. 291.

BABCOCK, H. W. and JOHNSON, J. J. (1941) *Astrophys. J.*, **94**, 271.

BACCALIN, C., BASSI, P. and MANDUCHI, C. (1955) *Nuovo Cim.*, Series 10, **1** (4), 657.

BALAZS, N. L. (1956) *Phys. Rev.*, **104** (5), 1220.

BARCLAY, F. R. and JELLEY, J. V. (1955) *Nuovo Cim.*, Series 10, **2** (1), 27.

BARCLAY, F. R. and JELLEY, J. V. (1956) *The Oxford Conference on Extensive Air Showers*, A.E.R.E., Harwell, p. 74.

BARKER, P. R., BINNIE, D. M., HYAMS, B. D. and ROUT, R. J. (1955a) *Phil. Mag.*, **46** (374), 300.

BARKER, P. R., BINNIE, D. M., HYAMS, B. D., ROUT, R. J. and SHEPHERD, J. (1955b) *Phil. Mag.*, **46** (374), 307.

BASSI, P. (1951) *Nuovo Cim.*, Series 9, **8**, 807.

BASSI, P., BIANCHI, A. M. and MANDUCHI, C. (1952) *Nuovo Cim.*, **9** (9), 861.

BASSI, P., CLARK, G. and ROSSI, B. (1953) *Phys. Rev.*, **92**, 441.

BAY, Z., CLELAND, M. R. and MCLERNON, F. (1952) *Phys. Rev.*, **87**, 901.

BECK, G. (1948) *Phys. Rev.*, **74** (7), 795.

BELCHER, E. H. (1953) *Proc. Roy. Soc.* A**216**, 90.

DE BENEDETTI, S. and RICHINGS, H. J. (1952) *Rev. Sci. Instrum.*, **23**, 37.

BIRKS, J. B. (1953) *Scintillation Counters*, Pergamon Press, London.

BLACKETT, P. M. S. (1948) *Rep. Conf. Gassiot Comm. Phys. Soc.* Emission spectra of the night sky and aurorae, p. 34, Physical Society, London.

BLUNCK, O. and LEISEGANG, S. (1950) *Z. Phys.*, **128**, 500.

BOGDANKEVICH, L. S. and BOLOTOVSKII, B. M. (1957) *Zh. eksp. teor. fiz.* **32**, 1421.

BOLOTOVSKII, B. M. and KOLOMENSKII, A. (1952) *Dokl. Akad. Nauk*, **85**, 59.

BOLOTOVSKII, B. M. (1957) *Usp. fiz. Nauk*, **62** (3), 201.

BOOTH, N. E., HUTCHINSON, G. W. and LEDLY, B. (1958). *Proc. Phys Soc.*, **71**, Pt. 3, (459), 293.

BOOTH, N. E. and LEDLEY, B. (1957) *J. Nuclear Instrum.*, **1** (6), 345.

BORN, M. (1933) *Optik*, Springer, Berlin.

BRABANT, J. M., CORK, B., HORWITZ, N., MOYER, B. J., MURRAY, J. J., WALLACE, R. and WENTZEL, W. A. (1956a) *Phys. Rev.*, **101** (1), 498 and (1956b) *Phys. Rev.*, **102** (6), 1622.

BRABANT, J. M., KENNEY, R. W. and WALLACE, R. (1956c) *Bull. Amer. Phys. Soc.*, Series II, **1** (5), 251.

BRABANT, J. M., MOYER, B. J. and WALLACE, R. (1957) *Rev. Sci. Instrum.*, **28** (6), 421.

BREITENBERGER, E. (1955) *Progress in Nuclear Physics*, Vol. 4, p. 56, Pergamon Press, London.

BREMMER, H. (1949) *Terrestial Radio Waves*, p. 282, Elsivier Publishing Co., New York.

BRENNAN, M. H. and LANDECKER, K. (1956) *Rev. Sci. Instrum.*, **27** (2), 112.

BUDINI, P. (1953) *Nuovo Cim.*, Series 9, **10** (3), 236.

BUDINI, P. and TAFFARA, L. (1953) *Nuovo Cim.*, Series 9, **10** (10), 1489.

CASSELS, J. M. (1956) *CERN Symposium, Geneva*, Vol. 2, p. 74.

ČERENKOV, P. A. (1934) *Dokl. Akad. Nauk, SSSR*, **2**, 451.

ČERENKOV, P. A. (1936) *Dokl. Akad. Nauk, SSSR*, **3**, 413.

ČERENKOV, P. A. (1937a) *Dokl. Akad. Nauk, SSSR*, **14**, 101.

ČERENKOV, P. A. (1937b) *Dokl. Akad. Nauk, SSSR*, **14**, 105.

ČERENKOV, P. A. (1937c) *Phys. Rev.*, **52**, 378.

ČERENKOV, P. A. (1937d) *Byull. Akad. Nauk, SSSR*, **4–5**, 455 and 492.

ČERENKOV, P. A. (1938a) *Dokl. Acad. Nauk, SSSR*, **20**, 651.

ČERENKOV, P. A. (1938b) *Dokl. Acad. Nauk, SSSR*, **21**, 116.

ČERENKOV, P. A. (1938c) *Dokl. Acad. Nauk, SSSR*, **21**, 319.

CHAMBERLAIN, O., SEGRÈ, E., WIEGAND, C. and YPSILANTIS, T. (1955) *Phys. Rev.*, **100** (3), 947.

CHAMBERLAIN, O. and WIEGAND, C. (1956) *CERN Symposium, Geneva*, Vol. 2, p. 82.

CHUDAKOV, A. and NESTEROVA, N. M. (1957) Paper read at the UPAP conference, Varenna, Como, Italy. (See also Nesterova and Chudakov 1955.)

CHUVEYEV, K. (1952) *Dokl. Akad. Nauk, SSSR*, **87** (4), 551.

CHUVILO, I. (1956) *CERN Symposium, Geneva*, Vol. 2, p. 83.

CLARK, G. W., SCHERB, F. and SMITH, W. B. (1957) *Rev. Sci. Instrum.*, **28** (6), 433.

COCCONI, G. (1949) *Rev. Mod. Phys.*, **21**, 26.

COLLINS, G. B. and REILING, V. G. (1938) *Phys. Rev.*, **54**, 499.

COWAN, C. L., REINES, F. and HARRISON, F. B. (1954) *Phys. Rev.*, **96**, 1294.

COX, R. T. (1944) *Phys. Rev.*, **66**, 106.

CRANE, H. R. (1948) *Rev. Mod. Phys.*, **20**, 278.

CRANSHAW, T. E. (1952) *Progress in Nuclear Physics*, Vol. 2, p. 271, Pergamon Press, London.

CRANSHAW, T. E. and GALBRAITH, W. (1954) 7th Series, *Phil. Mag.*, **45**, (370), 1109.

CRANSHAW, T. E. and GALBRAITH, W. (1957) 8th Series *Phil. Mag.*, **2**, (18), 804.

CURIE, EVE. (1941) *Madame Curie*, Heinemann, London.

CURRAN, S. C. (1953) *Luminescence and the Scintillation Counter*, Butterworths Scientific Publications, London.

CURRAN, S. C. and BAKER, W. R. (1948) *Rev. Sci. Instrum.*, **19**, 116. U.S. Atomic Energy Comm. Rep. M.D.D.C.—1296 (1944).

DAINTON, F. S. (1948) *Chem. Soc. Ann. Rep.*, **45**, 5. (A short note on page 16.)

DANOS, M. (1955) *J. Appl. Phys.*, **26** (1), 2.

DANOS, M., GESHWIND, S., LASHINSKY, H. and VAN TRIER, A. (1953) *Phys. Rev.*, **92** (3), 828.

DAVIDSON, P. W. (1952) *Nucleonics*, **10** (3), 33.

DAVIS, R., Jr. (1956) *Bull. Amer. Phys. Soc.*, Series 2, **1**, (4), 219.

DEDRICK, K. G. (1952) *Phys. Rev.*, **87**, 891.

DEE, P. I. and RICHARDS, E. W. T. (1951) *Nature, Lond.*, **168**, 736.

DÉJARDIN, G. (1936) *Rev. Mod. Phys.*, **8**, (1), 1.

DEUTSCH, M. (1953) *Progress in Nuclear Physics*, Vol. 3, p. 131, Pergamon Press, London.

DICKE, R. H. (1947) *Phys. Rev.*, **71**, 737.

DUERDEN, T. and HYAMS, B. D. (1952) *Phil. Mag.*, 7th Series, **43** (342), 717.

DUMOND, J. W. M. and COHEN, E. R. (1953) *Rev. Mod. Phys.*, **25** (3), 691.

EIDMAN, V. YA. (1956) Transactions of the Gorky Research Physiotechnical Institute and Radiophysical Faculty of the Gorky State University. *Scientific Notes* No. XXX.

ENGSTROM, R. W. (1955) *R.C.A. Rev.*, **16** (1), 116.

FERMI, E. (1939) *Phys. Rev.*, **56**, 1242.

FERMI, E. (1940) *Phys. Rev.*, **57**, 485.

FIDECARO, G. (1956) *CERN Symposium, Geneva*, Vol. 2, p. 80.

FILOSOFO, I. and YAMAGATA, T. (1956) *CERN Symposium, Geneva*, Vol. 2, p. 85.

FITCH, V. and MOTLEY, R. (1956) *Phys. Rev.*, **101**, 496.

FOWLER, G. N. and JONES, G. M. D. B. (1953) *Proc. Phys. Soc.* A **66**, 597.

FRANK, I. M. (1942) *Izv. Akad. Nauk (Fiz.)*, **6**, 3.

FRANK, I. M. (1943) *Zh. fiz., SSSR*, 7, 49. (Same topic as preceding reference.)

FRANK, I. M. (1944) *Dokl. Akad. Nauk, SSSR*, **42** (8), 341

FRANK, I. M. (1952) *Vavilov Memorial Symposium*, p. 172, U.S.S.R. Academy of Sciences, Moscow.

FRANK, I. M. (1956) *Usp. fiz. Nauk*, **58** (1), 111.

FRANK, I. M. and GINSBURG, V. (1945) *Zh. fiz., SSSR*, **9** (5), 353.

FRANK, I. M. and TAMM, IG. (1937) *Dokl. Akad. Nauk, SSSR*, **14** (3), 109.

GALBRAITH, W. and JELLEY, J. V. (1953) *Nature, Lond.*, **171** (4347), 349.

GALBRAITH, W. and JELLEY, J. V. (1955) Part I. *J. Atmosph. Terr. Phys.*, **6** (5), 250.

GARWIN, R. L. (1952) *Rev. Sci. Instrum.*, **23** (12), 755.

GETTING, I. A. (1947) *Phys. Rev.*, **71**, 123.

GINSBURG, V. L. (1940a) *Zh. fiz. SSSR*, **2**, 441; (1940) *Zh. eksp. teor. fiz.*, **10** (6), 589.

GINSBURG, V. L. (1940b) *Zh. fiz. SSSR*, **3**, 101; (1939) *Zh. eksp. teor. fiz.*, **10** (6), 608.

GINSBURG, V. L. (1942) *Zh. eksp. teor. fiz.*, **12**, 425.

GINSBURG, V. L. (1943) *Zh. fiz.*, *SSSR*, **7**, 115. (Same topic as preceding reference.)

GINSBURG, V. L. (1947a) *Dokl. Akad. Nauk*, **56** (3), 253. Translated by Defence Scientific Information Service. Defence Research Board, Canada. T103R (1954).

GINSBURG, V. L. (1947b) *Byull. Akad. Nauk, SSSR*, **11** (2), 165.

GINSBURG, V. L. (1952) *Vavilov Memorial Symposium*, p. 193, U.S.S.R. Academy of Sciences, Moscow.

GINSBURG, V. L. and FRANK, I. M. (1946) *Zh. eksp. teor. fiz.*, **16**, 15.

GINSBURG, V. L. and FRANK, I. M. (1947a) *Dokl. Akad. Nauk*, *SSSR*. **56** (6), 583. Translation T103R (1954) by Defence Research Board, Canada.

GINSBURG, V. L. and FRANK, I. M. (1947b) *Dokl. Akad. Nauk*, *SSSR*, **56** (7), 699. Translation T103R (1954) by Defence Research Board, Canada.

GOLDANSKII, V. I. and ZHDANOV, G. B. (1954) *Zh. eksp. teor. fiz.*, **26** (4), 405. A.E.R.E. Lib/Trans. 536.

GORDON, C. M. and HOOVER, J. I. (1957) *Nucleonics*, **15** (1), 92.

GREENFIELD, M. A., NORMAN, A., DOWDY, A. H. and KRATZ, P. M. (1953) *J. Opt. Soc. Amer.*, **43** (1), 42.

GREISEN, K. (1956) *Progress in Cosmic-Ray Phys.*, Vol. 3, North Holland Publishing Co., Amsterdam.

HALPERN, O. and HALL, H. (1948) *Phys. Rev.*, **73**, 477.

HANSON, R. J. and MOORE, D. C. (1956) *Nuovo Cim.*, Series 10, **4** (6), 1558.

HARDING, J. M. and HENDERSON, J. E. (1948) *Phys. Rev.*, **74** (10), 1560.

HARRIS, J. and OGILVIE, K. W. (1956). *Rev. Sci. Instrum.*, **27** (2), 113.

HARRISON, F. B., GODFREY, T. N. K. and KEUFFEL, J. W. (1952) *Nucleonics*, **10** (3), 33.

HAYAKAWA, S. and KITAO, K. (1956) *Progr. Theor. Phys.*, *Japan*, **16** (2), 131.

HEIBERG, E. and MARSHALL, J. (1956) *Rev. Sci. Instrum.*, **27** (8), 618.

HEITLER, W. (1944) *The Quantum Theory of Radiation*, Oxford.

HOFSTADTER, R. (1956) *CERN Symposium, Geneva*, Vol. 2, p. 75.

HORWITZ, N. (1955) *Phys. Rev.*, **98**, 165.

HUGHES, A. L. and DU BRIDGE, L. A. (1932) *Photoelectric Phenomena*, McGraw-Hill, New York.

HULST, H. C. VAN DE. (1953) "The Chromosphere and the Corona" in *The Sun* (ed. G. P. Kuiper), Chicago University Press.

HUQ, D. (1956) M.Sc. Thesis, University of Birmingham.

HUYBRECHTS, M. and SCHÖNBERG, M. (1952) *Nuovo Cim.*, Series 9, **9**, 764 (*see also* SCHÖNBERG, M. (1950) *Bull. Cent. Nucl. Univ. Libre. Brux.*, **20**, 1; (1951) *Nuovo Cim.*, **8** (3), 159; and (1952) *Nuovo Cim.*, Series 9, **9**, 210 and 372).

INDENBOM, V. L. (1951) *Zh. eksp. teor. fiz.*, **21**, 737.

IVANENKO, D. D. and GURGENIDZE, V. S. (1949) *Dokl. Akad. Nauk*, *SSSR*, **67** (6), 997.

IVANENKO, D. D. and TSYTOVICH, V. N. (1955) *Zh. eksp teor. fiz.*, **28** (3), 291; *Soviet Phys.* (1956) (*J. Exp. Theor. Phys.*), **1** (7), 135.

JANOSSY, L. (1948) *Cosmic Rays*, University Press, Oxford; p. 127.

JAUCH, J. M. and WATSON, K. M. (1948) *Phys. Rev.*, **74** (10), 1485, and 950, and (1949) *Phys. Rev.* **75**, 1249.

JELLEY, J. V. (1951) *Proc. Phys. Soc.* A **64**, 82.

JELLEY, J. V. (1953) *Progress in Nuclear Physics*, Vol. 3, p. 84, Pergamon Press, London. Russian translation. *Usp. fiz. Nauk.* (1956) **58** (2), 231.

JELLEY, J. V. (1956) *CERN Symposium, Geneva*, Vol. 2, p. 76.

JELLEY, J. V. and GALBRAITH, W. (1955) Part II. *J. Atmosph. Terr. Phys.*, **6** (6), 304.

JELLEY, J. V. and WHITEHOUSE, W. J. (1953) *Proc. Phys. Soc.* A**66**, 454.

JENKINS, F. A. and WHITE, H. E. (1937) *Fundamentals of Physical Optics*, 1st ed., McGraw-Hill, New York.

JESTER, M. H. L. (1955) University of California Radiation Laboratory, Report No. 2990.

JONES, W. B., KRATZ, H. R. and ROUVINA, J. (1957) *Rev. Sci. Instrum.*, **28** (3), 167.

JOOS, G. (1946) *Theoretical Physics*, p. 328, Blackie & Son, London.

KAGANOV, M. I. (1953a) *Zh. tekh. fiz.*, **23**, 507.

KAGANOV, M. I. (1953b) *Zh. tekh. fiz.*, **23**, 514.

KAGANOV, M. I. (1953c) *Zh. tekh. fiz.*, **23**, 523.

KANTZ, A. and HOFSTADTER, R. (1954) *Nucleonics*, **12** (3), 36.

KASSNER, J. L. and WILLARD, H. H. (1930) *J. Amer. Chem. Soc.*, **52**, 2391.

KINSEY, B. B. and WENTZEL, W. (1956) *CERN Symposium, Geneva*, Vol. 2, p. 68.

KLEPIKOV, N. (1951) *Vestnik Moscow State University*, No. 8, p. 61.

KOLOMENSKII, A. A. (1952) *Dokl. Akad. Nauk*, *SSSR*, **86** (6), 1097.

KOLOMENSKII, A. A. (1953) *Zh. eksp. teor. fiz.*, **24**, 167. Translated by Associated Technical Services (Trans 59G6R). East Orange, N.J. U.S.A.

KOLOMENSKII, A. A. (1956) *Dokl. Akad. Nauk*, *SSSR*, **106** (6), 982.

KOMPFNER, R. (1952) *Rep. Progr. Phys.* (Phys. Soc. London), **15**, 275.

KRUSE, U. E., MARSHALL, L. and PLATT, J. R. (1956) *Astrophys. J.*, **124**, 601.

LAMPERT, M. A. (1956) *Phys. Rev.*, **102** (2), 299.

LANDAU, L. (1944) *Zh. fiz. SSSR*, **8** (4), 201.

LANDECKER, K. (1952) *Phys. Rev.*, **86**, 852.

LANGER, L. M. and MOFFAT, R. J. D. (1952) *Phys. Rev.*, **88**, 689.

LASHINSKY, H. (1956) *J. Appl. Phys.*, **27** (6), 631.

LAW, R. R. (1952) Nucleonics, 10 (3), 38.

LAWSON, J. D. (1954) Phil. Mag., 45 (366), 748.

LEWIS, I. A. D. and WELLS, F. H. (1954) Millimicrosecond Pulse Techniques, Pergamon Press, London.

LI, YIN-YUAN. (1950) Phys. Rev., 80, 104.

LI, YIN-YUAN. (1951) Phys. Rev., 82, 281.

LINDENBAUM, S. J. and YUAN, L. C. L. (1956) CERN Symposium, Geneva, Vol. 2, p. 68.

LINHART, J. G. (1955) J. Appl. Phys., 26 (5), 527.

LINSLEY, J. (1954) Phys. Rev., 93 (4), 899.

LINSLEY, J. (1955) Phys. Rev., 97 (5), 1292.

LINSLEY, J. (1956) Phys. Rev., 101 (2), 826.

LINSLEY, J. and HORWITZ, N. (1955) Rev. Sci. Instrum., 26 (6), 557.

LUNDBY, A. (1956) CERN Symposium, Geneva, Vol. 2, p. 68.

MALLET, L. (1926) C.R. Acad. Sci. (Paris), 183, 274.

MALLET, L. (1928) C.R. Acad. Sci. (Paris), 187, 222.

MALLET, L. (1929) C.R. Acad. Sci. (Paris), 188, 445.

MANDÒ, M. (1954) Nuovo Cim., Series 9, 12 (1), 5. Translated by Technical Information Bureau for Chief Scientist, Ministry of Supply, London. Translation No. T.I.B. T4395 (1955).

MARCH, A. (1931) die Grundlagen der Quantenmechanik, 2, Leipzig.

MARSHALL, J. (1951) Phys. Rev., 81, 275.

MARSHALL, J. (1952) Phys. Rev., 86, 685.

MARSHALL, J. (1954) Ann. Rev. Nuclear Sci., 4, 141.

MARSHALL, J. (1956) CERN Symposium, Geneva, Vol. 2, 63.

MARSHALL, L. (1956) Astrophys. J., 124, 469.

MATANO, T., MIURA, I., ODA, M., SUGA, K., TANAHASHI, G. and TANAKA, K. (1957) Report INSJ-3 of the Institute for Nuclear Study, University of Tokyo, Tokyo, Japan. Also reported by Oda at the UPAP conference, Varenna, (1957) Como, Italy.

MATHER, J. W. and MARTINELLI, E. A. (1953) Phys. Rev., 92 (3), 780.

MATHER, R. L. (1951) Phys. Rev., 84, 181.

McDONALD, F. B. (1956) Phys. Rev., 104 (6), 1723.

McINTYRE, J. A. and HOFSTADTER, R. (1950) Phys. Rev., 78 (5), 617.

DE MENT, J. (1942) Fluorescent Chemicals and Their Applications. Chemical Publishing Co., New York.

MICHELS, W. C. and PATTERSON, A. L. (1941) Phys. Rev., 60, 589.

MILLAR, C. H. and HINCKS, E. P. (1957) Canad. J. Phys., 35, 363.

MILLAR, D. D. (1957) Paper H 11, read at the UPAP Conference, Varenna, Como, Italy, June 21st–26th.

MOFFAT, J. and STRINGFELLOW, M. W. (1958) J. Sci. Instrum., 35, (1), 18.

MORTON, G. A. (1949) R.C.A. Rev., 10, 525.

MORTON, G. A. (1952) Nucleonics, 10 (3), 39.

MOTZ, H. (1951) *J. Appl. Phys.*, **22**, 527.
MUZIKÁŘ, Č. (1955) *Czechoslovak J. Phys.*, **5** (1), 1.

NAG, B. D. and SAYIED, A. M. (1956) *Proc. Roy. Soc.* A235, 544.
NEAMTAN, S. M. (1953) *Phys. Rev.*, **92** (6), 1362 and (1954). *Phys. Rev.* **94**, 327.
NESTEROVA, N. M. and CHUDAKOV, A. E. (1955) *Zh. eksp. teor. fiz.*, **28** (3), 384; (1955) *Soviet Phys.* (*J. Exp. Theor. Phys.*), **1** (2), 388.

OGILVIE, K. W. (1955) *Canad. J. Phys.*, **33**, 555 and 746.

PAFOMOV, V. E. (1956) *Zh. eksp. teor. fiz.*, **30**, 761; *Soviet Phys.* (1956) (*J. Exp. Theor. Phys.*), **3** (4), 597.
PAFOMOV, V. E. (1957) *Zh. eksp. teor. fiz.*, **32** (3), 610.
PAWSEY, J. L. and SMERD, S. F. (1953) "Solar radio emissions", in *The Sun* (ed. G. P. Kuiper), Chicago University Press.
PIERCE, J. R. (1955) *J. Appl. Phys.*, **26** (5), 627.
POLIKAROV, A. (1954) *C. R. Acad. Bulg. Sci.*, **7**, (2), 29.
PORTER, N. and SHERWOOD, A. C. (1956) *The Oxford Conference on Extensive Air Showers*, A.E.R.E. Harwell, p. 71.
PORTER, N. (1957) *Nuovo Cim.*, Series 10, **5**, 526.
POST, R. F. (1952) *Nucleonics*, **10** (6), 56.
PRICE, B. T. (1955) *Rep. Progr. Phys.* (Phys. Soc. London), XVIII, 52.

RAFFLE, J. F. and ROBINS, E. J. (1952) *Proc. Phys. Soc.*, B **65**, 320.
RAJCHMAN, JAN. (1938) Thesis, Swiss Inst. of Technology, A. Kundig, Geneva.
RICH, J. A., SLOVACEK, R. E. and STUDER, F. J. (1953) *J. Opt. Soc. Amer.*, **43** (9), 750.
RICHARDS, E. W. T. (1956) A.E.R.E. Report No. C/R 1901. Harwell.
RIDLEY, B. W. (1956) *Progress in Nuclear Physics*, Vol. 5, p. 188, Pergamon Press, London.
RODDA, S. (1953) *Photo-electric Multipliers*, Macdonald, London.
RODIONOV, S. F. (1957) *Opt. spektrosk.*, SSSR, **2** (5), 606.
ROSSI, B. (1952) *High Energy Particles*, Prentice Hall, New York.
ROSSI, B. and GREISEN, K. (1941) *Rev. Mod. Phys.*, **13** (4), 240.
RYLE, M. (1949) *Proc. Phys. Soc.* A62, 491.

SAYIED, A. M. (1958) *Proc. Phys. Soc.* **71**, Pt. 3, (459), 398.
SCHIFF, L. I. (1955) *Quantum Mechanics*, p. 267. McGraw-Hill Book Co., New York.
SCHMIDT, G. (1956) *Mag. Fiz. Folyo.*, **4**, 453.
SCHÖNBERG, M. (1950) *Bull. Centre. Phys. Nucl. Libre. Brux.*, **20**, 1.
SCHÖNBERG, M. (1951) *Nuovo Cim.* **8**, (3), 159.
SCHÖNBERG, M. (1952) *Nuovo Cim.* **9**, (2), 210 and **9** (4) 372.
SHIROBOKOV, M. YA. (1949) *Zh. eksp. teor. fiz.*, **19**, 481.
SITENKO, A. G. (1954) *Dokl. Akad. Nauk*, SSSR, **98**, 377.
SITENKO, A. G. and KAGANOV, M. I. (1955) *Dokl. Akad. Nauk*, *SSSR*, **100**, 681.
U

SITENKO, A. G. and KOLOMENSKII, A. A. (1956) *Zh. eksp. teor. fiz.*, **30** (3), 511; *Soviet Phys.* (1956) (*J. Exp. Theor. Phys.*), **3** (3), 410.

SKARSVÅG, K. and LUNDBY, A. (1953) Joint Establishment for Nuclear Energy Research, Kjeller, Norway. JENER Report No. 22.

SMITH, S. J. and PURCELL, E. M. (1953) *Phys. Rev.*, **92** (4), 1069.

SOKOLOV, A. (1940) *Dokl. Akad. Nauk, SSSR*, **28**, 415.

SOKOLOV, A. A. and LOSKUTOV, YU.M. (1957) *Zh. eksp. teor. fiz.*, **32** (3), 630.

SOMMER, A. (1951) *Photoelectric cells*, 2nd ed., Methuen, London.

SOMMER, A. and TURK, W. E. (1950) *J. Sci. Instrum.*, **27** (5), 113.

SOMMERFELD, A. (1904) *Götting. Nachricht.*, **99**, 363.

SOMMERFELD, A. (1905) *Götting. Nachricht.*, **201**.

SOMMERFELD, A. (1954) *Optics*, p. 328, Academic Press, New York.

SUTTON, R. B., FIELDS, T. H., FOX, J. G., KANE, J. A., MOTT, W. E. and STALLWOOD, R. A. (1955) *Phys. Rev.*, **97** (3), 783.

SWANN, W. F. G. (1938) *J. Franklin Inst.*, **226**, 598.

TAMM, IG. (1939) *Zh. fis.*, *SSSR*, **1**, 439.

TANAKA, K. (1954) *Phys. Rev.*, **93** (3), 459. Univ. Calif. Rad. Lab. Report No. 1286 May (1951).

TANIUTI, T. (1951) *Progr. Theor. Phys.* (*Japan*), **6** (2), 207.

THOMAS, C. C., Jr., SUN, K. H. and MARUSICH, E. A. (1957) *Nucleonics*, **15** (4), 98.

TIDMAN, D. A. (1956a) *Nuovo Cim.*, Series 10, **3** (2), 503.

TIDMAN, D. A. (1956b) *Nuclear Phys.*, **2** (4), 289.

TOLLESTRUP, A. V. and WENTZEL, W. A. (1954) *Phys. Rev.*, **93** (4), 950.

VAVILOV, S. I. (1934) *Dokl. Akad. Nauk. SSSR*, **2**, 457.

VEKSLER, V. I. (1956) *CERN Symposium, Geneva*, Vol. 1, p. 80.

VLADIMIRSKII, V. (1947) *J. Tech. Phys.* (*USSR*), **17**, 1277.

WADA, W. W. (1949) *Phys. Rev.*, **75** (6), 981.

WEBBER, W. R. (1956) *Nuovo Cim.*, Series 10, **4** (6), 1285.

WEBBER, W. R. and McDONALD, F. B. (1955) *Phys. Rev.*, **100**, 1460.

WEISZ, P. B. and ANDERSON, B. L. (1947) *Phys. Rev.*, **72**, 431.

WELLS, F. H. (1952) *Nucleonics*, **10** (3), 37.

WIDMAIER, W. and ENGSTROM, R. W. (1955) *R.C.A. Rev.*, **16** (1), 109.

WILD, J. P., MURRAY, J. D. and ROWE, W. C. (1953) *Nature, Lond.*, **172**, 533.

WILLIAMS, F. C. (1938) *J. Inst. Elect. Engrs*, **82**, 561.

WINCKLER, J. R. (1952) *Phys. Rev.*, **85**, 1054.

WINCKLER, J. R. and ANDERSON, K. (1952) *Rev. Sci. Instrum.*, **23** (12,) 765.

WINCKLER, J. R. and ANDERSON, K. (1954) *Phys. Rev.*, **93** (3), 596.

WINCKLER, J. R., MITCHELL, E. N., ANDERSON, K. A. and PETERSON, L. (1955) *Phys. Rev.*, **98** (5), 1411.

WYCKOFF, H. O. and HENDERSON, J. E. (1943) *Phys. Rev.*, **64**, (1), 1.

NAME INDEX

Oda, M. 198
Odian, A. C. 195, 196
Ogilvie, K. W. 158, 190
Owen, R. B. 107

Pafomov, V. E. 37, 40, 76
Patterson, A. L. 29
Pawsey, J. L. 251
Peterson, L. 269
Pierce, J. R. 49, 264
Platt, J. R. 253
Polikarov, A. 221
Porter, N. 138, 139, 140, 158, 175, 179, 198
Post, R. F. 107
Price, B. T. 51, 52, 133
Purcell, E. M. 264

Raffle, J. F. 107
Rajchman, Jan 99, 105
Reiling, V. G. 79, 80
Reines, F. 158, 256
Rich, J. A. 90
Richards, E. W. T. 70, 90
Richings, H. J. 108
Ridley, B. W. 256
Robins, E. J. 107
Rodda, S. 98
Rodionov, S. F. 219
Rossi, B. 64, 135, 227
Rout, R. J. 158, 190
Rouvina, J. 180, 196
Rowe, W. C. 251
Ryle, M. 217

Sayied, A. M. 25, 26, 77
Schaetti, N. 120
Scherb, F. 158, 176, 180
Schiff, L. I. 27
Schmidt, G. 50
Schönberg, M. 52
Segrè, E. 3, 191
Shepherd, J. 158, 190
Sherwood, A. C. 198
Shirobokov, M. Ya. 31
Sitenko, A. G. 36, 37, 41, 52, 58
Skarsvåg, K. 264
Slovacek, R. E. 90
Smerd, S. F. 251
Smith, S. J. 264
Smith, W. B. 158, 176, 180

Sokolov, A. A. 27, 30
Sommer, A. 98, 105, 109
Sommerfeld, A. 21, 42, 52, 237
Stallwood, R. A. 186, 187
Stringfellow, M. W. 154, 195
Studer, F. J. 90
Suga, K. 198
Sun, K. H. 267
Sutton, R. B. 186, 187
Swann, W. F. G. 51

Taffara, L. 52
Tamm, Ig. 1, 2, 10, 13, 15, 22, 23, 25
Tanahashi, G. 198
Tanaka, K. 37, 198
Taniuti, T. 27
Thomas, C. C. Jr. 267
Tidman, D. A. 27, 29
Tollestrup, A. V. 242
Trier, A. Van. 47, 95
Tsytovich, V. N. 36, 55
Turk, W. E. 105

Vavilov, S. I. 9
Veksler, V. I. 56, 59, 266
Vladimirskii, V. 50

Wada, W. W. 269
Wallace, R. facing page 194, 193, 194
Watson, K. M. 25
Webber, W. R. 202
Weisz, P. B. 2, 82, 83
Wells, F. H. 107, 108
Wentzel, W. A. 193, 242, 243
White, H. E. 20, 41, 156
Whitehouse, W. J. 158, 256
Widmaier, W. 104
Wiegand, C. 3, 191
Wild, J. P. 251
Williams, F. C. 106
Winckler, J. R. 202–205, 269
Wyckoff, H. 80

Yamagata, T. 193, 195, 196
Ypsilantis, T. 191
Yuan, L. C. L. 242

Zhdanov, G. B. 221, 224, 229, 230

SUBJECT INDEX

301